7-5-84

To

Russell and Frances Moen

"With all the Best"

from

[signature]

Cutting Energy Costs

The 1980 Yearbook of Agriculture

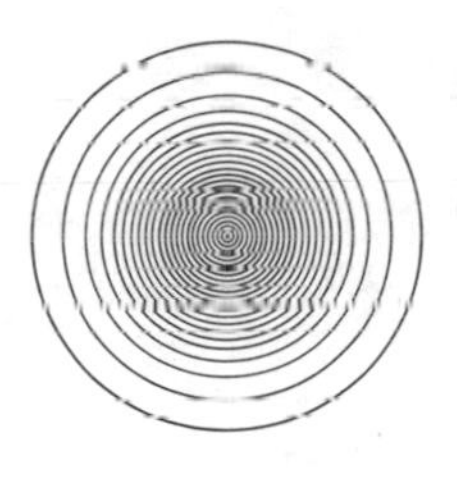

U.S. Department of Agriculture

For sale by the Superintendent of Documents, U.S. Government Printing Office
Washington, D.C. 20402

FOREWORD

Farmers, urban residents, and people from every walk of life want to know how to use less energy and cut energy costs. This book tells of many ways to do that.

All of us are well aware of how the increases in energy costs have cut into our incomes.

Farmers especially have been struggling to hold down their production energy requirements so that Americans can continue to get their food at reasonable cost. In fact, a new agricultural revolution may be in progress—one in which agriculture's own renewable energy supplies may be used increasingly to fuel farm machinery, heat farm buildings, dry grain, and serve many other purposes.

Some of agriculture's renewable energy supplies already are being used in gasohol to fuel the family car.

Communities—and local leaders—are organizing ways to reduce their energy outlays.

The U.S. Department of Agriculture has a variety of programs in the energy field, all of them working hard to ease the Nation's energy crunch.

And we feel that this book, which contains a large amount of useful material for handy reference, is a major contributor to the Department's efforts. Every American should find something worthwhile in this volume.

Bob Bergland
Secretary of Agriculture

PREFACE

Conservin' is deservin'—which is to say that energy conservation deserves a cash return, and may bring you one. Your energy conservation also deserves the esteem of other people, who may be inspired to a conservation effort themselves.

There are dozens of ways to save energy. It's something all of us can do—not just to be patriotic, but because it helps us first, and also helps everyone else.

One particularly useful chapter in this book that can help you conserve energy is *The Do's and Don'ts of Home Insulation*, by Barbara Griffin. It is virtually a small encyclopedia on home insulation, with many illustrations.

That chapter is just one example of the practical value of this book. Other chapters will have special appeal to farmers, foresters, homemakers, community leaders, young people, science buffs, and anyone concerned about energy.

Authors of this book are specialists mainly from the *U.S. Department of Agriculture*, and the *State Land Grant Universities.* The book was put together under the overall guidance of James C. Webster, *Assistant Secretary of Agriculture for Governmental and Public Affairs.*

Many individuals in the *Office of Governmental and Public Affairs* contributed to the publication effort, including Hal Taylor, Claude Gifford, David Sutton, Warren Bell, and Denver Browning.

Glenda Pifer, of the *Science and Education Administration-Extension*, chaired the Committee that planned the book. Members of the Committee were:

William A. Bailey, *Office of Transportation*
Daniel Ball, *Farmers Home Administration*
John Barringer, *Rural Electrification Administration*
William E. Carnahan, *SEA-Extension*
William Cox, *SEA-Extension*
Earle Gavett, Energy Staff, *Office of Budget, Planning, and Evaluation*
John Hornick, *Forest Service*
Jerry Newcomb, *Agricultural Stabilization and Conservation Service*
Marilyn Ruffin, *SEA-Agricultural Research*
Paul Schleusener, *SEA-Cooperative Research*
Donald Van Dyne, Energy Staff, *OBPE*

Jack Hayes
Yearbook Editor

Contents

II. FAMILY LIVING

III. COMMUNITIES

IV. ALTERNATIVE ENERGY SOURCES

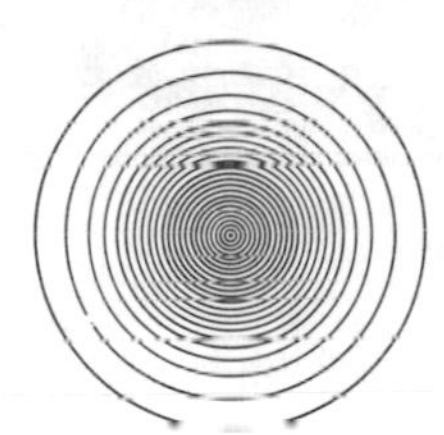

Section I

Agriculture, Forestry

J. VALBUENA

Where Farm Energy Goes

Part One of Overview
By Donald R. Price

Energy is basic to life. The survival of humanity depends on an adequate supply. Production of food, supply of clean water, and construction of shelter are inextricably connected to various types of energy inputs. A shortage of energy rapidly creates a shortage of these life-sustaining essentials.

Certainly food shortages cause human suffering, starvation, and social unrest. A continuous and dependable flow of food must be maintained because the consequences of an interruption are catastrophic by nature.

Energy has been substituted for labor and land in American agriculture, resulting in a food-producing capacity matched nowhere in the world. The United States is blessed with fertile soils and favorable climatic growing conditions, and American farmers are the stewards of this great resource.

Our farmers, with the assistance of agricultural scientists, have accomplished unbelievable levels of productivity since the early 1940's. Plant and animal genetics, pest control, and use of fertilizers can be credited with providing much of the increase. Mechanization can be identified as a major contributor. With the exception of plant and animal breeding, most of the success required an increase in energy input.

While productivity more than doubled since 1950 and labor was reduced by about half, the energy input to agricultural production quadrupled.

It is important to put into perspective the energy use in agricultural production relative to other sectors of our energy consuming society. Less than 5 percent of energy consumed in the United States is used in food production on the farm; most studies put the figure at about 3 percent. However, consumption in the total food and fiber system is over 20 percent.

Even though total consumption of energy in agricultural production is low relative to other major sectors, it has become very essential. Timely delivery of fuel is critical to many operations. Regional

---

DONALD R. PRICE *is Director, Office of Energy Programs, New York State College of Agriculture and Life Sciences and College of Human Ecology, Cornell University.*

differences, variability in weather, and fuel types must be considered. Fuels consumed on farms must be capable of meeting variable and high peak flow demands. Failure to provide for such conditions could result in total crop failure in some regions.

There is an important unique interrelationship between food and energy. Agriculture consumes energy in the production process, as just described. However, the products that result from this process contain large quantities of energy.

Farms Big User of Solar Energy

Agriculture is the only major sector that uses solar energy on a broad scale. The process of photosynthesis makes it possible for plants to convert the sun's energy into a readily storable and usable form for other uses.

Much of the energy produced on the farm through crops eventually finds its way to supplying energy needs of humans. At the same time these energy needs are being met, other required nutrients are supplied as well.

Feed grains and several different legume crops are converted to other storable forms of food energy through livestock production. The only economically feasible way to harvest crops from some land areas is by animal grazing. Land that would otherwise remain unproductive thus provides food energy through livestock production.

If it were not for the large quantities of energy needed to transport, process, package, market, and store food, and for end use preparation, the energy produced from farm crops would exceed the energy input in the production process. However, the additional energy input has allowed the food processing and distribution industry to provide a high quality product packaged and available to the convenience of consumers.

Beyond meeting food energy needs of people in the United States and many foreign countries, there are other important benefits.

In recent years the monetary returns from agricultural exports were over half the payments for foreign oil. These exports required less than 5 percent of total U.S. energy consumption.

The struggle with balance of payments is a serious concern and the capacity to export large quantities of U.S. agricultural products has tremendous value in balancing payments through world trade.

The two illustrations of the benefits from agriculture relative to energy are probably sufficient unto themselves. But, there is more. Besides supplying human energy needs and paying for oil imports, agriculture is being looked to as a supply of liquid and gaseous fuels.

Technology is available and gradually being applied to intercept agricultural residues and animal manures to extract energy before they are returned to the land as fertilizer. The increased cost of conventional liquid fuels and electricity is helping move such technologies towards economic feasibility.

Potential for Grains

Further, there is keen interest in growing crops specifically for conversion to liquid fuels. The grain crops are currently considered prime candidates.

The starch in grains may be readily converted to ethanol and used as a substitute for gasoline. Ethanol that is anhydrous (200 proof) may be mixed with gasoline (usually a 10 percent mixture) to make gasohol. Gasohol may be burned in automobiles and trucks without engine modification.

Ethanol with some water — such as 180 proof — may be burned in internal combustion engines with minor engine modifications.

Many controversial issues are related to the use of food products as a liquid fuel source. The availability of surplus grains may not continue more than a few years, depending on weather conditions in grain production areas and the ability of lesser developed countries to increase domestic production.

Because the current ethanol production technology is rather energy-intensive, it is questionable whether any real net energy is gained when all energy inputs are counted. This concern is particularly important if natural gas or fuel oil are used as the energy inputs to the conversion process. If coal, wood, municipal wastes, or agricultural wastes are the energy input, there is less concern about the energy balance.

Agriculture has always been the backbone of the U.S. economy and an area of achievement for which Americans can be justly proud. Now in a time of major national and international concern for energy resources, American agriculture is being focused in on as a potential source of energy to help manage a very difficult problem. It is most important to keep sight of the balance between agricultural production as a food source and as a potential source of energy.

A history of low fossil fuel prices relative to food prices resulted in a growing dependence on these fuels in the food and fiber system. The economics along with a desire to eliminate hand labor tasks caused a rapid substitution of mechanical labor for human and animal labor.

Increased use of energy had the effect of reducing risks of crop failure, and spoilage, and it increased crop yields. Energy was expended to increase the quality and total quantity of food, while less land was needed thanks to the use of energy-intensive fertilizers. Use of fertilizers has been credited with providing a full one-third of grain production.

Crop Needs for Energy

Energy use in the food and fiber systems is characterized by considerable diversity and varying intensity depending on the region, crop, or process involved. For example, energy required to produce major feed grains is about 2,000 Btus per pound. In comparison, input per pound of cotton produced is nearly 24,000 Btus and for tobacco the requirement is close to 30,000 Btus.

Illustrating regional differences, low-intensity corn production in North Dakota required approximately 1,200 Btus per pound of corn, medium-intensity corn production in Illinois called for 1,700 Btus per pound, while high-intensity irrigated corn in New Mexico needed about 8,400 Btus per pound.

Varying types of energy are often required for different activities in food production. At the farm, liquid fuels are the major direct energy use while natural gas, LP-gas, and electricity are the major types used in food processing. On-farm energy use for dairies requires a major input of electricity for milk cooling, operating milking systems, and supplying hot water for sanitation purposes.

The food system, therefore, is very much affected by shortages of any of the current forms of energy.

Another unique and potentially troublesome concern in agriculture production is the timeliness factor. The biological nature of food production, including the uncontrollable environmental conditions, result in an uneven flow of energy to the system. Timing of liquid and gaseous fuel requirements depends upon weather as it interacts with the physical and biological aspects of the environment. Weather conditions in some regions, such as in intensive corn-drying areas, can make a drastic difference in the energy requirements in any given year.

No segment of society should be exempt from the requirement to conserve energy. Every person can and should participate in the goal to use less energy and use it with greater efficiency.

There are some obvious major uses of energy where large quantities of energy can potentially be saved, as in transportation, But tremendous savings will also come from the accumulated savings from each individual.

Agricultural production falls into the category of small users, yet there are many opportunities to save and the active participation of workers is needed in all segments of agricultural production.

It is true that a real spirit of efficiency has been an active ingredient in the production system for many years. Farmers are recognized for their ability to be efficient in their farming operations and the result of their efforts has been low priced, high quality food. But there is room for improvement.

Nitrogen Fertilizers

Use of nitrogen fertilizers is credited with providing a third of the productive capacity of crops. If nitrogen fertilizers were limited to 50 pounds per acre, it is estimated that an additional 18 million acres of cropland would be required to maintain current production levels.

Fertilizers are big energy consumers, with an estimated 33 percent of the total energy input to crop production consumed by the use of fertilizers. Most of the inherent energy contained in fertilizers is the natural gas required to produce the nitrogen fertilizers.

Crops vary in their demand for nitrogen partly due to the natural capability some legumes, such as soybeans, have for fixing their own nitrogen. Corn is a major grain crop in the United States and the corn plant does not have the natural capability to fix its own nitrogen. Scientists are researching the plant breeding characteristics to determine if it may be eventually possible to develop this capability in a new variety of corn.

Applications of supplemental quantities of nitrogen to corn can result in a net return of six units of energy for every unit expended in fertilizer production. This helps plants transform more solar energy into usable and storable products.

Since fertilizer is a significant indirect energy component and its use is essential, what can and is being done to conserve? Several new conservation technologies have been developed to improve the efficiency of energy use. For example, heat given off from natural chemical reactions that take place in the production cycle is used in the drying stage.

Another obvious conservation practice is to apply only as much fertilizer as can be effectively used by plants. Plant scientists have identified these optimum levels for most plants, and farmers have begun following the recommendations and reduced their fertilizer applications in many situations.

A companion to this practice is applying fertilizer at a time when the plant can use it before it volatilizes or leaches away.

Using legumes as a source of nitrogen was a common practice of the 1950's. Legume crops such as clover were rotated with the corn crop. This can still be done today; however, the net result is lower production capacity for corn.

Animal manures can serve to reduce the use of processed fertilizers. The fertilizer value of animal manures is recognized by farmers and most manure is applied back on the land.

The manure should be applied just before plowing and planting in order for the plants to benefit from the maximum amount of nutrients available. Much of the manure applied today either leaches away, is carried off the field in surface water, or volatilizes away while in storage or lying on the land surface.

Tillage Operations

Experiments show that under some conditions one or more tillage operations can be eliminated without reducing yields. Yields from reduced tillage vary considerably with type of soil, water availability, and type of crop.

Some soils where reduced tillage is employed still produce about the same yield, while other soil types may produce appreciably less with reduced tillage. The tillage operation accounts for a small proportion of total energy requirements; thus, total savings are not substantial.

Irrigation uses about 13 percent of the energy in production agriculture in the United States. It is a valuable use because crops are now being grown on land that before irrigation was not able to support production.

By carefully scheduling the application of water, both energy and water can be conserved. As more is learned about plant-water relationships, improved scheduling can have even greater effects.

Trickle irrigation with vegetable and some fruit crops reduces energy used to move the water, and less water is required because less is wasted. Improvements in pump design and efficiency of operation can reduce energy requirements for pumping. Time of day operation can be helpful by operating pumps during off-peak power use times.

There are many other examples of methods and practices to conserve energy on the farm. The few given were to illustrate the potential that exists. Many excellent publications are available from Cooperative Extension Offices throughout the United States to assist farmers and homeowners with developing and practicing conservation measures.

Alternative Sources

Many farmers are quite skilled in repairing and building mechanical equipment, and most are capable carpenters. The farming operation often leaves periods of time when the workload is slack. These two combinations offer the ingredients needed to become involved in solar, wind, or small hydro systems.

The cost of alternative energy systems has hindered their more rapid development. If you have the skill and the time to build your own system the economics are much more encouraging.

Available space to put up solar or wind systems is usually not a problem on the farm. An area is almost always available without obstruction of the sun or wind. The large area will often reduce the cost of construction and allow greater use of the wind and sun.

Because of the factors just discussed it is quite likely that solar and wind applications will have their first widespread use on farms.

Already some solar applications are very popular with farmers. One such is a solar-heated swine farrowing house. Many of these have been constructed throughout the Midwest. Solar drying of corn is another application that will likely become fairly common within a few years.

On farms located near streams and rivers, interest in water power is growing. Again, the economic feasibility depends on how much of the system can be built by the farmer. New equipment is currently under development by government and industry to meet the requirements of small scale hydro sites.

Considerable space is desirable for large wind turbine systems. If a large system can be erected by the farmer with used or scrap parts, the economics can look very good. Average windspeed for any given area is important to the success of wind energy systems. Windspeeds over 15 miles an hour are needed.

Using wind for power is not a new concept on farms, of course. Farmers discovered many decades ago that the wind is an ideal source of power in remote areas for pumping water. Many windmills are still being used today for this purpose.

Windpower can be used to pump water, and to generate electricity for heating water and supplying other electrical needs at the farmstead. Electrical energy can be stored in batteries so electricity is available for periods when the winds are low.

Cost of a modern system may be too high to attract many farmers. However, if costs are reduced by providing much of the labor for developing a system, it may be a desirable investment for farmers located in windy areas.

A combination of alternative sources such as wind and solar along with the use of biomass materials available on the farm may be the concept of the future. An effective program in energy conservation along with producing energy on the farm could eventually make some types of farms nearly self-sufficient in energy.

Not all the new technologies need be incorporated at one time. However, over a period of several years an integration of several new energy sources along with conservation could lead to a nearly independent operation from an energy standpoint.

Summary

Sufficient food supply to feed the rapidly expanding world population must be of serious concern to everyone. Future energy policies of the world must consider carefully the relationship and interdependence of food and energy.

Our changing energy resource supply situation does not imply that today's modern farming practices will be abandoned for more primitive practices. The need for food produced in the United States will, in a few years, become so important to the world that our production capability cannot be jeopardized.

Instead, research and development programs will make it possible to increase production without a corresponding increase in energy consumption. These new improved efficiency technologies, especially those that use alternative energy sources, will and should be exported to developing countries.

The future of the food and energy situations need not be considered bleak. Research and development already underway will provide new technologies that will allow significant improvements in the efficiency of food production, processing, and packaging. The potential from solar, wind, water, and biomass may allow some types of farms to come close to energy self-sufficiency within a few years if the price and availability of fuels becomes even more serious.

Further Reading:

Critical Food Issues of the Eighties, M. Chou and D. P. Harmon, Jr., Pergamon Press, Maxwell House, Fairview Park, Elmsford, NY 10523. $10.95.

Less Energy, More Food

Part Two of Overview
By Dick Vilstrup

Man has historically needed energy to prepare food. Starting with wood in the primitive campfire, people have used heat to boil, bake, dry and preserve food for further use.

Today, food processing is still an essential part of our food system and makes a major contribution in improving food quality and palatability, extending edible life, increasing convenience, and creating new ingredients and food forms. Modern processing generally requires energy for heat, freezing, or mechanical technology.

The American food system is critically dependent on adequate supplies of energy. Moving food from the farmer to the consumer requires massive amounts of energy for marketing, transportation, processing, storage, distribution, retailing, and final preparation.

New production and processing technology that insures consumers sufficient quantities of quality food requires 16.5 percent of the total energy supply used in the United States. An additional 5.5 percent is needed for natural fiber and forestry.

A breakdown of the 16.5 percent of the energy used in the U.S. food system indicates that 29.1 percent of the energy is used in food processing or manufacture, 26 percent for in-home food preparation, 17 percent for out-of-home preparation, 4.9 percent for retailing, and 3 percent for the wholesale food trade, with only 17.6 percent for production.

The Federal Energy Administration estimates of energy use include direct, indirect, capital and transport energy costs.

Note that the major portion of energy is used beyond the farm gate. About 18 percent of the energy requirements is used for production, while 82 percent goes for processing, marketing, transporting, and preparing food for consumption.

Today, over 75 percent of the food produced on farms is processed before final shipment to consumers.

DICK VILSTRUP *is Extension Marketing Economist and Professor, University of Wisconsin. He also is Director of the Agricultural Transportation Energy Conservation Project, for the Wisconsin Energy Extension Service.*

Processing industries require energy for washing, cutting, steaming, boiling, freezing, drying, milling, refining, baking, canning, and packaging food. Energy needs in the food processing industry have increased rapidly during the past 30 years.

In the past few years there has been a shift toward more energy intensive and highly processed or packaged foods. The demand for convenience food and the dramatic increase in eating meals outside the home has accelerated this trend. Increased consumer demand has been noted for smaller containers and pre-cooked, oven ready products which require additional energy in processing.

Current socio-economic lifestyles, with spouses employed in full or part-time jobs, has stimulated the expanding need for energy in commercial food processing and the restaurant trade. Btu's of energy needed for commercial eating establishments now exceed energy used in farm production or in marketing and distribution.

The food marketing and processing sector of the food system continues to increase and totaled $140.5 billion, or about 68 percent of the food marketing bill in 1978. The cost of energy for plastics for packaging, specialized services for the institutional trade and the expansion of the fast food industry has accelerated this trend.

Energy costs for food items represent a large share of the consumer dollar. A U.S. Department of Agriculture (USDA) study indicates an average of 9 percent of the consumer food dollar goes for energy costs. Foods with the highest energy costs per dollar of processed products are sugar, butter, cheese, condensed milk, and canned fruits and vegetables.

Energy Used in the U.S. Food System

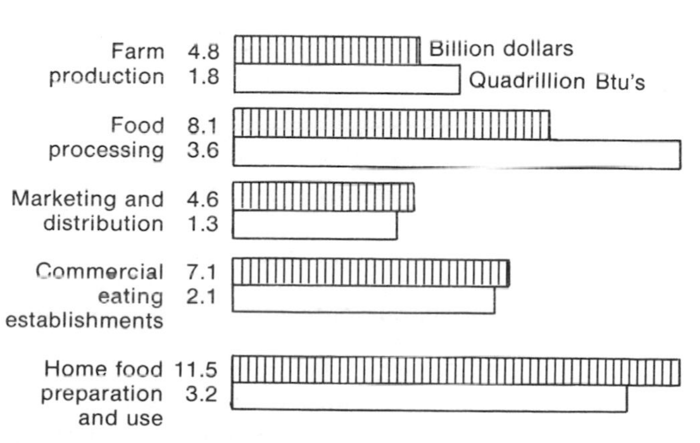

1976 data for farm production. 1975 data for all other categories.

1979 *Handbook of Agricultural Charts*, Agricultural Handbook 561, USDA.

Food products with the lowest energy costs per dollar of processed product include fluid milk, bakery products, meat products, and ice cream.

The processing industry uses all types of fuel, but relies basically on fuel oil, natural gas, coal, and electricity. The cost and uncertain supply of fossil fuels have focused attention of management on efficiency, conservation, and alternative fuels such as coal.

Processing Energy Costs for Selected Food Groups

Food groups	Energy cost cents per dollar of processed products[1]
Sugar	16.7
Butter, cheese & condensed milk	10.7
Canned fruits & vegetables	10.6
Frozen fruits & vegetables	10.5
Flour & cereals	9.9
Meat products	9.7
Ice cream	8.7
Fluid milk	8.6
Soft drinks	8.5
Bakery products	6.7
Alcoholic beverages	6.3

[1] Energy costs in the processing stage only; energy used in distribution and marketing is not included. Energy cost based on national average price of $2.33 per million Btu's.

Source: *Farm Index*, June 1977.

Energy accounting studies indicate energy use in food processing accounts for 7.6 percent of the total manufacturing fuels and electricity consumed. In 1975, food processing used 11,476,000 barrels of distillate oil, or 10.9 percent of distillate used in all manufacturing. Food processors also used 13,893,000 barrels of residual oil, 3,893,000 short tons of coal, 441 billion cubic feet of natural gas, and 38,299 billion kWh of electricity.

Adequate energy supplies are needed by food processors at critical times during a season. Timeliness is essential in preserving quality of harvested crops or perishable food ingredients. For example, many vegetable and fruit canning plants operate only a few weeks a year and a critical shortage of fuel during this harvest period would have a major impact on the industry. It is often difficult for food processing plants to store large quantities of fuel oil or coal in urban areas. The most convenient source of fuel for processing has been natural gas piped directly to a plant.

Energy use varies by type of food industry, depending on volume and kind of operation. Meat packing, grain milling, fruit and vegetable and milk industries consume significant total quantities of energy because of their size, but are generally not considered energy intensive. Beet sugar processing is the most energy intensive industry, followed by other refining and freezing operations.

Meat packing and processing, conducted nationwide, requires energy in the form of fossil fuel, electrical power, and heat. Energy is used in assembly, slaughter, boning, grinding, cooking, freezing, canning, packaging, refrigeration, storage, transportation, handling, and display for the ultimate consumer.

The movement toward eating meals away from home has increased sharply. It is now estimated that over a third of meals are prepared outside the home.

Out-of-home preparation is the third largest category of energy use in the food industry (17 percent). It includes fast food restaurants, coffee shops, cafeterias, hotels, motels, and other eating facilities. Energy is used in refrigeration, cooking, heating, air-conditioning, water heating, lighting, and energy needed to manufacture packaged items such as paper napkins, cups, boxes, and straws. The substantial energy needed to manufacture disposable containers and supplies represent a potential challenge for increased energy conservation.

Energy Use in Home Food Preparation

Energy used for in-home preparation is significant and accounts for 26 percent of the energy consumed in the food system, and represents 4 percent of total U.S. consumption. The primary use of energy for in-home consumption occurs in storing food (refrigeration and freezing) and in preparing food in ovens, ranges, and small appliances. In addition, consumers also expend considerable energy in transportation to and from retail stores.

The food marketing system includes a complex wholesale and retail network to move food from processor to consumer. About 7.9 percent of total energy in the food system is consumed in the movement through wholesale and retail channels. Energy is needed for refrigeration, storage, packaging, and transportation as wholesale firms move merchandise to retailers and industrial, commercial, institutional, farm, and professional businesses. Retailers, buying merchandise for resale to consumers, require energy for heat, electricity, refrigeration, packaging material, transportation, and facilities to provide the essential service.

Energy for transportation is essential in maintaining a smooth flow of food and fiber from farmer to consumer. Transportation is the key link between agricultural food production and the consuming public. Trucks, highways, barges, and rail lines are vital lifelines for nearly every community in the Nation. Processors are also totally dependent on a modern and efficient transportation system for the inputs and distribution of food products.

Use of fossil energy in agricultural transportation systems is significant. The transportation industry almost totally depends on fuels from petroleum. Transportation services are vital in shipping production supplies and to move raw farm products to producers and consumers.

The fuel and fiber system required 2,892 million gallons of diesel fuel and 411 million gallons of gasoline in 1977. It is estimated that energy needed for transportation represents over 12 percent of the total supply needed in the food system and accounts for over 2 percent of total energy used nationally.

Presently, nearly half the trucks on our major highways carry food and agriculturally related products. The food system depends on timely shipments during planting and harvesting seasons. Perishability of food products requires rapid and efficient distribution of supplies to specific markets.

Fuel estimates from USDA reported that the shipment of farm inputs required 619 million gallons of fuel. Moving farm commodities from farmers to processors required 1,416 million gallons. An additional 1,268 million gallons of fuel were needed to transport manufactured food products from processors to warehouses and supermarkets.

Estimated Transportation Fuel Requirements in the Food and Fiber System, 1977

Item	Ton-miles	Diesel fuel	Gasoline
	millions	million gallons	
Farm inputs	82,539	505	114
Agricultural commodities	141,098	1,119	297
Manufactured food products	116,077	1,268	*
Total	339,714	2,892	411

*not applicable.

Source: J. A. Barton, Transportation fuel requirements in the food and fiber system, *Agricultural Economics Report 414*, January 1980.

Dominant need in the food system is for fuel for trucking, which uses 77 percent of the total. Rails use about 20 percent, while most of the remainder is accounted for by barge and river traffic.

The pattern of energy use is undergoing many dynamic changes. Historically, food processing and packing plants were geographically located near intensive production areas. Several relatively cheap sources of energy were available, and strategic planning focused primarily on supply of raw material and availability of transportation.

Food Firms Switching to Use of Coal

Food firms are now making an orderly transition from primary reliance on oil and natural gas to accelerated use of coal, where feasible.

Conserving energy in the food system will be a high priority in the 1980's. Abrupt changes or minor disruptions in the availability of energy can seriously affect performance of the food processing and marketing system. New energy policies which encourage increased conservation, alternate fuels, energy recycling, and technological efficiency will be needed in the future.

Several new energy programs and developments show promise in the food field. These include—

- Adoption of new technology with the capability to use fuels efficiently.
- Reduction in bulk volume of perishables, cutting water content, compacting.
- Improved routing, scheduling, and elimination of wasteful empty backhauls where feasible.
- Automated control systems to minimize energy use in warehouses for frozen food and in retail store counters.
- Standardized modular shipping containers, encouragement of uniform packaging, reduced sorting, and less inefficient loads.
- Use of food processing wastes for generating heat, electric power, or fuel.
- Improved truck and trailer design to increase mileage, improve airflow and reduce friction during shipment.
- Increased use of natural cooling and controlled atmosphere storage for fruits and vegetables.
- High temperature pasturization of milk to reduce need for refrigeration and increase shelf life.
- Recycling heat or energy for multiple uses.
- Eliminating unnecessary regulations and practices that encourage energy waste in transportation and processing.
- Training of truck drivers, maintenance staff and dispatchers in energy conservation techniques.

How to Grow Crops With Less Energy

By W. W. Frye and S. H. Phillips

An individual farmer can obtain significant savings through more efficient management of energy in crop production.

Production efficiency can be maintained while decreasing fuel requirements through selection of one of the reduced tillage systems or modifying and combining these systems to fit geographical and individual farm situations.

Management is more critical and more herbicides are required as tillage is decreased, but the additional energy represented by the pesticides does not nearly offset the energy conserved by reduced tillage.

Management of commercial nitrogen fertilizers to improve efficiency — and the growing of legume crops as cover crops or in rotation or association with non-legume crops — are especially promising for energy conservation.

Modern high-horsepower tractors allow farmers to till deeply, frequently, and rapidly. It has been estimated that tillage practices result in movement of enough soil each year in the United States to build a superhighway from Los Angeles to New York.

With costly energy, means of reducing tillage is an important goal of farmers in the United States and throughout the world. Historians will record the 1970's as the peak years in tillage, and the 1980's as a period of readjustment to reduced tillage operations. The technology has been developed that will allow farmers to grow crops efficiently at lower costs by adopting reduced tillage or no-tillage systems.

Reduced tillage is not new but has evolved since herbicides were introduced in the 1940's. Research programs in establishing legumes in pastures without plowing or disking — and new systems related to no-tillage production of several crops — added confidence that drastic changes in tillage methods were possible in the future. Shortages of farm labor, larger acreages, higher volume pro-

W. W. FRYE *is Associate Professor of Agronomy, University of Kentucky. Shirley H. Phillips is Assistant Director of Extension for Agriculture at the University.*

duction, and improved technology encouraged further development and adoption.

Reduced tillage systems may also be termed minimum tillage or conservation tillage. Minimum tillage is the least amount of tillage required to create suitable soil conditions for seed germination, crop growth, and weed control. It may range all the way from use of several tillage operations to eliminating all tillage operations except planting.

In this chapter we discuss four tillage systems. These are conventional or moldboard plow tillage, chisel plow tillage, disk tillage, and no-tillage. Field operations usually involved are shown in the table. Each system has particular advantages and disadvantages.

Although minimum tillage methods were developed mainly for erosion control, they offer one of the greatest opportunities to reduce energy requirements in field crop production. Energy savings are mostly with tractor fuel due to fewer tillage operations.

Conventional tillage requires relatively large amounts of fuel for plowing and disking to prepare a seedbed. Generally, fuel savings are related to the amount of reduction in tillage and may be quite substantial with no-tillage. Less machinery is needed for reduced tillage, which contributes to the decrease in overall energy used in crop production.

Estimates for tillage systems vary, depending on

Modern high-horsepower tractors allow farmers to till deeply, frequently and rapidly. But they require energy. This tractor and three 5-bottom plow hookup in Washington State are preparing a field for another crop of fall wheat.

EARL R BAKER

the number and kind of field operations assumed and the energy values assigned to each operation or input. For our estimates, we have adopted the values in the table as representative energy requirements for several field operations. These are similar to other estimates by researchers.

Need for additional herbicides with reduced tillage offsets some but not all of the energy represented by the fuel saved in tillage, as shown in the table.

Estimated Energy Requirements for Several Field Operations and Inputs in Four Tillage Systems

	Tillage System			
Input or Operation	Conventional Tillage	Chisel Plow	Disk	No-Tillage
	gallons diesel fuel/acre			
Moldboard plow	1.84			
Chisel plow		1.12		
Disk	0.63	0.63	0.63	
Apply herbicides and disk second time	0.73	0.73	0.73	
Spray herbicides				0.13
Plant	0.43	0.43	0.43	0.50
Cultivate (once)	0.42	0.42	0.42	
Herbicides	1.75	2.01	2.25	2.88
Machinery and repair	1.86	1.61	1.25	0.60
Total	**7.66**	**6.95**	**5.71**	**4.11**

In some States, higher rates of nitrogen fertilizer are recommended for no-tillage than conventional tillage corn. There is greater potential for leaching, denitrification and immobilization of nitrogen in no-tillage. There is also a greater potential for yield increase from adding nitrogen fertilizers in no-tillage than for conventional tillage.

Research in Kentucky, Maryland and Virginia showed that conventional tillage produces more corn than no-tillage at low nitrogen rates, but no-tillage usually produces more than conventional tillage at higher rates of nitrogen. The energy represented by the increased yield of corn usually repays many times the energy represented by the additional nitrogen fertilizer.

Eco fallow is a management system commonly used in dryland winter wheat areas of the United States. With this system, herbicides are substituted for tillage in keeping fields void of vegetation during fallow years. It is considered a practice that conserves energy, soil and moisture.

Ways to Boost Food Output

Demand for food rises as populations, standards of living, and exports increase. There are two main ways for a nation to boost food production in response to these demands.

One is to add to the amount of land under cultivation, and the other is to increase the application of agricultural technology.

Generally, the more productive land and best sites for irrigation are cultivated while less productive land is left idle or used for other purposes when not needed for crop production. Thus, when additional land must be brought into cultivation it is almost always less productive land which may be marginally suited or, in some cases, unsuited for cultivation.

Increasing food production in this way has serious impacts on soil erosion, and results in

Eco-fallow, using herbicides to keep fields free of vegetation during fallow years, is widely used in the dryland winter wheat areas of the U.S.

D CK DODDS

326-621 O - 80 - 3 : QL 2

inefficient use of energy for cultivating more acres with low yields.

By using agricultural technology, U.S. farmers increased food production for several years while decreasing the amount of land under cultivation. During that time, production costs per unit were generally declining. Consumers benefited from an abundance of inexpensive, high quality food.

Dramatic increases in crop yields since World War II have paralleled the rise in fertilizer use. It is impossible to say how much of these bigger yields were due to fertilizers because the increases were due to a "complete package" of technology, service and management, including improved plant materials, pest control, culture techniques, harvesting, storage transportation and marketing. It is safe to say, however, that fertilizers are a major component of this "package."

Higher yields resulting from fertilizers are usually very economical. In many cases the greater yields may be worth several times the cost of the added fertilizer in terms of both dollars and fossil energy.

Fertilizers are a valuable input resource because they step up both the yield and quality of crops. Soils have the capacity to supply essential plant nutrients from the mineral and organic constituents, although the capacity varies widely among different soils. Crops have certain nutrient requirements for optimum yield production which differ considerably, both in amount of nutrients and kinds of nutrients.

Nutrients removed from the soil by harvesting crops — and loss by leaching, soil erosion or volatilization — must be replenished by the soil or fertilizers for optimum growth of the next crop.

Fossil fuel energy is used in manufacturing, mining, refining, transportation, and application of fertilizers. Most of the energy consumed by the fertilizer industry is in the manufacture of nitrogen. Natural gas is used as the source of hydrogen for the manufacture of about 94 percent of the ammonia compounds; 93 percent of the nitrogen in commercial fertilizers is from ammonia compounds. Yet only about 2 percent of the total natural gas used is for the production of ammonia for fertilizer.

Estimates of the amount of energy represented by a pound of fertilizer vary somewhat. For our discussion and calculations we selected intermediate values of 25,000 Btu per pound of nitrogen; 3,000 Btu per pound of P_2O_5 equivalent; and 2,000 Btu per pound of K_2O equivalent. (Divide Btu values by

147,000 to convert to gallons diesel fuel equivalent.) These estimates do not include energy used in applying fertilizers in the field.

There are some differences in energy represented by different forms of nitrogen fertilizers, with anhydrous ammonia being somewhat lower than urea and ammonium nitrate, which are about equal.

For efficiency and economy, fertilizer rates need to be adequate but not excessive. Nitrogen fertilizer rates should be recommended considering such factors as cropping history of the field, crop to be grown, and productive capacity of the soil. Recommendations for phosphorus, potassium and other nutrients which are potentially deficient in the area should be made from the results of soil tests.

Nitrogen fertilizer rates for corn, for example, usually are within the range of 75 to 175 pounds of nitrogen per acre, depending on climate and soil conditions. Recommendations based on soil tests for both phosphorus and potassium most frequently fall between 60 and 150 pounds P_2O_5 or K_2O.

In most soils, nitrogen is the most important fertilizer nutrient for production of non-legume crops because it tends to be deficient and to limit yields more than other nutrients. It is also the most energy-expensive and represents an area where improved efficiency and conservation can be effective.

Two Practices With Nitrogen

Two management practices which show the greatest potential to improve the efficiency of nitrogen fertilizer are: 1) delaying the application to coincide with the need for nitrogen by plants, and 2) use of legumes grown as cover crops or in rotation with row crops, or in association with pasture grasses.

Delayed Application. During the first four weeks after planting, corn plants take up only a small amount of their nitrogen requirement. If nitrogen fertilizers are applied at planting, much of it may be lost by leaching or denitrification before the crop uses it.

Whether delaying the application of nitrogen fertilizer for four weeks will improve nitrogen efficiency depends largely on climate and soil conditions.

On well-drained soils, the most likely loss of nitrogen is leaching of nitrate. On imperfectly-drained soils, the greatest loss is likely to be by denitrification of nitrate to gaseous forms. Higher rainfall increases losses by both means and on both well-drained and imperfectly-drained soils.

Leaching and denitrification losses are also more likely to occur under no-tillage than under conventional tillage.

Improved efficiency with delayed application of nitrogen fertilizer is taken into account in some States' fertilizer recommendations for corn production.

For example, in Kentucky, publications listing fertilizer recommendations say that rates of nitrogen can be decreased by 35 pounds per acre, if as much as two-thirds of the nitrogen is delayed four to six weeks after planting no-tillage corn on moderately well-drained soils, and for conventional tillage corn on moderately well and poorly drained soils. The nitrogen fertilizer saved by this practice represents about 875,000 Btu of energy per acre or about 6 gallons of diesel fuel equivalent per acre.

It should be pointed out, however, that the nitrogen fertilizer recommendations on moderately well drained and poorly drained soils are 50 and 75 pounds per acre, respectively, more than on well drained soils if the nitrogen fertilizer is all applied at planting. Thus, even with the advantages of delayed application, at least 15 pounds per acre more nitrogen is recommended for soils with impaired drainage as a safeguard against the greater potential nitrogen loss.

Nitrogen From Legumes. Until recent years, legume crops have been relied upon to provide nitrogen for non-legume crops throughout the recorded history of agriculture. There is renewed interest and research on the use of legumes as winter cover crops and in rotation or association with non-legume crops.

Results with winter annual legumes as cover crops for no-tillage corn in several States indicate that a substantial amount of the nitrogen needed by the corn can be supplied by legumes.

In Kentucky in 1979, grain yields of no-tillage corn following a cover crop of hairy vetch but with no nitrogen fertilizer were equal to corn yields on other plots with 88 pounds per acre nitrogen fertilizer added.

Others have reported even greater additions of nitrogen from legume cover crops for no-tillage corn. In Delaware, winter cover crop consisting of a mixture of hairy vetch and crimson clover resulted in corn yields comparable to those obtained by applying 100 pounds per acre of nitrogen fertilizer. Nitrogen fertilizer savings of such magnitudes would represent considerable conservation of energy.

Herbicides

Herbicides eliminate or decrease the number of cultivations for weed control and have essentially eliminated the drudgery of hand hoeing. The use of herbicides is an excellent example of using energy and technology as a substitute for labor.

Different herbicides require different amounts of energy in manufacturing the active ingredient, and some are carried in petroleum compounds which add to the energy that they represent.

A commonly accepted value for the energy to manufacture herbicides is about 44,000 Btu per pound of active ingredient, but that apparently does not include the petroleum base used as carriers for some herbicides.

For comparison purposes, we used the estimates of Siemens at the University of Illinois (see table earlier in chapter). His estimates were 0.5 gallon of diesel fuel equivalent per pound except for the contact herbicide commonly used in no-tillage. For that herbicide, he used a value of 1.25 gallons of diesel fuel per pound of active ingredient.

Studies have shown that herbicides are economical in terms of energy input/output ratios and dollars.

Crop Drying

Artificial drying of crops on farms has become a common practice since World War II. About half of the corn produced in the United States is dried artificially on the farm, and another fourth is dried

DICK DODDS

The moisture content of harvested crops must be lowered to store the crop without spoilage, insects or overheating. Crop drying facilities, such as this one in Lancaster County, Nebraska, allow the farmer to grow higher yielding, later maturing varieties of grain. This one uses a portable drying system that permits drying in stages, thus cutting the use of electricity.

off the farm. This permits early crop harvesting and a reduction in the moisture content below some critical level in order to store the crop without spoilage, insect infestation, or overheating.

Crop drying facilities allow farmers to grow higher yielding, later maturing varieties of grain, and to double-crop in some cases.

Almost all on-farm drying is done using LP gas. Off-farm drying is mostly with LP gas and natural gas. Solar drying units are coming to the forefront and much research is presently underway on this technology.

To reduce the moisture by 10 percent in the grain from an acre of corn with a yield of 125 bushels would require about 16 to 20 gallons of LP gas, depending on the type of dryer used.

The major means of conservation in crop drying are field drying to lower moisture level, low temperature drying, use of solar dryers, sealed storage of high moisture grain for livestock feed, and dryeration. In dryeration, the grain is removed hot from the dryer without cooling and held with no airflow for 4 to 12 hours. Then the grain is cooled slowly with aeration.

Studies of energy-conserving farms have identified certain practices common to all that should be considered by every farmer. These include:

- — Soil tests to determine fertilizer needs.
- — Use most productive soils in preference to marginal soils for crops with high energy requirements.
- — Use best agronomic practices to obtain efficient use of nitrogen fertilizer and optimum yields.
- — Use legumes in pastures or in rotation with non-legumes, where possible, to reduce need for commercial nitrogen.
- — Combine operations to reduce number of trips across fields.
- — Practice minimum tillage.
- — Use pesticides judiciously.
- — Store fuel properly and eliminate loss in transfer from storage to tractors.

Further Reading:

Agriculture Depends Heavily on Energy, American Chemical Society, 1974, *Chemical and Engineering News*, 52(10), pp. 23-24.

Potential for Energy Conservation in Agricultural Production, Report No. 40, Council for Agricultural Science & Technology, 250 Memorial Union, Ames, IA 50011. Free.

Greenhouse Production With Lower Fuel Costs

By T. H. Short and W. L. Bauerle

Greenhouse agriculture has existed since transparent materials were first developed. Many solar technologists and hobbyists suggest that a "solar greenhouse" with a massive vertical north wall and a high sloping south transparent roof is the ultimate future commercial greenhouse.

Sketches, however, date this type of structure to at least the early 16th century. Horse manure was usually placed under the ground beds to supply both heat and fertilizer. Even vegetable growers up until the mid part of the 20th century used manure in the base of "hot beds" for heating the small south sloping green houses. Such greenhouses were productive, but not nearly as productive as modern greenhouses with good temperature control.

Most modern commercial greenhouses resemble large factory buildings rather than a "solar greenhouse." Like a factory, productivity for profit is a major goal and the structure must facilitate easy movement of labor, material, and equipment.

A typical tomato greenhouse will produce 110 tons of fruit per acre through the labor of 2.5 people. This sort of productivity is 15 to 20 times that of the best field production in the best climates. The greenhouse grown product is consistently of very high quality while the field grown product quality is a variable dependent on weather conditions.

Estimates of commercial greenhouse acreage in the United Sates range from 6,270 to 20,000 acres. Most of the 6,270 acres are in year-round intensive production while the remaining area is used for seasonal transplant production or as temporary tunnel covers for starting crops in the early spring.

Ohio has traditionally been the leading State in both greenhouse vegetable and flower production. This tradition resulted mostly from Western European immigration patterns and a local need for high quality winter produce before the development of interstate highways. The highest percentage of

TED H. SHORT *is Associate Professor, Department of Agricultural Engineering, Ohio Agricultural Research and Development Center (OARDC). William L. Bauerle is Associate Professor, Department of Horticulture, OARDC.*

new construction since 1975 has occurred in the Southeast and Western States.

Large gutter-connected glass greenhouses with roof-ridge ventilators were first built in the early 1900's. During the late 1960's, fiberglass glazing became especially popular for connected greenhouses in the West and Southeast. Most new construction since 1970 in cold climates has been in the form of frame supported double-layer (air separated) plastic — a concept developed at the Agricultural Experiment Station of Rutgers State University. Double-layer air separated plastic provides a double glazing with low initial costs and a 30 to 40 percent energy savings over most single glazings.

The ultimate in open construction for good light penetration and machinery movement may be in the form of air-supported greenhouses such as the one-acre commercial bubble near Wooster, Ohio, that is used to grow lettuce and tomatoes.

A greenhouse in year-round intensive cropping will require a night temperature of 55° to 65° F depending on the type of crop being grown. This has resulted in an average annual fuel use of 100,000 gallons per acre of #2 fuel oil or 14 million cubic feet per acres of natural gas (14 billion Btu/acre) for Northeast Ohio glasshouse growers. This heating requirement is lower in warmer climates, but summer ventilation requirements are proportionally higher.

Greenhouses typically have a surplus solar heat supply during the day and excessive heat losses at night. An unventilated, unheated greenhouse in northeastern Ohio, 42° N. latitude, will reach over 85° F on a bright sub-freezing winter day and 120° F on a bright summer day. The following night temperature, however, will drop very rapidly to the outside air temperature if no heat is added.

Night temperature must not be allowed to drop below, or fluctuate from, 60° F for more than a few nights if plant and fruit quality are to be maintained. Day temperatures are allowed to range from 72° to 82° F in proportion to solar radiation. When the greenhouse temperature goes above 82° F, the greenhouse is ventilated with natural or evaporatively cooled air to both cool and minimize plant water stress. Sustained temperatures over 90° F can cause permanent damage to most crops.

Heat loss through greenhouse coverings is mostly affected by the thin boundary layer of stagnated air at the surfaces of each glazing material. Therefore, if one compares a tight double covered greenhouse (double glass, double plastic, double-plastic-over-glass, double fiberglass, glass and a tight internal single-layer-non-porous curtain) to a tight single covered greenhouse such as glass, the average energy savings will be about 40 percent.

If one compares this same tight glass greenhouse to a single layer plastic or fiberglass greenhouse, heat use will be nearly the same, especially after condensation develops on the inner plastic surfaces to minimize thermal radiation losses at night.

Approximations of Thermal Resistance, R, for Different Greenhouse Glazing Methods and Materials

Greenhouse Covering	R Value °F hr ft²/Btu
Single Glass (Sealed)	0.9
Single plastic	0.8
Single Fiberglass	0.8
Double Plastic, Polyethylene	1.4
Double Wall Acrylic	2.0
Double Glass (Sealed)	2.0
Double Plastic Over Glass	2.0
Single Glass & Thermal Blanket	2.0
Double Plastic & Thermal Blanket	2.5
Double Plastic, Poly-Pellets*	20.0

*A 5 inch thick layer of polystyrene pellets between a double plastic glazing.

Modifying Existing Greenhouses

Existing greenhouses can be modified for energy conservation by changing the exterior glazing or by internal insulation such as curtains. Areas like north walls and foundations can be permanently insulated, but the roof should be of major concern since this is where the major heat losses occur.

Applying a silicone sealant between glass laps can reduce infiltration of cold air into glass greenhouses. The extent of savings depends heavily on previous condition of the greenhouse, windiness of the location, and outside temperature conditions. Older glass greenhouses with wooden frames and in poor repair usually realize the most savings.

Usually it is not profitable to seal new glass greenhouses except during construction. With outside temperatures below 25° F the laps are usually frozen closed because of the large amount of condensate on the inside glass surfaces. At temperatures above 25° F, the heating requirement on a windy night may sometimes equal that for the coldest night conditions.

During the winters of 1978-79 and 1979-80, a lapsealed experimental greenhouse at the Ohio Agricultural Research and Development Center, compared to unsealed glass, had a fuel savings of 9 to 11 percent during freezing temperatures, 20 to 24 percent in above freezing temperatures, and 30 to 35 percent in early fall and late spring. Anticipated annual fuel savings for a similar greenhouse should be 20 to 25 percent after lapsealing.

One internal roof insulating concept is to pull curtain material under the roof at sundown and open the curtains at sunrise. To be effective, the curtain material must be non-porous and tight fitting when closed. The greatest advantage of a curtain system is that it can be used with any type of external glazing such as glass, fiberglass, or double plastic.

There have been numerous developments in closing and opening mechanisms, and of materials—including a series of air-inflated plastic tubes. The most adaptive type of greenhouse for curtains is a modular truss frame type with very few internal support posts. The least adaptive type greenhouse is one with extensive structural framing and one that uses the overhead framing to support trellised crops and hanging baskets. Average annual fuel savings with a good curtain system will be approximately 35 percent.

Older single glass greenhouses are usually best modified externally. The principal technique used commercially has been the application of double plastic over glass (DPOG). This technique was initially researched and developed at the Ohio Agricultural Research and Development Center in 1975. Annual fuel requirements were found to be reduced by 57 percent with a wood frame glasshouse in average repair.

One result of the DPOG research has been renewed awareness of the importance of controlling the night temperature and daytime carbon dioxide (CO_2) levels within the greenhouse. Plastic over glass will always reduce light transmission, with a potential yield reduction of 5 to 10 percent for high light crops such as tomatoes, cucumbers, and roses. For medium and low light crops, yield and quality can be maintained or increased if growing practices are proper.

Some vegetable and rose growers have actually reported yield increases with DPOG over their crops because of better control of night temperature. Also, a tighter sealed greenhouse allows growers who supplement CO_2 to maintain higher than normal levels. If CO_2 is not supplemented, chances are very good of CO_2 deficiency and poor plant growth.

A double wall acrylic glazing can be used to totally replace a single layer of glass for an average 50 to 60 percent fuel saving. Double wall acrylic is manufactured in rigid sheets about 4 feet wide and in standard lengths of 8, 10, 12, 14 and 16 ft.

The acrylic material consists of two layers separated about 0.6 in. with ribs spaced every 0.6 in. It diffuses and transmits 83 percent of the light compared to single glass at 89 to 90 percent, but the total amount of light reaching the plants is about the same because supporting roof bars can be spaced every 4 ft. instead of every 2 ft.

Acrylic is one of the more expensive greenhouse coverings, but it has a very long life and is nearly maintenance free.

Pellets Pumped Between Walls

For most climates, over 75 percent of all supplemental greenhouse heating is required at night. Further, studies in Ohio and Japan indicate that a polystyrene pellet nighttime insulation technique could reduce greenhouse nighttime energy requirements by 80 to 90 percent. Five inches of pellets are pumped between the walls of a double wall greenhouse at sundown and removed at sunrise for a nighttime insulation value of R = 20.

A similar system is used on a small scale in commercial Japanese glass greenhouses where snow is not a problem. The Japanese form a double wall by installing rigid plastic sheeting material approximately 3 in. behind the glass.

In most cold climates, however, especially with gutter-connected houses, snow can accumulate in localized areas and damage or break brittle materials such as glass. Snow also interferes with light transmission the following day if not melted off. Because snow load forces are better distributed over the supporting framework of air-inflated double plastic covers than with glass, the Ohio approach has been to use conventional double-plastic covers that are air inflated during the day and filled with pellets at night.

Polystyrene pellets should have a minimum diameter of 1 in. and should be treated with a fire retardant. Pellets are pumped directly through blowers with an air/pellet ratio of approximately 25:1. A 1 horsepower blower rated at 1,000 cfm at 3,450 rpm and 1 in. water column pressure will pump about 0.75 cu. ft. of pellets per second.

The mixture must be pumped into the plastic layers at pressure less than 1 in. water column pressure to prevent rupturing the plastic. This is accomplished by evacuating air from between the plastic sheets with a similar-sized blower while filling. The evacuation procedure can also control the thickness of fill and maintain film tension on the insulated system at night.

Static electric cling of the pellets to the plastic and each other can be controlled by such chemicals as glycerine. Approximately 1 gallon of glycerine (mixed with an equal amount of water) added to each 1,000 cu. ft. of pellets prevents static problems for many months. Other antistatic chemicals recommended for garments have also been effective. The precise life of the antistatic agents is unknown.

Moisture in the pellets and between the plastic must be minimized during sub-freezing weather. A thin layer of pellets can freeze on the inside surface of the outside cover. Likewise, moisture in the pellets can reduce the insulation effect. Therefore, all air inlets to blowers are designed to be outside the humid greenhouse. On dry days, the pellet storage can be air-dried with one of the blowers.

Pellets should be stored ouside the greenhouse growing area in a dark, dry location to prevent any slow deterioration of the polystyrene by sunlight. Large thin wall plastic tubes can be used horizontally or vertically for storage as the pellets weigh only 1 lb/ft^3. The life of the pellet is indefinite since proper handling causes no apparent deterioration.

Modifying Heating and Ventilation

Almost every conservation practice requires some modification of an existing heating and ventilating system. A tighter single glazing tends to require more ventilation to reduce condensate dripping on plants. A double glazed structure will have less condensation even at higher humidities because of a warmer inner surface. These changes in humidity and condensation can have a great effect on the grower's ability to properly control plant growth and quality.

All heating systems should discharge the heat as low and as close to the plants as possible. Steam or hot water pipes are usually placed low and between the rows of a trellised vegetable crop or beneath the benches of most potted crops.

Root zone heating is an important concept being developed and studied along with energy conservation systems. There is evidence that many plant tops will tolerate lower night temperatures if the roots are maintained at 70° to 80° F.

One system for potted crops is to install 3/4 inch plastic pipe on 2 to 4 ft. spacings within a 4 inch layer of porous concrete (concrete without sand). For soil grown crops such as lettuce, the plastic pipes are placed directly in the soil (sand preferred) to heat the root zone. Water temperature within the pipes is usually maintained at 100° F.

For conventional double plastic greenhouse structures, root zone or floor heating will take care of 15 to 25 percent of the heat requirement during the coolest periods. For polystyrene pellet insulated greenhouses, the soil heating is predicted to provide all of the heat necessary for high production and optimum temperature control.

Cultural practices that growers use for optimum plant growth are often related to some of the unique features of the greenhouse itself. Much of a successful greenhouse grower's production is based on his ability to control plant growth under different light conditions by controlling fertilizer, water, and carbon dioxide rates, and temperature and humidity levels. For each control variable, too much and too high, or too little and too low can have a very adverse effect on yield and quality of any crop.

Plants always need less water as the humidity rises and after tightly sealing a greenhouse. A tight seal often increases condensation and dripping from a single glazed greenhouse even though the humdity remains the same. Therefore, a tight greenhouse should preferably be a double glazed greenhouse to prevent inside water condensation that will drip on the plants. Double glazing will result in higher winter humidities for better plant growth and drier ceilings as long as the greenhouse is properly managed with a trickle irrigation system.

Plant temperature at night is one of the more important control factors for the greenhouse grower to manage. The optimum plant temperature may actually be different for roots and tops even though one temperature for both has typically been recommended. For the fruiting of a crop such as tomatoes, night temperature of the plants must be maintained above 58° F to have significant fruit set. Vegetative growth of the same tomato or other totally vegetative crops, however, may be more affected by proper root temperature (65° to 75° F) than top temperature.

Plant temperatures during the day are controlled in proportion to solar radiation. This control function is usually allowed to occur naturally since any rise in solar radiation also increases the greenhouse temperature above a daytime base of 65° to 70° F. If the daytime temperature is set too high when light intensity is low, excessive respiration can result in plants that are elongated and weakened. This results in poor quality and low production. If the temperature is too low, limited growth occurs.

Carbon dioxide must be available at ambient (330 parts per million), or above, levels for good production. Vegetable and rose growers usually supplement CO_2 to 1,000 to 1,500 ppm. It requires approximately 75 pounds of CO_2 per acre per hour to achieve 1,500 ppm. Without supplemental CO_2, it has been demonstrated that CO_2 levels in commercial greenhouses can drop to 200 ppm in 20 minutes on a bright sunny day. This makes enrichment increasingly important as infiltration is reduced with energy conservation systems. CO_2 can be provided from different burner sources, including a boiler stack if a clean fuel is burned efficiently.

Alternate Energy

The relatively large amount of low temperature heat required in greenhouses makes them good candidates for using waste heat from electric power plants and other industrial sources. Greenhouses can also be heated with active solar collectors or solar ponds.

For all alternate energy considerations, an energy conserving greenhouse design will be much more feasible than any conventional design. Conventional designs require large, expensive heat exchangers for low temperature waste heat applications. Further, a conventional greenhouse has too high a heating requirement for any active solar collector system. Floor or soil heating with nighttime insulation tends to be as good an application for alternate energy systems as it is for fossil fuel heated greenhouses.

There is every reason to believe the greenhouse industry has a greater potential for the future than ever before. The consistent quality horticultural product comes from the greenhouse, not the field. Field production has relied on expensive mobile fuels and the interstate highway systems, while the greenhouse can use local low-grade fuels such as coal or waste heat being generated close to population centers.

The energy dilemma of the 70's can shape a future for the greenhouse industry that will be brighter than ever before. The industry, however, will need to make major technological changes to conserve energy. And the supporting energy industries must develop energy systems compatible with commercial greenhouse production.

The most crucial problem of the early 1980's will be to continue reducing the energy consumption and operating costs of the existing greenhouse growers. One economical alternative has been the use of double plastic-over-glass (DPOG).

DPOG reduces heat requirements 50 to 60 percent and has received wide adaptation by the industry since 1977. New greenhouses and the existing double plastic greenhouses must be designed to adapt to some highly insulative nighttime insulation system.

Night curtain systems are an intermediate step in the right direction. A major step will be the polystyrene pellet system under development in Ohio which shows promise of reducing night heating by 90 percent. More research and development of the handling and control systems is expected to bring the pellet system into commercial use.

Further Reading:

Building Hobby Greenhouses, Agriculture Information Bulletin No. 357, U.S. Department of Agriculture, #001-000-03692-1, for sale from Superintendent of Documents, U.S. Government Printing Office, Washington, DC 20402. $1.

Conserving Energy In Ohio Greenhouses, Special Circular 102, Ohio Agricultural Research and Development Center, Mailroom, Wooster, OH 44691. Free.

Conserving Heat In Glass Greenhouses With Surface-Mounted Air-Inflated Plastic, Special Circular 101, Ohio Agricultural Research and Development Center, Mailroom, Wooster, OH 44691. Free.

Energy Conservation and Solar Heating for Greenhouses, NRAES-3, Northeast Regional Agricultural Engineering Service, Distribution Center, Cornell University, 7 Research Park, Ithaca, NY 14850. $1.50.

Hobby Greenhouses and Other Gardening Structures, NE-77, Northeast Regional Agricultural Engineering Service, Distribution Center, Cornell University, 7 Research Park, Ithaca, NY 14850. $2.

Cheaper Ways to Grow Tree Fruits and Nuts

By Larry K. Jackson

Fruit and nut growers can reduce energy consumption in many ways.

Some of the suggestions given in this chapter will vary from one geographic area to another and from crop to crop. Due to space limitations, crops and geographic areas have not been discussed individually, but suggestions are offered in general categories for consideration by growers.

Fertilize at recommended levels. Over-fertilization is not only wasteful and expensive but may in some cases actually reduce yields. Growers should stay within established recommended guidelines when possible.

Proper use of soil and leaf analyses allows more precise determination of optimum amounts of fertilizer to apply. Adjustments can often be made before deficiencies actually occur, and wasteful excesses eliminated before they cause harm.

Many fruit crops can be fertilized with reduced frequency. In other words, consider using the same amount of plant food per acre per year but with fewer applications. Slow-release and organic fertilizers can be of real benefit in these programs.

In regard to liming, bear in mind that most crops have an optimum pH level. Proper and timely adjustment of soil pH will increase plant growth and enhance utilization efficiency of applied fertilizer.

Applying certain soluble mineral elements through irrigation systems (fertigation) may provide some growers with an opportunity to reduce both application and material costs.

Use of nitrogen-fixing cover crops can often provide an inexpensive source of nitrogen and provide a "sink" for other applied nutrients which will be released after the crop is incorporated and begins to decompose.

Many growers have access to manure, composts and other biological wastes which can often be used as an inexpensive source of supplemental plant food.

LARRY K. JACKSON *is Extension Horticulturist, Fruit Crops Department, University of Florida.*

Pest Control

Integrated pest management — use of chemicals and biological control in conjunction with careful pest monitoring and consideration of variables such as weather and intended market — can save most growers both energy and money.

Spray application techniques vary considerably. Concentrate and/or aerial sprays are frequently substituted for ground applications, because where feasible, they usually provide faster control at a lower cost. Both pesticide and energy consumption are minimized.

Growers should consider the use of biologically resistant plant cultivars wherever possible. Such resistance is the most economical form of plant protection available.

Consider management of weeds as an alternative to control. It may be satisfactory to tolerate considerable weed growth during certain periods of the year with some crops. Mowing is usually less expensive than cultivation, and should be considered as an alternative weed control method.

Where weeds must be strictly controlled, chemicals are generally accepted to be less expensive and energy-intensive than traditional mechanical weed control procedures.

The 4 "R's" — using the *right* quantity of the *right* chemical at the *right* time in the *right* place — are more important today than ever before. Growers must know the pests, their life cycles, the chemicals and rates recommended for control, and the most efficient application techniques.

Sophisticated air blast sprayer used by most tree fruit growers for rapid, efficient pest control.

326-621 0 - 80 - 4 : QL 2

Efficient Water Use

Water management is treated in detail elsewhere in this section of the Yearbook. However, efficient water use is important not only because of energy considerations, but also because water itself is a precious natural resource. Several areas of water use efficiency are suggested below.

Irrigation scheduling. The accounting method, where daily water use is calculated and subtracted from the soil water balance, can help you determine the optimum time to irrigate. Other methods are also available to growers which can help guide irrigation decisions.

Low volume irrigation. Recent advances in low volume irrigation technology have made systems available which are energy-and-water-efficient and often relatively inexpensive. One new system in use today is trickle or drip irrigation. Such systems have strategically placed emitters which slowly release small amounts of water directly in the rooting zone of the plants being irrigated. Low volume of micro-sprinklers, which are scaled-down versions of larger gun-type systems, also appear very promising.

Minimizing weed growth, especially around young plants, greatly reduces water needs for most fruit crops. This is especially true on light, sandy soils.

Scion and rootstock cultivars differ in ability to crop efficiently with less water. This is a new concept and little is known about water use efficiency in many crops. The subject doubtless will receive increasing attention in the future.

Most fruit crops should be pruned regularly. This not only is horticulturally sound, but energy-efficient as well since it lessens brush disposal problems, increases efficiency of spray applications, and facilitates cultural and harvest operations.

Overdoing Cultivation

Many growers over-cultivate crops for esthetic rather than horticultural reasons. Where soil compaction is a problem or weeds cannot be managed by herbicides or mowing, cultivation may be necessary. However, minimize cultivation, not only to save energy but also to reduce wear on equipment and injury to crop roots near the soil surface.

Use of wind machines, irrigation, or a combination of heaters and wind machines will usually save considerable energy compared to the use of heaters alone for protecting fruit crops from cold damage.

Passive cold protection methods are also very important. These include proper variety and site selection, clean cultivation, irrigation of the orchard floor to facilitate heat transfer, and optimizing orchard geometry to aid air drainage.

Mechanical topper to trim citrus trees.

Late pruning, fertilizaton and herbiciding sometimes decrease cold-hardiness and should be avoided or done cautiously. By the same token, plants should not be allowed to go into the fall and winter months in poor condition. Weak plants are predisposed to cold damage.

Regular use of plats or maps greatly increase the efficiency of orchard managers. Areas with special problems or needs can easily be identified and treated. Resets can be located quickly and given the special care they need.

Remote sensing techniques using aerial photography with infrared color film is now available in most areas. These new techniques furnish growers detailed information on their orchards and even help to determine individual tree condition.

When possible, equipment should be matched to the tractor. Both under-and-over-powering implements are very energy-inefficient.

Implements should be the right size to operate efficiently within the geometric pattern of the orchard. For instance, if a 10-foot middle needs cultivating, use a 10-foot disc instead of making 2 passes with a 5- or 6-foot disc.

Alternative power sources for farm equipment may also prove quite energy-efficient. Diesel engines use less fuel than gasoline or LP engines, for example. All equipment, of course, should be kept in peak operating condition to assure maximum efficiency.

Harvesting, Marketing

Once the crop is produced and ready to pick, some of the largest consumers of agricultural energy come into play. Often there is little an individual grower can do, but here are some energy ideas to keep in mind.

A clean, level orchard floor will greatly increase harvest efficiency. Remove overhanging limbs which may obstruct movement of personnel and equipment. A well-prepared orchard requires less energy to harvest.

Consider pick-your-own or direct marketing techniques. Many growers — especially those near large population centers — use their customers to harvest much of the crop. Pick-your-own (PYO) fruit operations are often successful if properly managed, and provide growers with a convenient market for their product.

Most customers see PYO operations as an opportunity to buy top-quality fruit of their choice economically and as a source of recreation to the family.

Some growers use direct roadside marketing or a combination of PYO and roadsiding. Still others sell their fruit directly to large outlets, local grocery stores, or to a farmer's market.

Energy-Saving Ideas For Berry Growers

By Jerome Hull, Jr.

Energy conservation in agricultural production is realized by reducing or eliminating production and harvesting practices for which energy is required, or by instituting an alternative method that is less

JEROME HULL, JR., *is Extension Specialist, Department of Horticulture, Cooperative Extension Service, Michigan State University.*

energy-consuming. It is also achieved by increasing agricultural production per unit of energy used.

Agricultural research and grower innovation will result in new or modified berry production and harvesting methods. Development of satisfactory postplant nematicides will enable strawberry growers to avoid preplant fumigation. The postplant treatment might be combined with a herbicide treatment to eliminate one passage of equipment through the field.

Eliminating a preplant fumigation in the fall will facilitate growing green manure crops late into the year preceding spring planting. This would increase the amount of readily decomposable organic material that could be produced and worked into the soil.

Plant breeding to develop varieties with resistance to major insects and disease will enable growers to minimize pesticide applications. Pheromones to monitor insect activity, plus routine inspections of plantings for pest activity, will permit timely pesticide applications. Pesticide application equipment will be put to work less frequently and smaller quantities of pesticides formulated from petroleum products will be required.

Micro encapsulation of pesticides may result in greater pesticide effectiveness and prolonged residual activity, thus enabling producers to apply lower rates or less frequent applications of the active ingredient and still achieve satisfactory control. An increased interval between applications would save on pesticide and equipment usage.

Harvesting into a small trailer to facilitate harvesting and save energy.

Pesticides Via Sprinklers

Most strawberry plantings have sprinkler irrigation systems for frost control. The systems are designed to apply water to the entire planting continuously throughout periods of subfreezing temperatures. These irrigation systems could be adapted for applying pesticides rather than using conventional spray equipment. Development of satisfactory systemic pesticides should make the irrigation application technique very feasible.

Herbicides and herbicide application methods can reduce tillage for weed control. Herbicides with little or no residual active ingredient could be applied to eliminate noxious perennial weeds before planting. Wick and rope applicators can be used to apply herbicides to foliage of weeds exceeding strawberry plant height without injuring strawberry plants.

Herbicide programs providing effective control of grasses and perennial weeds would enable growers to maintain plantings for additional fruiting seasons, and avoid the extensive energy use required for preparing, planting and establishing a new planting.

Plant analysis most accurately reflects the nutrient status of perennial fruit crops. Analysis of plant samples for nutrient content would result in fertilization programs designed to apply only those nutrient elements required for optimum plant growth and fruit production.

Growth-regulating chemicals offer opportunities to modify plant growth for more efficient management. Most berry crops ripen their fruit over a period of time, rather than maturing the entire crop at once. Growth regulators concentrating the ripening period would reduce the number of times harvesting equipment needs to travel through the planting. Chemical tipping compounds might control terminal growth on black raspberries, and promote lateral branching and increased fruit-bearing surface.

Mechanized harvesting can result in greater fruit recovery. Harvesting strawberries by hand for processing in Michigan yielded about 4 tons per acre while mechanical picking resulted in nearly 5.5 tons. Fruit was satisfactory for slicing, puree and juice, but the machine more effectively gleaned all the fruit from the planting than did hand pickers.

Increasing acreages of berry crops are being marketed "pick your own," where the customer harvests the fruit. This saves much of the fossil energy the producer would otherwise need for harvest. However, the energy extended by customers driving to the farm will offset the farmer's energy savings.

How Vegetable Growers Can Cut Energy Costs

By R. E. Gomez and D. J. Cotter

Producers are supplying consumers year-round with an abundance of fresh and processed nutritious vegetables. The commercial vegetable enterprise is very large, occupying about 3.3 million acres in 1980. While this is an increase of only about 75,000 acres since 1970, the total value has increased from $1.65 billion in 1970 to $3.08 billion in 1980.

About three-fourths of commercial vegetable production goes to fresh market outlets while one-fourth is processed. Both types of production are energy-intensive.

During the 1970's a study in California showed that fresh vegetable production required, on the average, 1.5 calories of fuel and electrical energy for each food calorie produced. Canned vegetables consumed 4.4 calories and frozen vegetables 5.2 calories, excluding energy in the containers.

Conservation is fast becoming an economic necessity because vegetable production does require large quantities of energy. It must be remembered, however, that nonedible calories are transformed into edible ones and that some processed foods require fewer energy inputs when prepared in the home.

Vegetable producers should plan carefully on matters affecting energy and income. For example, is it better to specialize in one crop and benefit from production efficiencies, or produce several and spread the risk of crop loss and market failure?

Many factors need to be considered, such as crop rotation and succession, type of crops, varieties, equipment and energy needs, labor requirements, water and nutrient availability and cost, and pest management programs. By carefully examining each farm enterprise and the crops, producers can make farming less chancy and more energy-effective.

RICARDO E. GOMEZ *is Program Leader-Horticulture, Science and Education Administration-Extension, USDA.* Donald J. Cotter *is Professor, Department of Horticulture, New Mexico State University.*

New Ways to Measure Yields

Since the fresh vegetable producer does not have a price guarantee, the best means a producer has to assure profits is to strive for high yields at the right time. For many years vegetable production efficiency has been measured by yield per acre. In the future we will also measure production efficiency in terms of yield per quantity of water (mainly in the West) and yield per unit of energy input.

Energy conservation begins with records. They must be kept so that decisions can be made. Some of the important records are: a) location of each crop planted; b) date and yield; c) pesticide application (type, amount, results); d) fertilizer application (amount, date, results); e) soil analyses (prior to and after crop harvest); f) machinery time per operation; and g) fuel costs. The more complete the records, the better the decision you can make.

Crop succession and rotation influence energy input by affecting weeds, diseases, and insects as well as nutrient requirements of the future crops. Consulting experts in horticulture, weed control, plant pathology, and entomology as to the possible rotational effects on pests and soils will enable the producer to draw up a final schedule for crops.

Similar crops are often hosts to the same insects and diseases. Even some nonrelated crops act as hosts to the same pests. In some cases, a pest organism may always be present and its effect on crop plants must be minimized by variety selection and/or cultural practices.

More Data Needed on Irrigation

Irrigation (where necessary) increases yields and quality, but also contributes to production costs and energy expenditure. Use of water by many vegetable crops has not yet been tallied up. Only when data are available can a producer reasonably predict the amount of water needed for his crop. Careful water monitoring with tensiometers or other types of measuring devices can give a producer a better picture of irrigation needs.

Trickle, drip, or subsurface irrigation systems have not been used extensively on most vegetable crops. More experimental testing by commercial operators is warranted. Even though the initial cost seems high, these techniques can help decrease the amount of water, nutrients, and pesticides needed, and can also be used for salinity management in areas with salt problems.

In the arid areas of the West or where irrigation is needed for germination and early plant development, accurate soil leveling would be a way to save energy, water, and labor costs. Technology changes such as laser land leveling should be considered by both large and small producers. When a field is properly leveled it is less prone to flooding and to certain diseases. Efficient use of fertilizers, particularly nitrogen, is enhanced by applying the right amount of water coupled with the correct distribution of that water.

Adding Organic Matter

During soil preparation, adding organic matter such as crop residues or manures can benefit soil structure and water and nutrient holding capacities. Organic matter added to soil is particularly important to promote better growth and development. Proper growth makes for more efficient use of water and nutrients.

Soil analyses can be used to predict nutrient needs, organic matter requirements, and to estimate water requirements and frequency of waterings. These analyses are run by many Land-Grant Universities and a host of private laboratories throughout the United States.

Planting pregerminated seed can also improve stands and yield even though it is costlier than dry-seeding methods. Pregerminated seed, along with precise planting techniques, can reduce the amount of labor at thinning, the amount of water required, and the time between planting and emergence. Similarly, using high quality viable seed enables a grower to select a lower seeding rate to reduce cost.

Mulching for weed control, moisture retention, and earliness can also reduce unit energy input by increasing yields. Plastic mulches, however, are oil based and require energy in their manufacture and in field application.

A grower must choose among the trade offs — to mulch or not, to use plastic or not, or whether to use organic mulches. The latter approach is ideal in summer but delays soil warming and crop growth when applied early in spring.

Capping

Pre-irrigation and planting seed in moist soils followed by covering seed with two to four inches of soil on the seed beds (capping) should also be considered. These techniques have been used extensively in some field crops and have been tried successfully in some vegetable production areas. However, small seeded crops cannot be planted in this manner.

High density planted, single harvest, short-season varieties will also play an important role in the near future.

Mechanical harvesting promises to change fresh

vegetable production drastically. A major benefit to the grower is that peak labor requirements are reduced. Producers can, therefore, predict schedules and better use available labor on a continual rather than sporadic basis.

While the shortrun effect on labor may be viewed as detrimental, in the longrun farm labor is more highly paid and work productivity remains high.

Plant geneticists and breeders often foresee some of the changes before they take place. Their foresight results in a timely array of varieties adapted to the new constraints and opportunities of the times and are often more palatable to the consumer.

Vegetables For Small Families

One recent societal trend is towards smaller families and consuming groups, single-parent families, couples, and retirees. Development of vegetables small enough to be used by single people or couples should also be of prime importance to plant breeders.

The vegetable producer must start to think in terms of a yet more intensive type of crop culture — multiple or sequence cropping. Properly researched techniques that enable more to be planted in a given area can lead to lower costs of production and lower consumption of energy.

Early application of pesticides may be warranted to preserve a desired plant population, especially when crops are precision planted. Encapsulating seed with nutrients, particularly phosphorus or micronutrients or pesticides, coupled with precision planting, has a great future for tomorrow's vegetable producer.

Integrated pest management holds a legitimate and important place in the vegetable farmer's operation. By using established levels in managing pests efficiently, the producer can sometimes cut down on use of pesticides. This will have a marked effect on the production costs, and also reduce overall energy expenditures of the Nation. The other beneficiary is the environment. Pesticides are necessary to assure plentiful food, but a clean healthful environment benefits us also.

Low volume or ultra low volume spraying for pest control should be considered for use on a wider scale, and in conjunction with pest monitoring and biological control. Cost levels need to be followed closely.

The right pesticide must be used and the correct amount at the right time to attain desired results and cause least possible impact on the environment.

Instructions on labels as well as State and Federal usage regulations must be followed.

Minimum Till Culture

No-till or minimum till culture can take place if plant canopies can be developed quickly and densely enough to shade out weeds. Therefore, high density plantings can contribute to energy and production cost savings.

Fertilizer efficiency needs to be investigated further, especially of those nutrients readily moved by water. Soluble fertilizer materials in irrigation water can save costs for growers who apply small amounts at the appropriate plant development stage.

Not much is known about when and how much should be applied at what growth stage. New techniques will allow growers to improve the timing. Again, the producers, researchers, and Extension personnel, working as a team solving plant nutrient problems, can bring about a more enlightened attitude towards energy and resource conservation.

Too much fertilizer not only is a waste of material, but could result in reduced yields and hurt other plant growth and development processes. Further excesses can become hazards to the environment.

Minimizing Transport Expenses

Another way to save energy costs on a nationwide scale is to minimize transportation requirements and costs. One method is to produce a large assortment of vegetables regionally to meet most needs. This is contrary to today's criteria of growing crops in regions where they are best adapted. But if energy and transportation costs become high enough, long distance transport may become prohibitive.

Direct marketing offers another avenue for energy savings, especially for local producers. The internal quality of much locally grown produce is excellent. Many consumers are willing to accept vegetables of lower external quality if they know the internal quality is as good or better than in produce available through traditional outlets. Direct marketing could effect an attitude change in this paradox between internal and external quality requirements.

The Land-Grant Universities, through research and Extension, have a responsibility to present information to make the public aware of nutritional aspects of the various vegetables and the possibility of substituting one vegetable for another. Educational programs will have to be increased and made available for more people.

To sum up, energy is used either directly by the producer in fuel for vehicles and other equipment, pumps, and graders, or indirectly in the form of fertilizers, organic matter, pesticides, irrigation equipment, and plastic mulches. Labor also contributes to energy costs. Therefore, there are many direct and many more indirect energy costs which could be reduced with proper planning and execution. With energy savings, we could still produce vegetables efficiently and remain competitive with other areas of the world.

Tips on Energy Saving For the Home Gardener

By Ricardo E. Gomez

Since the early 1970's there has been an increasing trend towards more gardening activities around the home. A total of 77 percent of households are engaged in the care of some type of plants.

Even though each individual area is small, the aggregate areas of plants around the home is large. For example, the average home vegetable garden is around 600 square feet, yet the total area devoted to home grown vegetables is comparable to that used in California for the commercial vegetable industry.

Energy savings in such individually small areas seem negligible. But when taken as a whole they can't be disregarded. So all homeowners share the responsibility of using energy efficiently.

Energy is used as fuel for lawnmowers and other equipment, to maintain water pressure, and to produce chemicals and other materials for gardening. Therefore, whenever any activity or practice is minimized, an energy savings is bound to occur.

Of course, a reduction in the size of the maintained area will cut down on energy related expenditures around the home. For example, in some areas of the West two gallons of water are used on

---

RICARDO E. GOMEZ *is Program Leader-Horticulture, Science and Education Administration-Extension.*

plants (mainly turf) for every gallon used indoors. By maintaining only half the area, water use can be cut a third.

Here are some tips for reducing energy consumption while still growing plants properly.

Information Sources

The County Extension agent in your area (listed under county government or the Land-Grant University in the telephone directory) is an excellent source of information and publications on locally successful gardening practices such as adapted varieties, soil requirements, pests, and how to use vegetables and other edible crops. Obtain as much information as possible before you start gardening.

Plan ahead as to where and what to plant, taking into consideration the ultimate size of the plant rather than the size when it is acquired or planted. Many homeowners have to remove ornamental plants at a late date because they are too large. Plant at the correct spacing for mature specimens to save money, time, and energy.

Vegetable gardeners do not need to plant more than necessary, but thinning at the proper stage to provide ample room for the crop is required.

A soil test — conducted by a university laboratory or other — will help you determine the nutrients required for a particular type of plant. This soil test should be done every two to four years. Remember that overdoing it with fertilizers can harm plant development.

Composting materials (other than diseased or insect-ridden plants or weed seeds) should be attempted. Add this compost to the soil in the fall. Other types of organic matter such as manures or green manure crops should also be applied during fall. This timing allows for the start of the decomposing process and can result in water and nutrient savings (need to apply less) during the growing season.

Proper Use of Water

Watering, if needed, should supply the plant with enough so it can live and not drown. Too much water can lead to diseases or improper development.

During drought or in arid areas, more frequent watering is required. However, water early in the morning and only if the plants need it.

Watch for wilting symptoms in the early part of the day. If they occur — then water. If wilting occurs in the afternoon, there should be no major problems and plants will probably not require watering.

Daily waterings usually are not required, but may be needed due to an insufficient amount used. This causes plants to have a shallow root system which in turn calls for frequent waterings. Deep watering, less frequently, can promote deeper rooting and more drought resistant plants.

Controlling weeds can also affect water consumption. Weeds are plants out of place and require water for their development. Therefore, they need to be controlled. Whenever possible, control weeds and insects mechanically. However, these pests can be overwhelming.

If pesticides are needed, read the label and follow it carefully. More is definitely not better. Make sure you have identified the weed, the insect, or the disease before attempting to control it. If you need help, contact your county agent or other knowledgeable source of information.

Native Plants Save Energy

Use of native plants for landscaping and utilitarian purposes around the home can save energy. These plants are better adapted and require less care than exotic types.

Use disease and other pest-resistant or tolerant varieties that are adapted to the area, the space available, the type of culture, and your purpose for growing them. Allow for the proper spacing when you plant and, if possible, label the plants. Map the area and write the variety, date of planting, types of pesticides used, yield, and other pertinent information and start keeping permanent records. They will help you in the future.

Do not prune or thin plants because your neighbor is doing so. Do it only when you need to get rid of diseased parts, to provide more light, to train or make plants more productive, or to give them the space required.

Don't try to fool Mother Nature very often. Mulches and greenhouse type devices (hot caps, tents) can be used successfully in the garden, but learn their limitations. Do not try to extend the season in the fall by fertilizing late. This often results in winter injury. Let the plants go dormant as they should.

The chapters in this section on commercial horticultural crops should be read by the homeowner since he can always use some of the techniques or ideas presented, or may be able to adapt them to his special circumstances.

An Energy-Saving List For Dairy Production

By L. E. Stewart and R. F. Davis

Milk and meat from dairy cattle are major contributors to our food supply. Foods from dairy cattle provide major sources of protein, minerals — particularly calcium and phosphorus, and vitamin A and B complex vitamins, including Vitamin B_{12}. The quality of protein from milk and dairy products is high, and nutritional requirements can be met with smaller amounts than when animal products are not in the diet.

Hides provide an important source of fiber for a wide variety of uses.

Dairy production is an important agricultural enterprise in the United States, placing first to third in agricultural income in 16 of the 50 States. Over 10 million dairy cows produce milk for our daily use.

While significant quantities of grain are included in dairy rations, over two-thirds of the total feed used in milk production is from forages which have little or no alternative use in our economy. Much of the land on which forages are grown is not suited to more intensive cultivation. Thus dairy cattle and other ruminant livestock serve as collectors, concentrators, and converters of non-food plants to high quality human food. Byproducts of dairy production include a wide variety of medicinal products.

Energy from fossil fuels is used in varying amounts in milk production. Very small amounts of energy are required for the harvesting of forages by grazing, with more intensive use in concentrated feeding systems particularly the feeding of high producing dairy cattle. Some energy is required indirectly by dairy production in the manufacture and construction of buildings, machinery, and equipment required for this activity.

Many functions of dairy production require direct input of energy as discussed below.

LARRY E. STEWART *is Associate Professor and Chairman, Department of Agricultural Engineering, University of Maryland.* Richard F. Davis *is Professor and Chairman, Department of Dairy Science.*

U.S. agriculture used 223.2 trillion Btu's of energy for operations directly relating to livestock production in 1978. This was nearly 11 percent of the total energy used in U.S. agriculture. The table lists forms and amounts.

Direct Energy Use for Livestock Production

Energy Form	Units	Quantity
Gasoline	1,000 Gallons	604,363
Diesel Fuel	1,000 Gallons	487,283
Fuel Oil	1,000 Gallons	10,218
LP Gas	1,000 Gallons	403,845
Natural Gas	Million Cubic Feet	5,141
Coal	Tons	36,522
Electricity	Million Kilowatt Hours	9,961

Milk production accounted for a significant portion of this energy. On-farm operations include feed processing and handling, waste disposal, water supply and heating, space heating, ventilation, lighting, milking and milk cooling, and vehicle use directly related to dairy production.

These operations are important steps in production of high quality milk for the consumer. Although these operations are performed on individual farms in many different ways, the following describes typical farming operations in terms of how energy is actually used in producing these important foods.

Feed Processing, Handling. Farmers must provide carefully balanced rations to dairy cows to produce the maximum amount of milk per animal. To accomplish this, grains must be mechanically reduced by grinding. Then they are thoroughly mixed with necessary protein concentrates, vitamins, minerals, and sometimes forages. Finally the mixture is conveyed to the animals in feeding areas.

Devices such as hammer or roller type mills are used to grind grains so the animals can use the feed in an efficient way. Vertical or horizontal mixers are used to insure that the feed each animal receives contains all nutrients needed for maximum production.

Auger, belt, or chain conveyors requiring little energy are frequently used to carry processed feeds from the storage area to the cattle. Trucks or tractor-drawn wagons with mechanized unloading are used on many farms to mix and distribute feed.

Dairy cows also are fed silage and hay. Silage is frequently stored in upright silos in which mechanical unloaders are used to move the material from the silo onto conveyors or vehicles that carry feed to the cattle. Silage stored in horizontal silos (bunker or pit type) is loaded on vehicles by front-end loaders or specially designed elevators for transport to feeding areas.

Hay for dairy cattle is generally baled and moved into storage. It is transported by conveyors or vehicles for feeding.

Disposal of Waste

Farmers must pay special attention to waste handling operations to provide sanitary products, insure animal health, and prevent environmental pollution. Dairy producers must remove wastes from animal production units on a daily basis to meet regulatory and sanitation requirements.

Methods most commonly used for waste removal are either mechanical scraping or water flush systems. In mechanical scraping, a tractor mounted blade pushes wastes from the production area into a manure spreader for direct distribution, or to an approved storage tank or basin for later distribution on the land.

The water flush system involves releasing water at a controlled rate over a paved surface to wash the wastes into a lagoon or storage tank. These fluid wastes are then typically pumped through an irrigation system so that fertilizer value of the manure can be used in crop production.

Water Supply, Heating. All livestock require a continuous source of clean water for drinking. Dairy operations require larger quantities of water for animal consumption and for washing milking equipment and milking areas.

Health officials regularly inspect dairy farms to be sure milk is produced under stringent sanitary conditions. A dependable supply of clean hot water is essential to the dairy farmer in meeting the health regulations.

Most milking parlors use space heating for the comfort of milkers during winter months. Hot air furnaces, electric heaters, or radiant panels are used to help operators in the cold, wet environment that may exist in such facilities.

Ventilation and Lighting

Sometimes dairy cattle are kept in buildings designed to provide maximum production efficiency. As a result animals are often rather concentrated and ventilation is needed to control moisture and odors within the production units.

A variety of fan ventilation systems are used to remove a controlled amount of air from these

326-621 O - 80 - 5 : QL 2

facilities that will prevent moisture and odor buildup without removing excessive heat from the building.

Lighting is for two purposes. One is to allow animals to locate feed and water, the other so workers can observe the animals and perform tasks related to their care.

Milking, Cooling. Automatic milking systems have been developed to quickly and carefully harvest the milk crop. These systems are electrically operated and controlled.

Vacuum systems are used to withdraw milk from the cow and then convey the milk to refrigerated tanks. Again, health regulations require the milk to be quickly cooled in these tanks to insure a high quality product. All components of the milking system are automatically washed and sanitized upon completion of each milking operation.

Farm trucks and autos are used in providing many functions related to milk production. Worker transport, on-farm animal transport, and hauling of feeds and other supplies are the primary users of energy in this aspect of livestock production.

Energy Conservation

Farmers, like all U.S. citizens, are striving to reduce energy use in every possible way. Following are some of the important things dairy producers can do to cut energy use in their operations.

Savings on Feed

- Use low horsepower grinders operating for longer time periods to minimize energy consumption in feed grinding and mixing.
- In large operations, use three-phase electrical service to reduce cost of motors and improve system efficiency.
- Use conveyors and augers to replace vehicles in distributing feed.
- Maintain all equipment according to manufacturers' specifications (lubrication, alignment, etc.).
- Let cattle self-feed to eliminate mechanical equipment where possible.
- Set up gravity flow of materials where the operational situation permits.
- Use controlled grazing to provide forage for animals at appropriate times of year.

Waste Disposal. Proper maintenance of mechanical equipment is essential. The system must conserve all of the plant nutrients so they can be returned to support crop production.

Select equipment carefully to provide an efficient flow of materials through the entire system. Waste water can be recycled for flushing wastes from animal housing areas.

Tips on Water Supply, Heating

Use intermediate storage water systems. These systems employ a low horsepower pump to fill a large reservoir of water to supply needs of cattle and for sanitation.

Maintain animal waterers properly to minimize spillage and leakage.

Insulating water heaters can reduce energy use as much as 10 percent. Set thermostat settings on water heaters no higher than maximum water temperatures needed. Drain water heaters periodically to flush out lime desposits and improve heating efficiency.

Insulate hot water lines that pass through unheated areas.

In space heating, insulate walls and ceilings of heated areas. Carefully size the heating unit to match environmental conditions needed. Maintain the heating system according to manufacturers' specifications. Insulate heating ducts. Keep thermostats at lowest acceptable settings.

Note that wood stoves offer an alternative for some on-farm situations.

Use Natural Ventilation If Possible

Eliminate mechanical ventilation and use natural ventilation where possible by renovation of existing buildings and design in new construction.

When warm animal housing facilities are required, consider a convertible system which would be closed, warm and mechanically ventilated during cold months, open and naturally ventilated during warm months.

Reduce ventilation rates to minimum safe levels in heated buildings.

Turn off fans when ventilation is not required. Select fans with high cfm/watt rating. Clean fans and shutters frequently and provide proper lubrication and adjustment. Use temperature controlled, variable speed fans to optimize air flow and reduce energy use and loss.

In lighting, use lower wattage bulbs where practical. Turn off lights when not in use. Buy efficient bulbs and lamps.

Use task lighting to reduce whole area lighting needs.

Install dimmers where total wattage bulbs give more light than needed. Use photo-cells or timeclock controls on outside lights.

For milking and milk cooling, maintain vacuum pumps according to manufacturer's specification. Capture and use heat generated by vacuum pumps and milk cooling equipment. A major portion of hot water needs can be supplied from these sources. Adopt approved "clean in place" practices that permit lower water temperature and detergent re-use by recycling.

When using vehicles, maximize loads and minimize trips. Plan schedules carefully. Follow regular maintenance programs. Buy the right size vehicle for the job. Inflate tires properly and check weekly. Avoid excessive engine idling.

Producing Energy on a Dairy Farm

Extensive research and development is underway to find ways for dairy farmers to produce energy on the farm. Systems for producing alcohol and methane are of major interest with solar, wind and biomass use also being developed and demonstrated on farms.

Alcohol Fuels. Dairy producers have special interest in alcohol fuels they might produce, since they can also use the stillage (spent grains) byproduct remaining after distillation as feed for animals.

For example, one bushel of corn can produce 2.5 gallons of alcohol and 30 gallons of stillage containing 6 to 8 percent solids or 16 to 18 pounds of grain (dry weight) from an on-farm still. For continuous production, three gallons of stillage should have a feed value approximately equal to one pound of grain plus one pound of soybean meal or similar protein supplement.

The large quantity of water involved in the stillage presents some special problems in handling and maintaining sanitary conditions. Thorough evaluation of the economic feasibility of alcohol production on each individual farm is essential.

Methane From Wastes. Production of methane gas from animal wastes has been demonstrated as technically feasible and should become an economically feasible energy source in the near future.

It is estimated that for each 1,000 pounds of body weight of dairy cattle, 44 cubic feet of methane containing 26,000 Btu's can be produced each day.

Assuming 60 percent system efficiency, 100 dairy cows (1,500 pounds each) would produce 1.6 million Btu's of energy each day, equivalent to about 12 gallons of diesel fuel each day or 4,450 gallons per year. Properly handled, enough electricity can be produced from this source to approach meeting needs of the farm unit.

Solar Energy, Use of Wind

Equipment and methods for collecting and storing solar energy for dairy production have been demonstrated in many operations throughout the United States. Solar energy is used for hot water heating, space heating for dairy production units, and drying grain for animal feeding. Use for water heating has the advantage of continuous application and opportunity for direct storage of energy collected during periods of intense sunlight.

Wind systems have been developed to efficiently pump water or to generate electricity for use on dairy farms. Wind energy applications are very site specific. In other words, water can be pumped or electricity generated only where the wind blows in a relatively continuous fashion.

In coastal, mountainous or plains areas such conditions usually exist. In other parts of the country a dependable wind supply may not exist, and a wind system would have limited use in milk production.

Biomass Problems. Corn stover, straw and other crop residues can be collected, compacted and burned to produce energy for water or space heating and crop drying.

There is normally sufficient residue remaining on a corn field to provide more energy than needed for drying the crop. However, efficient methods for harvesting the residue have not been developed. Also, there is concern that removal of too much of the residue will reduce organic matter in the soil and also may contribute to increased soil erosion.

Additional research and development is underway and methods may be found to turn crop residues into a viable energy source.

Further Reading:

Agricultural Anaerobic Digesters, Bulletin 827, Ag. Mailing Room, 112 Agriculture Administration Building, The Pennsylvania State University, University Park, PA 16802. Free.

Energy and U.S. Agriculture: 1974 and 1978, Statistical Bulletin 632, ESCS Publications, U.S. Department of Agriculture, Room 0054-S, Washington, DC 20250. Free.

Small-Scale Fuel Alcohol Production, #001-000-04124-0, U.S. Department of Agriculture, for sale from Superintendent of Documents, U.S. Government Printing Office, Washington, DC 20402. $6.

How to Raise Hogs For Less Money

By C. Stanislaw and B. Driggers

Conserving energy on a hog farm is not always a simple or direct process. Every action must be viewed in the total context of net productivity. Adjusting the heat lower in the nursery, for example, will cause the pigs to compensate by lowering their feed efficiency. Diarrhea or respiratory problems also can occur.

Some form of compensation for an inferior environment can develop at any point in the chain of production. At all times the swine producer needs to be aware of the pig's environmental needs for maximum productivity. His energy conservation program must be directed at providing this optimum animal environment with greater energy efficiency. Compromising the environment itself to save energy is counterproductive.

Let's first take up energy conservation through building design and construction.

Confinement continues to be the trend in swine production, largely to reduce labor and to improve performance through greater environmental control. Thus, we must identify construction practices and materials usage that will aid in conserving energy.

Tight construction is essential to reduce infiltration losses. It has been estimated that through small cracks and openings in a building and around doors and windows, air infiltrates at the rate of 220 cubic feet per hour per foot of crack with a wind velocity of 15 miles per hour.

With an outside temperature of 30° F and an inside temperature of 75° F, typical conditions in some parts of the country during winter, the infiltration loss for a typical 3 ft. x 6.5 ft. poorly fitted door is equivalent to 0.9 gallons of LP gas per day. Most buildings will have several doors and windows which then will significantly increase heat losses because of infiltration.

Weatherstripping around doors will drastically

CHARLES M. STANISLAW *is Professor, Extension Swine Husbandry, Area Swine Specialist, North Carolina State University, Wilson. L. Bynum Driggers is Extension Professor, Biological and Agricultural Engineering, North Carolina State University, Raleigh.*

lower this kind of loss. Also, plastic film tightly fitted over windows will reduce infiltration and simultaneously provide a storm window effect which further cuts conduction losses through this area.

Insulation is absolutely essential to minimize heat loss in the winter and heat gain in the summer. Materials made for this purpose must be installed in the walls, ceiling, roof, under the floor or around the foundation.

The first illustration shows the effect of insulation on heat loss in relationship to the insulation thickness and its resistance or "R" value. In general, sufficient insulation should be provided to keep the heat loss below 5 Btu/hr per square foot.

The second illustration shows the relationship between insulation thickness and its "R" value.

A typical 20-crate farrowing house is 24 ft. x 56 ft. with 8-foot walls. When insulated to insure a heat loss of no more than 5 Btu/hr/sq. ft., the total heat

Effect of insulation upon heat loss through the walls, ceiling, or roof.

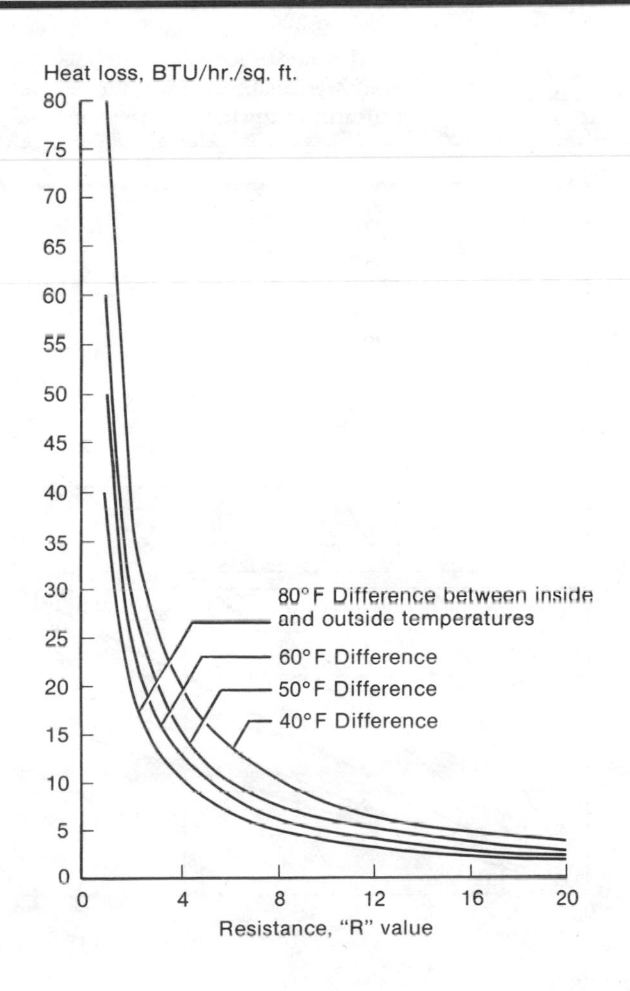

loss through the walls and ceiling is 13,120 Btu/hr or the equivalent of 0.14 gallons of LP gas per hour or 3.4 gallons per day.

A poorly insulated house where the heat loss is 15 Btu/hr per square foot will require 0.43 gallons of LP gas or equivalent per hour or 10.3 gallons per day.

Thus, it becomes apparent that insulation is the key to reducing heat losses through exposed areas.

Adequate amounts of insulation should be installed during initial construction because it is easier and cheaper to install at that time. In existing inadequately insulated buildings, additional insulation should be provided but many times it will be more difficult and costly to install. A one-time investment in adequate insulation results in a long term energy savings.

Ventilation Design

Proper ventilation is an essential compatible component of confinement swine housing. But over-ventilation can be costly because of the heating requirements for the ventilating air. It can also be costly as measured by pig performance when a building is under-ventilated.

A common misconception is that heating costs

Relationship between "R" value and insulation thickness.

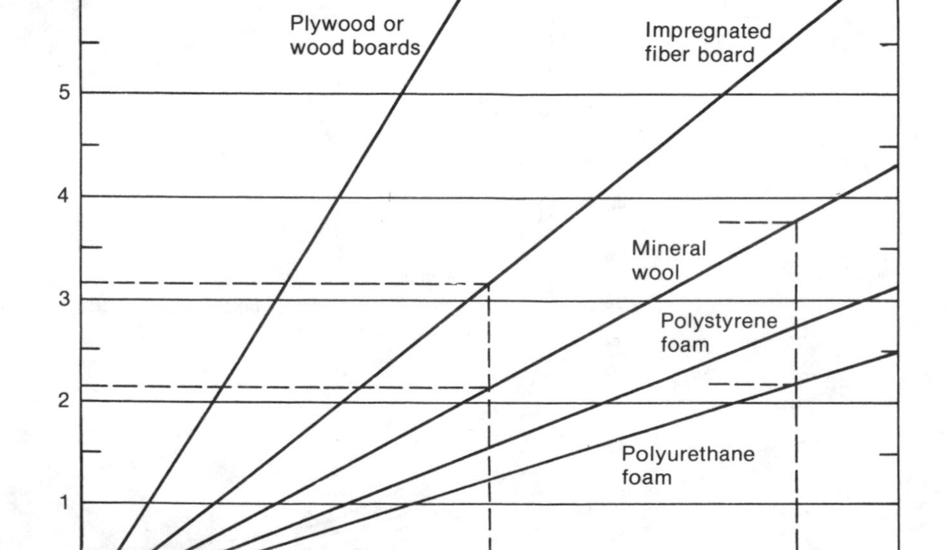

will be reduced when the inside temperature is dropped by lowering the thermostat setting. Losses through the structure will be less but the ventilation loss will be much greater.

Incoming cold air must be heated in order to increase its moisture-holding capacity. Cold air has little capacity for picking up moisture. In general, the moisture-holding capacity doubles as the air temperature is raised 20° F.

An example will illustrate the interrelationships between air temperatures, ventilation rate and heating requirements.

A farrowing house maintained at 70° F and 75 percent relative humidity (RH) while the outside air temperature is at 30° F and 75 percent RH requires a ventilation rate of approximately 25 cubic feet of air per minute (cfm) to remove the one pound of moisture produced per hour by the sow and litter. If the inside temperature is maintained at 50° F and 75 percent RH while the outside remains at 30° F and 75 percent RH, the ventilation required to remove the pound of moisture is 70 cfm.

To heat the 25 cfm from 30° F to 70° F requires 1,160 Btu per hour, but to heat the 70 cfm from 30° F to 50° F requires 1,625 Btu per hour.

With the minimum ventilation the heat requirement per day is 27,840 Btu or 0.30 gallons of LP gas or equivalent. But in the cooler room with the higher ventilation rate the LP gas requirement is 0.42 gallons per day, or an increase of 40 percent in the heating requirement.

Hence, the best approach to energy efficiency in enclosed, well-insulated confinement buildings is to maintain the temperature in the 70° F to 80° F range and provide good air distribution with precise control over the winter ventilation rate for moisture removal. Adjustments may be necessary in the ventilation rate for gas removal depending upon waste management practices employed in the building.

Equipment Management

The modern swine farm has a large variety of energy-consuming equipment. Any piece of this equipment, properly maintained or used, will require less energy to operate.

Hot air heating systems should have the air filters checked daily and cleaned if necessary. Swine buildings frequently are dusty, especially under minimum ventilation during the colder months. This further emphasizes the need for checking the filters regularly.

This same dust coats the louvers on ventilation fans. Moisture in the air cakes the dust, increasing the weight on the louvers and resulting in less air flow by the fan. Clean the louvers regularly.

Do not oil the louver hinges since oil will capture and hold dust particles, thus aggravating the problem. Use powdered graphite if lubrication is required.

Fan blades likewise can cake with dust and operate less efficiently. They should be cleaned periodically, also.

Many ventilation fans in swine buildings operate from an automatic variable speed control. Keeping such fans "balanced" with some heating systems can be difficult. This is especially so if the variable speed control has a very narrow range between high speed and low speed. Under these circumstances the fan speeds up and exhausts too much warm air every time the heater comes on.

In such situations, replace the automatic variable speed control with a manual variable speed control. With a manual control the fan stays at whatever speed the operator sets it.

Electric controls in farrowing houses that automatically dim heat lamps or other electric heating units as the temperature increases inside the building are a great energy saver.

These controls automatically adjust the heat output to the pigs from the warmest part of the day to the coolest part of the night. They also avoid the rapid temperature changes that can occur if the

Clean the louvers on hog house ventilators regularly. The added weight of accumulated dirt can cut air flow from the fan.

WM. CARNAHAN

operator only has the alternative of turning heating units completely on or off.

Accurate, dependable thermostats on all heating units are a must for energy efficiency. Coil sensors generally are more efficient than mercury bulbs. Mercury thermostats are especially unreliable because an accumulation of dust on the bulb and spring greatly increases the on-off range. Installing dust protectors or taping the openings are not recommended since they tend to "insulate" the thermostat against room temperature changes.

Even though animal behavior dictates actual control settings, an accurate thermometer is necessary in environmentally controlled buildings. A thermometer serves two functions: 1) it establishes the rough or approximate settings which are fine-tuned by animal behavior, and 2) it enables the operator to recognize thermostats that are changing in their sensitivity.

On-farm feed processing equipment is most energy-efficient if hammers and screens in the mill are promptly replaced when worn. Most proportioner type mills have the capability of bypassing some preground ingredients around the hammers and screens. When ingredients not requiring additional grinding are so bypassed, the energy load in the mill is reduced.

Fogging or sprinkling systems in the summer should be on thermostats and timers. Fogging for two or three minutes out of ten is as effective as constant fogging. Also, studies have shown that less drinking water is wasted with nipple waterers than with bowl waterers. Keep in mind that energy is required to provide all the water used on a hog farm, even if it is wasted.

Managing Animals

Pigs of all ages respond to their environment in a manner that clearly demonstrates how comfortable or uncomfortable they are. Every successful swine producer understands these responses and adjusts the environment as necessary. He knows that the most efficient animal is a comfortable animal.

One of the most frequently seen expressions of pig discomfort is piling up to keep warm.

Nursing pigs huddled against the sow, or even on top of her, are cold regardless of the actual room temperature. Likewise, pigs piled up at the source of supplemental heat are not getting enough warmth from the heat source. This may also indicate that the rest of the room is being kept too cold. Pigs piled along a wall or along the length of a pen partition are attempting to avoid cold drafts.

Comfortable pigs, however, are uniformly distributed over the entire floor.

Pigs under stress will have environmental needs different from those of similar pigs not under stress. Pigs that are weaned, moved, mixed or sick will require an adjustment in the environment to be comfortable. This is why no control settings are sacred. They must be changed as needs of the animals dictate.

The proper environment is provided most efficiently when all pens, crates, or other holding areas are fully stocked with animals. It costs no more to operate a heat lamp for a litter of ten pigs than it does for a litter of six. Likewise, energy requirements to heat a nursery are no less when the pens are only partially full. This same reasoning generally applies to energy required for ventilation. The more pigs that can utilize a given input of energy, the less energy cost chargeable to each pig.

Kansas livestock producer Arlan Benteman heats his swine farrowing houses with solar power. He should recover his initial investment within 7 years.

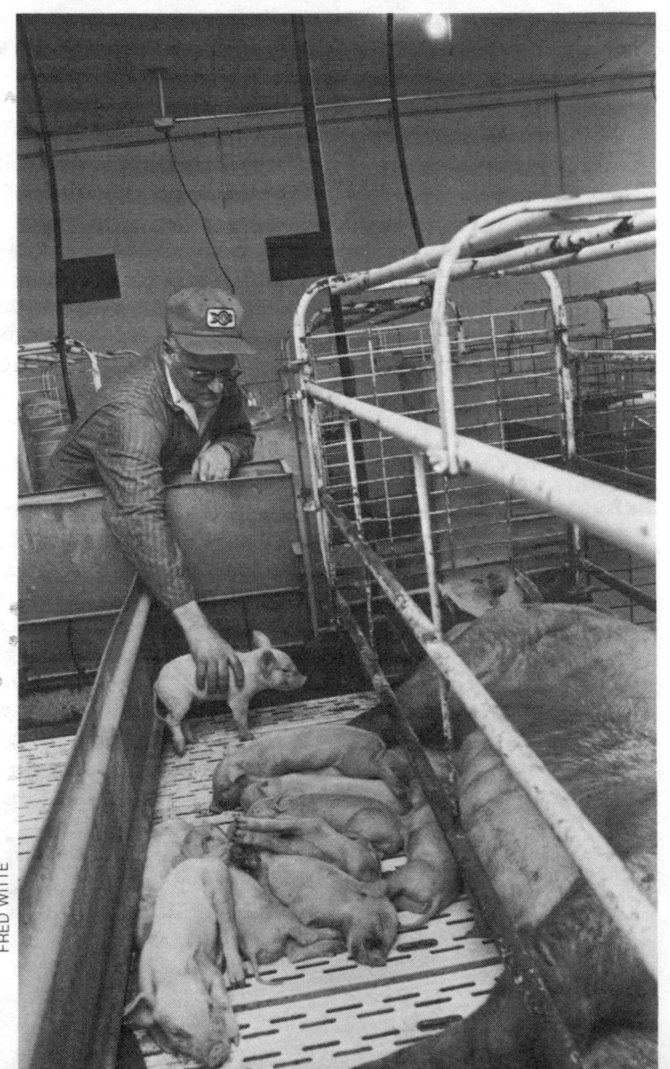

FRED WITTE

Obviously, the farm with the highest reproductive rate, lowest death loss, etc., will operate more efficiently in terms of energy utilization than one with suboptimum production of animals.

Swine production units are generally more energy-efficient if the facilities are designed so that only one age group of pigs occupies a given room or building at a time. This commonly is referred to as the all-in, all-out concept. It is a popular design to help promote animal health. Fortunately, it also promotes energy efficiency.

If two age groups of pigs occupy a single nursery room, the temperature must be maintained high enough for the younger pigs. This additional heat is wasted on the older pigs in the room since the older pigs have a lower heat requirement.

If two different age groups must occupy a single room or building, the arrangement should be with the older or larger pigs across the aisle from the younger or smaller pigs. That will create the same heating or ventilation demands at all points in the length of the building.

This arrangement is preferred because it is virtually impossible to provide two distinctly different environments in one room with any degree of energy efficiency.

New Concepts

Several alternatives to fossil fuel usage have been promulgated, but very little technical base for design as to the effectiveness, applicability, practicality, and cost effectiveness accompanies all the rhetoric.

Research in many areas is underway and in time meaningful results will be forthcoming, but for the present one must be realistic about the current state of development.

Solar. Application of solar energy to swine buildings as a means of heating ventilating air is suspect presently, in the authors' opinion. Some research has shown annual savings of 1 to 2 gallons of propane for each square foot of collector.

For immediate application, though, solar's greatest potential may be to heat or preheat water because water is a good storage medium. Heat stored in the water can be used during non-daylight hours when the collector is non-functional.

Methane. Possibilities of producing methane from swine waste must be considered because of tremendous public and producer interest.

The technical feasibility of methane production from swine waste as well as other types of waste has been documented. However, the economic justification for this process has not been demonstrated.

To be profitable, methane production depends upon economy of scale, cost of fossil fuel, and recovering solid residues for animal refeeding and liquid effluents for fertilizer.

Below-Ground Buildings. Below-ground buildings do not appear to be too practical. As pointed out previously, the greatest requirement for heat is to warm ventilating air, and below-ground construction would not contribute to energy savings in this respect.

The moisture load could be increased because of underground water intrusion. This would result in higher ventilation rates and subsequently higher heating costs.

Additional problems could be encountered in moving animals in and out and also removing waste from the buildings.

Geothermal. Several researchers have espoused theories on geothermal heating and cooling. To date, though, no specific design criteria and cost effectiveness of this process have been developed.

Wood-Burning Alternative

One practical alternative to fossil fuel consumption is a wood-burning heating system. Many producers have access to wood or forest residues, and furnaces or heaters are available for incorporation in swine buildings. However, wood is costly in many areas.

Energy content of wood is approximately 8,600 Btu per pound, but it can vary depending upon resin content. A cord of wood (128 cubic feet by volume) contains 80 cubic feet of solid wood after the air spaces are deducted.

If the wood weighs 40 pounds per cubic foot, typical for many hardwoods, the energy content is 27.5 million Btu per cord, equivalent to 299 gallons of LP gas.

All this energy will not be available, though, because of losses in the combustion process and the heating equipment.

Economics of Energy

Swine producers have become very conscious of the cost of energy and the need to conserve energy whenever possible. Yet energy is only one of many variable costs that producers incur each year.

Compared to other variable costs in a typical swine confinement setup, energy accounts for less than 10 percent of the total cost in producing feeder pigs, less than 1 percent for feeding them to market weight, and less than 5 percent for the entire operation.

This is illustrated by the energy consumption and cost data at the North Carolina Swine Development Center (see first table). The table includes data only for the most recent year available so that current energy costs would be more nearly represented. From this table it is obvious that opportunities for significant energy conservation are in producing feeder pigs.

Energy Consumption
North Carolina Swine Development Center, 1979

	Percent of Variable Cost		
Energy	Producing Feeder Pigs	Feeding Out	Farrow to Finish
Electricity	2.1	0.8	1.8
LP Gas	6.0	0.0	2.5

The second table, from the same farm, illustrates the actual energy used for various parameters within the feeder pig production phase. This distribution between the farrowing house and the nursery building is specific for the production system employed on that farm.

Energy Consumption
North Carolina Swine Development Center, 1970-79

	Farrowing		Nursery	
	kWh	LP Gas (gal.)	kWh	LP Gas (gal.)
Per sow maintained	234.6	18.1	360.0	39.6
Per litter farrowed	118.2	9.2	130.6	20.1
Per pig farrowed, live	11.6	0.9	12.8	2.0
Per pig weaned	13.5	1.0	14.9	2.3
Per pig marketed	14.6	1.1	16.2	2.2

In any system, however, attempts to conserve energy should be made in two areas.

One is to reduce actual energy needs by proper building, ventilation, heating, and insulation design, by proper equipment operation and by appropriate animal management. The other is by more efficiently using energy which is consumed.

Some Better Ways To Raise Poultry

By F. D. Thornberry

Development of America's highly efficient poultry industry and the accompanying economical consumer price of eggs and poultry meat has been the direct result of dependable energy sources.

This energy dependency will continue in the foreseeable future and can have a profound effect on all segments of the poultry industry — production, transportation, processing, and distribution. Interruption of energy supplies would cause a severe burden on the industry, consumers, and the Nation.

Recent USDA data show that brooding accounts for about 71 percent of the energy used in on-farm poultry production. Lighting and ventilation use 7 and 4 percent, respectively. Waste handling, and operation of feeding and egg collection equipment, are responsible for about 18 percent. Energy costs account for about 20 percent of total variable costs of producing caged eggs, and 30 percent for broiler production.

Energy use per production unit varies greatly between types of poultry and housing, regions, and individual producers. Climatic conditions cause some differences, but these are often modified by varying management practices, building design, and degree of mechanization.

Costlier energy causes economic hardship for poultry producers. As individuals, producers have little flexibility and exert a minimal influence on prices. They must absorb increased energy costs since they are unable to pass them on to the consumer.

The poultry industry also is totally dependent on feed grain supplies. In the future, the most important problem facing industry and consumers alike may be the availability and cost of feed grain.

Extremely high grain prices caused by high energy and fertilizer costs could conceivably push poultry and egg prices beyond an acceptable level. This could seriously injure the poultry industry.

FREDRICK D. THORNBERRY *is Project Group Supervisor in Poultry Science and Poultry Specialist, Texas Agricultural Extension Service, Texas A&M University.*

Costly energy, questions concerning energy supplies and inability of producers to pass on all of the production costs indicate a real need for improving energy management. Realistically, initial conservation of energy will stem from applying small energy saving techniques. Short term cost benefits will be needed to stimulate immediate change.

The potential for reducing energy use without a detrimental effect on production is significant. For most producers, identifying and adopting energy efficient practices and closer attention to detail will effect an immediate saving in energy dollars.

Development and maintenance of appropriate energy records are essential for an effective energy conservation program. Such records will assist in determining areas of excess use and in documenting post-adjustment savings.

Data needed include electrical and fuel consumption for poultry facilities, mileage or operating time and fuel consumed by vehicles, a list of major energy uses areas, and maintenance and repair records. Other items needed include flock performance and environmental temperature records, energy ratings for equipment, and installation and service manuals.

Changes in general poultry farm operational practices can significantly reduce energy expenditures for most operations. Management personnel must strive to make every employee conscious of energy conservation.

Rolling Stock Purchases

Purchases of rolling stock should be oriented to energy efficient vehicles of a size and horsepower suitable for the job required. Vehicles equipped with manual transmission often require less fuel to operate than those with automatic transmissions. Air-conditioning may not be essential for some vehicles and employees.

Adherence to recommended engine maintenance schedules, proper tire pressure, and correct driving procedures will lower fuel consumption. Driving procedures include minimal braking, smooth acceleration, and moderate speeds at an even pace. Engines should be turned off rather than allowed to idle when the vehicles are required to stop for extended periods of time.

Lights, air-conditioning, and heating units should be turned off when not needed. Thermostats should be checked and adjusted to provide comfort and minimize energy use for both summer and winter operations.

Insulation levels in heated or cooled work areas should be evaluated and increased if practical. Holes

326-621 0 - 80 - 6 : QL 2

and cracks around doors and windows should be sealed.

An inventory of spare parts should be maintained to keep travel for replacement parts to a minimum.

Energy costs for pelleting may offset nutritional advantages of pelleted feeds. Added feed storage capacity can reduce the frequency of feed delivery.

For egg farms, the frequency and volume of egg pickup and delivery may be altered.

Energy required to incinerate dead birds and organic refuse may make disposal pits or burying more feasible for some operations.

Well insulated water heaters of the minimum capacity needed should be installed adjacent to or in areas of major use, and hot water pipes should be insulated.

Purchasing decisions should be based on equipment operating costs as well as purchase price. Price alone can no longer be the final determinant. More expensive but energy efficient equipment may pay back the added cost many times with energy savings during projected life of the equipment.

Orientation of Housing

Improved housing is a key to reducing energy requirements in production. House orientation can have an important effect on energy efficiency. An east-west orientation minimizes the solar heat load in summer.

Virtually all layers, broilers and replacement pullets are maintained in confinement housing with

Cyclone solar collectors can save energy.

WM. CARNAHAN

varying degrees of environmental modification. Confinement rearing of turkeys is increasing.

Enclosed housing for broilers and layers is a reality in many Northern States. These houses permit greater bird density and improve feed efficiency in cold weather. They are a necessity in some northern areas, even though energy required for ventilation is increased.

In the South, curtain sidewall housing is most common. There, the economics of enclosed housing are not well documented. Greatly increased amounts of energy for proper ventilation and cooling in summer are required and improvements in winter feed efficiency are less dramatic.

Insulation is essential if poultry houses are to be energy efficient. Practically all new houses are insulated and many older structures have had insulation added. Amount of insulation used is a primary factor controlling energy use and efficiency. While adequate insulation is expensive, payback through energy savings and improved performance can generally be attained in 5 to 7 years.

Proper insulation of most types of poultry housing reduces energy costs in hot as well as cold weather. In winter, adequate roof or ceiling insulation can reduce heat loss and energy requirements in the form of extra brooder fuel or feed. In cold climates wall insulation is profitable.

Ceiling or roof insulation in summer can minimize radiant heat from the sun, reducing temperature stress problems and ventilation and cooling requirements. Roofs of older uninsulated houses are often coated with whitewash or white paint to reflect radiant heat and minimize heat stress.

A variety of insulation materials are in use. Insulation capabilities of different materials vary widely. Spray-on polyurethane insulation is popular for insulating existing houses. It is easy to apply and effective in sealing air leaks.

Plastic and cellulose type insulation materials are flammable, particularly when coated with dust — a normal situation in poultry houses. Insulation should be fire-retardant treated or protected from the potential of ignition.

Houses and poultry have been lost as a result of insulation ignited by backfiring motors, sparks from welding units, and electrical shorts caused by rodents chewing on unprotected wiring. Rodent damage can be a problem with all types of insulation. This calls for an effective rodent control program.

State Extension Service personnel can provide

The ceiling insulation in this Florida poultry house helps reduce radiant heat from the sun. Consequently, ventilation and cooling requirements are reduced in summer. During brooding or cold weather, the insulation reduces heat loss. This saves fuel and improves feed efficiency.

C.R. DOUGLAS

recommendations on insulation needs for a particular area of the United States.

Brooding a Big Factor

Brooding accounts for almost three-fourths of the on-farm energy required in poultry production. In the past, energy for brooding has often been used inefficiently. However, increasing fuel costs and the threat of shortages of natural and LP gases have created a realization that brooding efficiencies and resultant fuel savings must be improved dramatically.

Brooding practices are quite similar for all commercial species of poultry, although turkeys and replacement stock require more space than broilers. Fuel requirements are, of course, much higher in winter than other seasons. Usage in the South is higher than climatic differences require because lower levels of insulation and more open housing is used, resulting in greater energy loss.

The amount of insulation used in housing, tightness of housing, and management expertise of producers influence fuel requirements for brooding. A number of improved brooding practices can reduce fuel requirements. These include partial house brooding, winterizing houses, proper maintenance of brooders, and adoption of fuel efficient management practices.

Partial house brooding is receiving greater acceptance as a means of reducing fuel consumption. U.S. Department of Agriculture researchers in Mississippi have shown this practice can reduce fuel consumption as much as two-thirds over conventional brooding systems. Under most commercial conditions the practice can cut fuel required by at least 25 percent.

In partial house brooding, chicks, or poults are normally confined to 15 to 30 percent of the house during the initial 10 to 14 days of brooding. A plastic curtain is installed from ceiling to floor to separate the brooding area from the remainder of the house.

Proper ventilation, adequate insulation, and attentive management are critical. Mechanical ventilation is needed to provide adequate air movement for removal of moisture and to control ammonia levels.

Following the initial brooding period the curtain is generally moved to the center of the house for an additional 10 to 14 days, after which it is removed and the entire house placed in use.

Weather conditions determine how long brooders will be used. In freezing weather, some heat should

FRED WITTE

Partial house brooding is receiving greater acceptance as a means of reducing fuel consumption. The plastic curtain in the background confines the chickens to 15 to 30 percent of the house and can reduce fuel consumption as much as two-thirds over conventional brooding systems.

Adjusting a curtain used in partial house brooding on a contract broiler farm.

HERB BREVARD

be supplied to the unused portion of the house to prevent frozen water pipes and hoses.

Fuel requirements for brooding can be cut 10 to 15 percent and feed efficiency improved by winterizing curtain wall houses. This is easily done by tacking a layer of polyethylene to the inside of sidewall openings to reduce air leakage. If houses depend on natural ventilation via curtain manipulation, the plastic should not extend the complete height of the sidewall opening. Other sites of air leakage and heat loss should be sealed. Even small air leaks can be costly.

Extra ventilation and managerial attention may be required to prevent excessive moisture and wet litter or high house temperatures during periods of increasing environmental temperatures.

Sidewall curtains must be kept in good repair. Rodents should be controlled to minimize curtain damage and feed wastage. An initial brooding temperature of 84° F (29° C) to 86° F (30° C) rather than the commonly accepted 90° F (32° C) is acceptable under most conditions. A slightly higher brooding temperature may be needed if chicks or poults have been stressed, or high humidity conditions prevail. Reducing brooding temperatures 2° to 3° F every 3 to 4 days rather than 5° F per week can save fuel.

The maximum feasible number of poultry should be brooded under each brooder. Capacity can be increased by 10 percent or more by clustering brooders in groups and using a single brooder guard per cluster. Solid brooder guards are of assistance in holding more heat in the brooding area.

Pilot lights on alternate brooders can often be turned off in warm weather and during the latter stage of brooding. Cage brooded layer replacement pullets should be started in the top deck where room temperature is highest.

Proper brooder maintenance on a scheduled basis will minimize brooder failure during severe temperature periods. It will also reduce maintenance labor requirements when labor is needed for more intensive chores.

A thermometer should be used to check the accuracy of thermostat controls, to avoid wasting fuel and stressing poultry. Inspections for gas leaks should be frequent to minimize fuel loss and danger from fire or explosion.

Fuel efficiency ratings as well as initial cost should be a strong consideration when purchasing brooders.

Electrical energy requirements for many poultry operations can be reduced through modified practices and changes in lighting, ventilation, feeding, egg collection and waste management systems.

Lighting Schedules

Lighting practices which will conserve energy include reducing day-length or hours of light received per day, decreasing light intensity, and adding reflectors. Use of fluorescent rather than incandescent lights may also be considered.

Market poultry have performed satisfactorily under a variety of lighting schedules, including 23 hours of low intensity light and various intermittent lighting programs. Electricity for lighting can be reduced by adopting a proven intermittent program and using low intensity lighting at 0.5 foot candle at bird level.

Daylengths greater than 15 hours per day seldom improve laying flock performance. Similarily, a light intensity of 0.5 foot candle is sufficient to stimulate optimum egg production.

However, neither daylength nor light intensity should be reduced on laying flocks in production. Adoption of shorter end lighting programs and a reduction in light intensity should be considered for new flocks at the initiation of lay.

Intermittent lighting of layers as a means of reducing electrical usage has been advocated but has not gained widespread industry acceptance. Reasons include the necessity for enclosed housing and greater managerial attention.

Simple aluminum reflectors and periodic cleaning of bulbs will permit use of lower wattage bulbs to produce the same light intensity, and can reduce electricity requirements 25 percent. A clean 25-watt bulb and reflector provides about the same intensity as a clean 40-watt bulb with no reflector or a dirty 60-watt bulb with no reflector.

In new housing rows of lights should be staggered to improve light distribution. Distance between bulbs should be about one and one-half times the distance from the light to the floor, depending on ceiling height. Distance from the wall should be half the distance between bulbs.

Fluorescent lights are more efficient in energy usage than incandescent lights and should be considered for new housing. However, fluorescent fixtures and bulbs may have a higher initial cost than incandescent and also present greater maintenance problems.

Poultry house ventilation is a three factor process involving air exchange, moisture removal, and house temperature modifications.

Natural ventilation is commonly used in open-sidewall housing. It depends on natural air currents and requires no expenditure of electricity. Mechanical ventilation is necessary for enclosed housing and is used in conjunction with natural ventilation in many high density houses with open sidewalls.

Effective ventilation at minimum cost becomes increasingly critical with increases in housing size and bird density, or when brooding and management practices are drastically altered as with partial house brooding. Optimum ventilation rates depend on climate, desired temperature and humidity ranges, house construction, waste management system, and type and age of poultry.

Air Pressure Systems

Both positive (forced) and negative (exhaust) air pressure systems are used for mechanical ventilation of poultry housing.

Positive pressure systems force air movement into and through the house and are commonly used for ventilating and cooling poultry in open type housing. In contrast, negative pressure systems are commonly used in enclosed or curtain tight housing. Air is brought in through well-distributed wall or ceiling slot inlets or by cracking tight fitting curtains near the top of the wall.

Economical and effective ventilation using either of these systems depends on the proper selection and efficient performance of ventilating equipment. The producer is interested in initial cost, maintenance requirements, and operational cost as measured by the amount of air moved per watt of power consumed under given conditions.

Differences in fan efficiency occur not only between fans of manufacturers but also between fan types of a given manufacturer. Independent testing agencies evaluate many brands and types of fans to determine air flow and power requirements.

Data collected allow the selection of fan designs, sizes, speeds and motor size to provide the most economical ventilation for a given housing situation. Slow speed fans generally move air at a lower cost than high speed fans of the same capacity. Thus, additional or larger low speed fans are usually more economical. They may be rapidly paid for through reduced electrical requirements.

Evaluations of fans have revealed as much as 6.6 cfm/watt difference in efficiency between the least and the most efficient fans for a particular situation. This amounts to an operating cost difference of $145 per year for a fan delivering 8,000 cfm and used 3,000 hours per year. In large houses with a number of fans such a difference in efficiency can be quite significant.

In many areas of the United States, evaporative cooling in conjunction with mechanical ventilation is needed to attain satisfactory laying hen performance in high density houses during periods of high summer temperature. Properly engineered and maintained evaporative systems can reduce incoming air temperatures by 12° to 15° F when outside temperatures are in the high 90's.

HERB BREVARD

Slow speed fan in position to cool broiler chicks in summer heat wave. Slow speed fans are used to reduce energy costs. Fan is located near bird level and set at a 45° angle to maximize ventilation effectiveness.

Housing equipped with evaporative cooling systems must have roof or ceiling insulation. Houses must be tight enough to channel incoming air through evaporative pads when using a negative pressure ventilation system.

Failure to maintain pads in a functional condition can drastically reduce effectiveness of an evaporative system. Pads must be kept moist. Wood fiber pads are cheap but deteriorate rapidly. Extension Service studies in Texas have shown concrete coated fiber pads, though more expensive initially, have a much longer life expectancy with minimal labor requirements for maintenance and replacement.

Clogged fogging nozzles can reduce effectiveness of evaporative cooling pads. Nozzles should be checked frequently to assure correct operation. They can be cleaned with muriatic acid to remove mineral deposits. Filters should be installed in water systems to reduce clogging.

Inexpensive chlorination systems can be installed if sulfur or iron bacteria or algae are problems in nozzles and on cooling pads. Cooling pad water should be recirculated and water leaks and runoff kept to a minimum.

During cold weather, banks of evaporative pads should be sealed with a plastic curtain to minimize heat loss. Sufficient air intake areas should be maintained to allow for effective winter ventilation.

Sprinklers on roofs or fogging within houses are sometimes used to provide a degree of evaporative cooling and alleviate heat stress.

Proper installation and maintenance of ventilation and cooling equipment are vital if energy is to be used most efficiently and equipment life maximized. Manufacturer recommendations on installation, operation, service and maintenance should be closely followed.

Care of Fan Motors

Totally enclosed motors are essential to minimize damage from dust and humidity. Pressure lubricated or permanently lubricated bearings should be used. Time-delay fuses sized for the motor should be installed on individual fans to protect against overload.

Check fans weekly and lubricate motors when needed. Common fan problems include broken or worn belts, inoperative motors, clogged protective screens, pulleys out of alignment, and dirty blades and louvers. Motors, as well as protective screens and louvers, should be kept free of dust to maintain maximum energy efficiency.

Luis Moreno sweeps dust and feathers from fan guards in a Texas layer house. Fans move air through evaporative pads during hot summer months to cool the house.

BOBBE BAKER

Energy efficient ventilation and cooling of poultry houses can be complex. Assistance in determining ventilation and cooling requirements can be obtained from State Extension Poultry Specialists and Agricultural Engineers.

Mechanization of feeding and egg collection has increased dramatically as production unit size, labor availability, and costs have forced poultrymen to substitute energy for labor. Energy needs for feed distribution and egg collection and packing can be reduced to an extent through better management and maintenance practices.

Running time for mechanical feeders should be kept to the minimum necessary to distribute feed through the house. Feed leakage and wasted feed increases feeder running time and electrical consumption in addition to increasing feed cost.

Energy requirements and labor costs for egg collection and packing systems can be reduced by keeping egg collecting belts and equipment full by collecting once daily. However, increased shell damage from once daily gathering of eggs from flocks with poor shell quality may offset savings in electricity and labor.

Extension Service studies in Texas have shown that shell damage in the form of impact checks is directly proportional to the length of time eggs are

Magdaleno Moreno controls the flow of eggs on a collection belt on a Texas egg farm. Keeping belts and equipment loaded to capacity can cut energy requirements and labor costs in egg collection and packing systems.

BOBBE BAKER

allowed to remain in roll-out trays. It may be most economical to gather eggs from flocks with poor shell quality two to three times daily.

As with ventilation equipment, proper maintenance of mechanical feeders and egg collection systems is necessary for efficient energy usage and maximum equipment life. A recommended lubrication schedule should be maintained and motors kept free of dust. Collection and packing systems must be checked for adjustment on a frequent basis to minimize shell damage and maximize efficiency of energy use.

Selection of a watering system can also influence energy requirements. Continuous flow waterers are wasteful and increase water and accompanying energy requirements greatly over other watering systems. Water leaks should be kept to a minimum to reduce water demand and minimize waste management problems.

Intermittent watering programs can further reduce water and energy requirements. However, malfunctions which can be costly in terms of bird performance are common. Close supervision is required to prevent malfunctions.

Handling of Wastes

Energy requirements for waste handling can vary widely. A built-up or composted litter program for broilers, turkeys and pullets can reduce energy requirements for cleanout. Heat from bacterial action in the litter may provide some reduction in energy required during brooding. Energy requirements for handling caged layer waste will depend on the waste management system in use.

In-house dry storage of layer manure and periodic cleanout generally requires an increased ventilation rate. This is particularly true for high density houses. Energy is also required to dispense insecticides for fly control. Water leakage from waterers into manure beds can be a real problem in managing poultry manure.

Lagoon-flush systems, if properly constructed, minimize waste handling and fly problems. This system is increasing in popularity, particularly with egg producers who have minimal acreage for waste disposal and where markets for manure fertilizer are not readily available. Disadvantages may include an energy requirement to pump fill water for lagoons, particularly if well water is used. Fertilizer value of the manure is also usually lost.

In hot weather, pits can be flushed during the period of maximum temperature to aid in reducing house temperature.

Liquid storage of manure in pits beneath cages eliminates fly control requirements, permits greater flexibility in removing manure, and conserves much of the fertilizer value of the manure. However, farm water requirements are increased and considerable energy is used in spreading the liquid on grass or cropland. Odor complaints are possible when the liquid is dispersed.

Daily or frequent cleanout with a scraper system offers advantages but is energy intensive and requires a greater amount of equipment maintenance than other systems. Manure disposal or storage can be a problem during prolonged periods of wet weather.

Manure dehydration is not feasible except under exceptional conditions. Energy costs for dehydration are prohibitive and marketing, packaging, storage and transportation present problems.

The poultry industry depends heavily on natural

and LP gases, transportation fuels, fuel oil, and electricity. Possibilities for greater substitution of coal, wood, and solar or wind energy for those conventional fuels appear limited for the industry at the farm level.

Use of coal and wood for brooding is feasible but creates a variety of problems including storage, handling, and availability. Solar and wind energy will require further research, as will conversion of biomass and poultry manures to a usable energy form.

Dramatic increases in energy costs for mechanization, lighting, and brooding will be required to make other forms of energy competitive.

Shifts and adjustments in production patterns and locations based on energy availability will likely be minimal and slow because of unit size, investment, and complexity.

Conservation practices and selection of efficient equipment in brooding, housing and production systems — particularly in relation to ventilation and heating — appear to offer producers the greatest potential for reducing energy use and cost.

Further Reading:

Energy Use and Conservation in the Poultry and Egg Industry, AER No. 354, U.S. Department of Agriculture, ESCS Publications, Room 0054-S, Washington, DC 20250. Free.

Gas Brooder Maintenance, Extension Fact Sheet L-1772, Texas Agricultural Extension Service, Extension Publications, Texas A&M University, College Station, TX 77843. Free.

How to Produce Beef For Less Money

By Danny G. Fox

Energy use in agricultural production is about 3 percent of the total energy used in the United States annually. Less than 5 percent of the energy used in agricultural production is for beef production.

Therefore, total elimination of beef production would be of minor significance in increasing the availability of energy supplies in this country for other uses, especially when consideration is given to replacing beef as a source of food.

Of national concern is the adequate nutrition of many people in both the United States and the world in as energy efficient a way as possible. Two major concerns are the efficiency of converting food energy and protein to beef, and the proportion of this energy and protein used in beef production that could be used directly for human food.

About 70 percent of the energy and protein consumed by cattle is excreted during digestion and metabolism. About half the remainder is lost through body maintenance and death loss. However, about 80 percent of the energy fed to the total U.S. cattle population comes from forages which humans or simple stomached animals cannot use. Included are crop residues, non-grain plant parts, pasture, and hay.

Much of the grain fed to cattle is harvested, stored, and fed as high-moisture grain (rather than drying and marketing the grain) because of factors that limit the grain's value on the market, such as drought, early frost, mold, kernel damage, or contamination. Part of the non-forage feed also comes from byproducts of grain milling.

Cost of energy directly used in beef production (not including feed production) is still a relatively small fraction of the total cost. The equivalent of about 12 gallons of gasoline per cow is used to operate the cow-calf enterprise. At $1.20 a gallon, this represents less than 10 percent of the total cash

DANNY G. FOX *is Associate Professor, Animal Science, New York State College of Agriculture and Life Sciences, Cornell University.*

cost to keep a cow for a year. The equivalent of about 8½ gallons of gasoline per head is used to operate feedlots, or about 4 percent of the total cost.

However, energy used in producing feed for growing and finishing cattle is substantial. Energy to produce the feed (machine operation; fertilizer manufacturing, transport and application; pesticides; drying) for cattle fed in feedlots is about seven times greater than that used to operate the feedlot. Thus, a 15 percent savings in feed required would entirely offset energy used to operate the lot. Besides, there is more opportunity to improve feed efficiency than there is to reduce energy use in cow-calf and feedlot operation.

Hence, only a brief summary will be given to practices that will save energy in actual operation of cow-calf and feedlot enterprises. Much more discussion will be given to ways to reduce feed use per pound of beef produced. Many practices will be suggested and the potential for fuel savings will be given where estimates are available.

The sources of fuel used are gasoline, diesel, electricity, propane and natural gas. For ease of understanding, energy use has been converted to the equivalent of gasoline.

Specifics on management needed to carry out a practice will be brief. The Cooperative Extension Service in your State should be contacted for details.

Cow-Calf Operation

A large proportion of the fuel used in a cow-calf operation is for checking cattle and hauling supplemental feed to grazing cattle. Most pickups will use 2 to 4 gallons of fuel an hour. Thus, anything that can be done to reduce the number of trips will save fuel. Other practices will save fuel, either directly or by reducing use of products that require a lot of fuel to produce.

1) Feed supplement every other day rather than daily. This can result in savings for many operators of 100 to 300 gallons for the wintering period.

2) Rotational graze rather than continuous. Cattle are concentrated in a much smaller area, reducing the time and fuel required to check cattle and to distribute supplemental feed. This will also increase pasture production in most cases, giving greater carrying capacities and thus more weight produced for fixed fuel requirements. Up to 900 gallons a year could be saved on a large ranch where cattle are spread over wide areas.

3) Use legumes with the grass where possible to save on nitrogen fertilizer. In many cases the additional protein will benefit the cattle, especially grazing calves. Fuel energy required to produce, transport, and apply 100 pounds of nitrogen is about the equivalent of 22 gallons of gasoline.

4) Use grazing as much as possible. When use of harvested feeds increase, energy costs usually rise.

5) Shorten the breeding and calving season. Cattle require the greatest amount of care and observation during the breeding and calving season. If breeding is shortened, calving will also be shortened. A 60 day vs. 90 day calving season saves 30 days of intensive observation a year. This could mean 60 fewer trips per year to check cattle, which could save 100 to 300 gallons of gasoline a year, obviously depending on size of the operation and how widely dispersed the cattle are.

6) Do everything possible to increase weaning weights and percent of calf crop weaned. Many fuel costs are fixed, so increased beef produced per gallon of fuel used is a necessary goal to improve fuel efficiency. Close culling, cross-breeding, timing of calving season, pasture and supplemental feed management are some major factors involved.

Cattle Feeding

Feed production accounts for 86 percent of the energy used in beef production, with the other 14 percent for feedlot operation and feed processing. Most energy savings in the feedlot are related to properly matching equipment power requirements to a specific job, use of diesel rather than gas engines, proper maintenance of equipment, optimizing light use, and organizing feeding and manure removal to minimize engine operating time.

Much of the opportunity for reducing energy costs is in reducing the feed required per unit of gain, since it contains the majority of energy input in producing beef (machine use, fertilizer, irrigation, drying, etc.). For every ton of feed saved, fuel requirements are reduced by about 40 gallons. How can it be done?

- Optimize use of growth stimulants. Use them, re-implant as recommended, follow directions on how to properly implant. Their proper use can result in a net energy savings equal to 10 gallons of gasoline per steer fed from weaning to normal slaughter weight.
- Use feed additives that improve feed efficiency. They can save about as much as the growth stimulant. The two together thus save us up to 20 gallons of fuel in the United States per steer fed.
- Properly balance the ration. Be sure no nutrients are limited, or are greatly in excess of requirements. Seek help from the Cooperative Extension Service, feed companies, or consulting nutritionists to help formulate a feeding system.

326-621 0 - 80 - 7 : QL 2

Where possible, the major feeds used should be sampled and analyzed periodically. Then they can be accurately supplemented, considering their requirements according to stage of growth and potential rate of gain.

Calves should be sorted so that as near as possible those within a pen have similar nutrient requirements.

Feed requirements could be reduced 10 percent in many feedlots by improved ration formulation. Many farmer-feeders often are especially careless in this category. They either are not aware of the importance of these factors, do not take the time to balance them carefully or seek help, or do not follow the recommendations given. A cattle feeder careless with ration formulation and feeding 300 head can indirectly cost himself and the U.S. public the equivalent of 3,000 gallons of gasoline a year.

• Harvest and store the grains as high moisture. On the average, about 10 pints of moisture are removed per bushel of corn dried. This requires about .18 gallons of LP gas per bushel. If an average of 40 bushels are fed per steer, that's 7.2 gallons a head. In most cases, storage and feeding costs need not be greatly different if high moisture grain is used.

Any increase in storage costs, losses, or feeding costs with high moisture grain are more than offset by improvement in feed efficiency and savings in field losses through earlier harvest. More careful feeding management, however, is required. Greater attention must be given to feedbunk management and protein supplementation.

• Avoid unnecessary processing, and carefully choose a processing method. Losses are excessive when milo and most small grains are not processed. However, the major feedgrain, corn, does not always require processing for optimum efficiency. Processing generally improves feed efficiency if rations contain over 50 percent roughage, the corn is extremely dry (less than 10 percent moisture); or when cattle are over 10 to 15 months of age. But in some cases, such as steam flaking of corn, the energy cost of processing exceeds the energy used to produce the feed saved.

• Choose a feeding system carefully. Many feeding systems are employed because cattle have been used primarily to market feeds that otherwise would have a low market value. Net gasoline equivalent used per 100 pounds of gain varies from 17 to 24 gallons for feedlot finishing of a yearling steer. Rations containing higher proportions of hay and silage result in less energy for gain. However, this must be weighed against the longer time on feed and thus higher non-feed costs to select the most profitable system.

• Use byproduct feeds. Many byproducts of grain and food production and processing are under-utilized. Included are products from brewer's, distiller's, cereal, fruit, vegetable and milk processing and crop residues. Information is available through your Extension Service on how to use them. If energy and thus feed grains continue to become more expensive, byproduct feeds will become more profitable to use. For example, a cattle feeder discovered he could replace corn grain and protein supplement with corn screenings and wet brewer's grains, and saved $50,000 to $100,000 in feed costs per year. At the same time, he obviously was contributing to fuel conservation.

• Use manure efficiently. A steer excretes about .3 of a pound of nitrogen per day, or 72 pounds over a 240 day feeding period. This has a potential of saving 70 pounds of manufactured nitrogen fertilizer, which costs 15.8 gallons of gasoline equivalent. At best, not all of this nitrogen will be available to the plant, and in the past the cost of storing and hauling has exceeded the value. However, it has to be handled, and every effort should be made to capture as much of it as possible. Again, bulletins are available through Extension Service on this subject. In general, avoiding exposure to weather and incorporating into the soil as it is applied are the most crucial practices to improve recycling.

• Sell cattle at their optimum slaughter weight. A feedlot steer at low choice grade will burn over .4 of a gallon of gasoline equivalent per day. That's considering the fact he is eating 23 pounds of feed dry matter. Most State Extension Services and consulting nutritionists can offer valuable advice as to the most efficient slaughter point for the type of cattle being fed and cost-price relationships.

Further Reading:

Beef Production and Management, Reston Publishing Company, 11480 Sunset Hills Road, Reston, VA 22090. $15.95.

Energy Conservation in Agriculture, Special Publication #5, Council for Agricultural Science and Technology, 250 Memorial Union, Ames, IA 50011. Free.

Great Plains Cow/Calf Manual and *Great Plains Cattle Feeders Manual*, available through Cooperative Extension offices in the Great Plains States.

How to Raise Sheep Easier and Cheaper

By Tom Wickersham

Sheep are special animals. As small ruminants, they convert renewable resources (herbs, grasses, legumes, even weeds) to meat and wool. It might be argued sheep, on balance, supply energy rather than use energy. The bumper sticker "Sheep run on grass" states it succinctly.

Persons wearing woolen garments can be comfortable with lower thermostat settings. Sleeping under woolen blankets is delightful in cool bedrooms. Substitution of wool for manmade fabrics also saves energy because petroleum is the base raw material used in manufacturing synthetics.

Sheep farmers, ranchers, and lamb feeders do use energy in the production of over 5 million slaughter sheep and lambs and 102.8 million pounds of wool.

A 1974 study indicates about 58 percent of the total energy used is for general travel, 21 percent for feed processing and distribution, 11.5 percent for assembling and handling, and 6 percent for farm auto use. Other uses include 2.4 percent for waste handling, 0.81 percent for space heating, 0.35 percent for lights and 0.19 percent for supplying water.

Proportionately, sheep producers use more energy on general farm travel and assembling and handling than producers of the other meat animal species. The energy used is about three-fourths gasoline and one-fourth diesel fuel with only a percent-and-a-half for electricity.

Energy savings can be achieved by sheep producers just as all citizens can cut energy usage. It would be logical to focus first on the big usage areas: general travel and feed processing and distribution.

General Travel

Successful sheep producers have their flocks under constant surveillance and observation. This is necessary in the range areas to prevent predator losses and to move the sheep as part of good range management.

A herder with a horse or two and a dog or two

TOM WICKERSHAM *is Extension Livestock Specialist (Sheep), Department of Animal Science, Iowa State University.*

literally lives with a "band" (1,000 or more) of sheep from spring through the summer into the fall.

These herders need food, dog food, some horse feed, and salt for the sheep supplied on a weekly or bi-weekly basis. The supplies are taken to the herders from the headquarters with light trucks. Energy used in servicing these herders is absolutely essential, and any savings in this area and use would be minimal.

In other than range areas the same close observation of sheep is important. But these sheep are often in fenced fields. There are also many producers (Iowa and Ohio each have about 12,000). The flocks may have only 25 to 100 head, but require daily attention.

Characteristically, these sheep producers would get in the pickup or on the small tractor to go look at the sheep. There is opportunity to drastically reduce or eliminate the energy used in this function.

More and more, sheep farmers are getting working sheep dogs. There is growing interest in breeding and training these dogs for use with sheep. A good working dog can be sent perhaps as much as a quarter of a mile or more to gather and bring a flock of sheep to the flockowner.

This seemingly small daily saving of gasoline by the many sheep producers would cut energy use significantly. Every sheep farm could well afford a

Sheep are often fenced in so they can be kept under observation and protected from predators.

LOWELL GEORGIA

good sheep dog to save fossil fuel energy, human energy, and mental stress.

When energy was plentiful and cheap, little thought was given to ways of managing sheep to accomplish better results with the same energy, or the same results with less energy.

Good management of sheep calls for gathering, handling, and treating them several times yearly. For example, sheep need worming two or more times yearly, they are sheared yearly, vaccinations are given, feet are trimmed. and they are sorted and marketed.

With forethought, some of these management procedures can be combined. This would significantly reduce the energy expended, assuming that each time a flock is worked the sheep have to be gathered and driven to pens or corrals. Typically, this would involve a pickup or tractor being driven to the pasture, then slowly herding the sheep to the pens. Next, the vehicle would idle along using fuel as gates are opened and closed.

With some thought and prior planning, essential management procedures could be combined so that a flock would need to be herded together only three or four times yearly, instead of twice as often. This would save some energy without endangering the wellbeing of the sheep.

Sheepdog's instincts and training help herders work sheep, saving time and energy.

CHUCK BENN

Processing Feed, and Feeding

Relatively little food is processed for mature sheep in breeding flocks whether in the Western Range, Southwest, farm flocks, or New England States. Nature equipped sheep with incisor teeth for efficiently biting off forage, with lips and tongue that get feed back in the mouth where the molars grind and in a sense process it.

Feed processing methods have not proven greatly superior to those nature provided sheep in terms of converting feed to meat and wool. This suggests that processing feed is unnecessary, costly, and wasteful of energy.

Grinding and mixing diets for *young* lambs can be justified even though some energy is used. Rations for young lambs need to be carefully formulated and fortified. Further, grinding and mixing prevents lambs from sorting and unbalancing their diets.

Pelleting is the most common processing method used in lamb feeding. This process uses energy for grinding, mixing, extruding the feed through a die and for cooling and drying the finished pellet.

Large commercial lamb feeders like to feed pellets because the lambs can be self-fed rations known to produce good results, and each bite of feed is just the same, so lambs can't sort their feed. Perhaps the most important reason complete pelleted feeds are fed is that the feed manufacturer fills the self-feeders from huge trucks, thus eliminating much of the labor normally needed to feed lambs.

Lamb feeders would have to quit feeding complete pellets if energy use is to be reduced in commercial feedlots. Alternate feeds such as corn silage could be substituted. Higher energy costs may force lamb feeders to use feeding programs in which less processing of feeds is involved.

There is interest in raising sheep in confinement. Some research has been conducted on such systems. Few conclusions have been drawn. To date, little consideration has been given to the energy used in a confinement system.

Sheep producers are aware that in confinement, all feed has to be hauled to the sheep and the waste hauled away. This requires more energy than the traditional system in which sheep graze 6 or 7 months a year and spread their waste with no energy cost.

Assembling and Handling

The decade of the 70's produced a drastic decline in the number of lamb slaughtering plants. Fewer than 15 plants in the United States have a kill capacity of over 250,000 head yearly. Lamb producers and lamb feeders are faced with a marketing problem growing out of the high energy cost of transporting lambs to slaughter plants that are great distances away.

A beginning has been made by sheepmen to overcome this problem. It is saving energy and transportation costs. Lamb tele-auctions are being organized so a truckload (about 400 head) of lambs is booked for sale on a given day by producers in a county or multi-county area.

This truckload is subsequently auctioned and sold via a conference call made to several lamb slaughterers. The high bidder designates the shipment date within the week. Lambs are brought by producers from their farms a relatively short distance (usually under 30 miles) to an assembly point where they are weighed and loaded into the large truck and sent on their way.

This marketing method saves energy. Lamb producers with few lambs use relatively little energy getting their lambs to the nearby assembly point. The long hauls are made by the full semi-truck load unit.

A third energy saving is achieved by buying and selling over the telephone. That saves gasoline normally used by a lamb buyer driving an automobile over the country for days buying a few lambs at this farm or at that auction barn until the buyer has enough to fill a truck. Then the buyer would retrace the route or send a truck to pick up the lambs bought.

There is also movement toward direct selling of replacement ewes from western ranchers to farm flock State sheep producers in semi-truck units. Energy savings result from this procedure, and an added benefit of delivering healthier animals not stressed and exposed to disease in dealers' and traders' hands.

The 300 to 400 head in each semi-truck are unloaded at a central point. Individual producers come only a few miles to pick up the replacement ewes they previously ordered.

Sheep producer will gain trust and experience dealing with each other in local units and in different areas. Orders and package shipments can be consolidated in economical units, thereby achieving some economy and savings of energy.

Sheep producers will respond to the general appeal for conservation of energy, especially in use of the farm automobile. They will go to fewer shows and sales, especially those at long distances. However, they need to continue to travel to educational meetings to keep current with technology and need to participate with other sheep producers in their organizations.

Space Heating

Most sheep barns, sheds or shelters do not have heaters in them because supplementary heat is not needed. Sheep carry around the warmest overcoat ever made — their own fleece. In fact, sheep prefer a cold, dry (low humidity) environment to warm, moist conditions.

Less than 1 percent of the total energy expended in sheep production is for space heating. That energy used is during the lambing season to prevent chilling or freezing of newborn baby lambs.

To conserve energy, in many sheep barns only a part of the barn is heated — the maternity ward. It is often well insulated.

In areas where temperatures are very cold, the ceiling and sidewalls of barns are insulated. In these shelters, ewes are often sheared at the time of confinement, preparatory to lambing. This allows enough heat to escape from the shorn sheeps' bodies that the inside temperature will be kept well above freezing when outside temperatures are a good bit below zero. The sheep, in a sense make their own warm room.

Only winter-born lambs require supplementary heat for a few hours after birth. Sheep producers know losses from chilling are higher and costs will be somewhat greater as energy use and costs increase. Some are shifting to a later lambing program when temperatures are above freezing, eliminating the need for supplementary heat. As these shifts are made, less energy will be used in sheep production.

Energy-Saving Ideas For Food Processors

By R. Paul Singh

Most food consumed in the United States is processed. Food is processed to extend its edible shelf life, make it more convenient to prepare, make foods edible that are otherwise unpalatable, produce new food forms, and create ingredients for use in further food processing. To accomplish these tasks, food processors rely heavily on energy in the form of heat and mechanization.

Major energy used in the food processing industry comes from fossil fuels. The goal of this chapter is to take up current and future energy use in food and fiber processing, marketing, and distribution. The discussion will include an energy-accounting method that is an essential component of energy conservation technologies.

In the last few decades the food industry has grown rapidly. All indicators point toward continuing growth in the future. In 1977, the total food marketing bill was $123.5 billion. The food processing sector consumed $35.8 billion or 29 percent of the total. The other major sectors were wholesaling, $18.5 billion; retailing, $32.1 billion; public eating places, $27.2 billion; and transportation, $9.9 billion.

Several socioeconomic factors affect domestic demands for processed foods. Demands for convenience foods and food consumed outside the home continue to increase as more spouses are employed and family size decreases. It is expected the food processing industry will maintain a key role in meeting needs of the U.S. consumer.

Besides domestic needs, worldwide needs for food are expected to continue to grow, as illustrated by Chancellor and Goss (1976). Their study estimated that: a) the world population will increase to between 6.0 and 7.1 billion in the year 2000; and b) world requirements for food calories in the year 2000 will be nearly double those in 1970.

The United States has maintained its leadership in exporting agricultural goods. The agricultural

R. PAUL SINGH *is Associate Professor of Food Engineering, Department of Agricultural Engineering and Department of Food Science and Technology, University of California, Davis.*

M. LEMMON

The United States is the leader in exporting agricultural goods like this grain being loaded on the Missouri River near Kansas City. To maintain this leadership, and meet domestic food needs too, the food processing industry will require a reliable energy source.

trade showed a positive net balance of payments of about $12 billion for each year from 1974 to 1976. To maintain the export market leadership and meet domestic needs of food, the food processing industry will require a reliable supply of energy.

Several studies have focused on determining energy consumption by the food sector. These findings, summarized by the Federal Energy Administration (1976), provide a perspective of energy use in the U.S. food system.

Of the total U.S. energy consumption, about 2.9 percent was used for farm production, 4.8 percent for food manufacturing (processing), 4.3 percent for in-home food preparation, 2.8 percent for out-of-home preparation, 0.5 percent for wholesale food trade, and 0.8 percent for retail food trade.

These values include direct, indirect, capital and transport costs in energy use.

Energy Need After Food Is Produced

Substantial energy is expended after food leaves the farm gate. Only 18 percent of the energy in the food system is spent in food production, with the remaining 82 percent used to process, market, and prepare it for consumption. The largest share of that 82 percent is used by the food processing segment.

A study by Development Planning Research Associates, Inc., reported by Unger (1975), provides comparison of energy use within the leading energy-intensive manufacturing industries.

The food and kindred products industry group (Standard Industrial Classification 20) ranks sixth in terms of gross energy use after primary metals, chemical and allied products, petroleum and coal products, stone, clay and glass products, and paper and allied products.

The food industry, however, relies heavily on the other five industrial groups for goods and services. Within the same group of industries the food and kindred products industry ranks first in terms of total employment, value added, and the total value of shipments.

Of the 14 leading energy-consuming food and kindred products industries, meat-packing ranks as the highest energy consumer. Because of their volume, the meat-packing, prepared animal feeds, and fluid milk industries are the leading energy consumers.

Ranking based on energy used per dollar value of shipment indicates beet-sugar processing to be the most energy-intensive followed by wet-corn milling.

Cost of energy use in the food system is low in terms of per unit product cost. Doering *et al.* (1977) presented information on energy cost per unit of final product. Energy embodied in packaging is not included. Based on 1974 costs, the energy cost divided by market cost was less than 10 percent for most common food items. As energy costs rise, the energy cost per unit market cost will also increase.

The type of energy source used in the food sector varies among different segments. The processing industry uses all fuel types, whereas other segments, such as transport or home preparation, are overly dependent on a single source.

Most warehouse and retail establishments rely heavily on electricity for distribution. Considerable energy derived from liquid fuels is used by medium-

The meat-packing industry uses more than 99 trillion Btu's a year, making it the highest energy-consuming industry in the food and kindred products group.

G. ROBINSON

size transport vehicles such as route trucks and step vans weighing 8,000 to 14,000 lbs.

Flexibility With Fuels

The processing sector has greater flexibility in substituting one fuel source for another. Since a voluntary energy-conservation program was adopted in the food processing industry, these trends have been observed.

For example, the National Food Processors Association reports that the canned fruits and vegetables industry has relied increasingly on fuel oil, moving away from natural gas. The natural gas consumption for this industry decreased from 63 percent of total energy used in 1972 to 50 percent in 1978, while oil use increased from 20 percent of total energy consumption to 35 percent (Department of Energy, 1979).

In the past, energy has been a relatively underpriced resource. Although future energy prices are uncertain and subject to unpredictable political and even military events, energy prices may go higher—even substantially higher.

The supply of some sources of energy may be unreliable, as evidenced in the Midwestern States in the winter of 1976. This problem may be aggravated by political problems in oil-producing nations.

In view of these uncertainties it is important to recognize the need for timeliness of the energy supplies to certain food processing industries. For example, most fruit and vegetable canning plants operate during only 6 to 12 weeks of the year; an energy curtailment during that period would seriously affect the industry.

Short-term stockpiling of coal and fuel oil for processing plants in urban areas poses difficult logistical problems.

The most convenient supply of energy to the processing plant has been clean-burning natural gas brought through pipes. In contrast, shipment and storage of coal or fuel oil at or near the plant location could create serious problems. Plants in urban areas would require considerable expenditure to maintain a reliable energy-handling and delivery system. In addition, the industry will have to address the environmental impact of burning coal to general energy at plant locations.

A voluntary energy conservation program instituted by the Department of Energy (DOE) requires major energy-consuming firms to report on their energy efficiencies. Using 1972 as a base year, the goal for the food and kindred products industry was to improve efficiency by 12 percent by 1980.

Efficiency Level Upped by 17 Percent

In a recent survey of selected food industries (DOE, 1980), it is reported that the food industry improved its energy efficiency by 17 percent by 1978 over 1972 through installing steam traps and automatic controls on heating devices, eliminating excessive lighting, improving boiler efficiency, and other housekeeping measures.

No major effort has been directed towards energy-saving modifications of process equipment.

All major food processing operations have a potential for energy conservation. Equipment used in processing foods was designed during the era of plentiful energy supplies. Previous emphasis on equipment has been on capacity, product quality, and reduced labor requirement. With little or no concern about energy use, most present equipment consumes more energy than necessary.

Improving efficiencies of energy use in process equipment offers considerable challenges. It will be unrealistic to expect the industry to discard current equipment overnight in favor of newly designed energy-efficient equipment. The more practical approach is to modify current equipment and operating procedures.

New energy-saving equipment can be introduced gradually as other equipment becomes obsolete. Unfortunately, reliable data on energy use by processing equipment are not available.

A question often raised is how to initiate an energy-conservation program. Energy accounting is the first step toward any major energy-related improvements in the food industry.

Accounting Technique

An energy-accounting method useful in developing energy conservation technologies for the food industry was outlined by Singh (1978). The method involves the following steps.

Decide on Objective. If the analysis objective is to determine the feasibility of improving the thermal energy use efficiency of a process, only thermal energy sources (such as steam or heated air) need be accounted for. All energy types must be accounted for when determining total energy use of a process or a plant.

Choose a System Boundary. Selecting a correct system boundary requires experience and the ability to visualize the process completely. Several attempts may be needed to determine important energy inputs. This is more difficult when analyzing a large system. But selecting a system boundary is relatively simple for an energy analysis of food processing equipment.

Draw Flow Diagram. Energy used by different processing equipment during a certain base time can be presented concisely on the flow chart, and energy used in the system per unit product can be calculated.

Identify Mass, Energy Inputs. All mass and energy flows (steam, heated air, or electrical energy) that cross the system boundary must be correctly identified.

Measure Inputs. If the analysis involves a piece of processing equipment, measurement will involve such items as steam flow, product flow, or electricity. Repeated trials are needed to observe energy-use variation, if any, in relation to time and different product flow rates.

Identify Outputs. All energy outputs from the system and product flow across the system boundary must be included in the analysis. Certain forms of energy output may not be obvious in the first trial.

Measure Outputs. Measure product flow and energy outputs from system, including any increase in energy in the product, such as increased product temperature.

Once the information outlined in the above steps is systematically obtained, energy accounting can be carried out easily. The energy-accounting method presented above is a powerful tool to obtain quantitative information on energy use in food processing systems. The method permits determination of the relative importance of different processing operations in terms of their energy use.

Substantial Payoff Seen

The energy-accounting method is useful in finding energy use efficiencies of various equipment. It should be recognized that the method requires installing energy-sensing instruments followed by monitoring and analysis of data. Initially, such costs could be substantial for a large-scale accounting study. However, substantial payoffs are possible.

Using an energy-accounting diagram for canning whole-peeled tomatoes which shows the quantity and type of energy consumed at various locations in a processing plant, Singh *et al.* (1980) identified major energy-intensive unit operations that should be further examined in tomato processing plants.

A similar study conducted on an atmospheric retort used to sterilize canned foods helped develop modifications that showed a 50 percent reduction in energy. Such modifications, with payback periods of about one season, are already being implemented in the canning industry to conserve energy and reduce the impact of increasing energy costs (Griffith *et al.*, 1979).

Comparison of energy costs of different types of processing methods has been a subject of few research studies. The research data are still too meager to draw final conclusions. However, certain trends can be observed.

Energy Costs of That Can

In canning food products the major area of energy consumption is manufacturing the package, namely the metal can. The energy cost of a can may be as much as 190 percent of the energy used to process the product. Similarly for frozen foods, large amounts of energy are used in retail, wholesale and the home for low-temperature storage — up to 340 percent of energy used to process the food.

Rao (1980) has computed the energy consumption per 2.9 oz. serving of corn kernels from fresh refrigerated, frozen, and canned as 2937, 2541, and 2875 Btu respectively. These values account for energy consumed by various steps after harvest and before in-home preparation. It should be stressed that there is considerable variability in the data used to obtain the above values.

It is expected that as more data become available it will be possible to make better comparisons between different processing modes. In such comparisons, the influence of other factors — such as food quality and rates of processing capacity — cannot be overlooked.

Efficient use of solar energy in food processing has been limited to a few processes such as drying grapes for raisins and drying apricots. Recently, through Federal funding, several feasibility studies have been initiated to examine the use of solar energy.

For example, solar ponds are being investigated for preheating water for a food processing plant in Alabama. During the day, water in six 181′ x 16′ ponds collect solar energy. The hot water is then pumped to the plant for use in processing. The project is anticipated to supply 7 percent of the plant's total energy requirement.

Solar collectors on the roof of a cannery in Sacramento, Calif., have been used for heating water to 198° F. The hot water is used in can-washing lines.

Solar Used to Dry Garlic and Onions

A food dehydration plant in Gilroy, Calif., is drying onions and garlic by air heated with solar collectors. Water heated to 200° F in the collectors is pumped through a heat exchanger to heat air for use in the driers. The project is designed for dehydrating 250 million pounds of onions and garlic annually.

Due to the high cost of solar collectors and their poor efficiencies, the payback periods for such installations are currently not attractive. As the cost of collectors becomes more reasonable and as costs of conventional energy sources increase, more use of solar energy is expected.

Use of geothermal energy in food processing is obviously limited by geographical locations. A plant in Ontario, Oreg., is investigating the use of geo thermal energy to supply energy to blanchers and peelers for processing potatoes.

Certain food processors are re-examining plant wastes that were earlier discarded. Biomass wastes such as walnut shells, rice hulls, almond hulls, peach and cherry pits contain large amounts of energy. If properly harnessed, the wastes can be used as an energy source for the processing plants.

A canning plant in Modesto, Calif., is burning peach pits in the boilers to generate steam. The company expects fuel savings of approximately $190,000 per year.

Cogeneration is also being seriously considered by processing plants. Since many plants use both electricity and low pressure steam, the cogeneration principle allows much better efficiencies in energy generation.

Alternate technologies are expected to gain considerable importance in coming years as energy costs rise. Payback periods for adapting several of these technologies will decrease with increasing costs of fossil-fuel based energy sources.

Processing of Fibers

In the recent past there has been considerable interest in examining energy use in processing agricultural fibers such as cotton and its comparison with synthetic fibers.

For cotton, the major operations after harvest are ginning, processing or weaving followed by dyeing or finishing. According to Winkle *et al.* (1978), 100 pounds of baled cotton lint require 29 kWh of energy. For manufacturing cloth the energy requirements are estimated to be 6.5 kWh/square yard, while shirt manufacture consumes another 1 kWh/ square yard.

The analysis of Winkle *et al.* (1978) shows that in order to manufacture cotton shirts the energy requirement is less than the energy required for polyester/cotton blends. However, when energy consumption is compared on the basis of lifetime use — thus accounting for washing, drying and ironing — the energy requirement for polyester/ cotton blends is more favorable than for 100 percent cotton.

326-621 O - 80 - 8 : QL 2

Considering production, processing and lifetime use, energy-intensive maintenance of a cotton shirt is 115.5 kWh compared to 72.4 kWh for the 65/35, polyester/cotton blend.

This analysis clearly shows the importance of careful system analysis when energy use is examined. Certain products or processes may appear very frugal in their energy use when considered alone. However, the overall system may yield surprisingly different results.

Summing Up

The time for energy conservation and use of alternate energy technologies has arrived. The food processing industry has a considerable potential in realizing large energy savings through modifications of equipment and processes. As discussed in this chapter, the industry has already become more energy conscientious.

Judicious use of energy should help a processing plant in maintaining a competitive edge over others, in addition to keeping the price of food from increasing due to costly energy.

Further Reading:

Balancing Energy and Food Production 1975-2000, W. J. Chancellor and J. R. Goss, 1976, *Science,* Vol. 192, pp. 213-218.

Cotton versus Polyester, T. L. Winkle, J. Edeleanu, A. P. Elizabeth and C. A. Walker, 1978, *American Scientist,* Volume 66, pp. 280-290.

Energy Accounting in Canning Tomato Products, R. P. Singh, P. A. Carroad, M. S. Chhinnan, N. L. Jacob and W. W. Rose, 1980, *Journal of Food Science,* 45(3).

Energy Accounting in Food Process Operations, R. P. Singh, 1978, *Food Technology,* April, p. 40.

Energy Consumption for Refrigerated, Canned, and Frozen Snap Beans and Corn, A. Rao, 1980, *Journal of Food Process Eng.* 3(1).

Energy Use in the Food System, Federal Energy Administration, #041-018-00109-3, for sale from Superintendent of Documents, U.S. Government Printing Office, Washington, DC 20402. $2.65.

Energy Utilization in the Leading Energy Consuming Food Processing Industries, S. G. Unger, 1975, *Food Technology,* December, p. 34.

External Heat Exchangers on Retorts Save TVG $59,000/Yr., H. E. Griffith, A. Malvick and K. Robe, 1979, *Food Processing,* May, p. 156.

Industrial Energy Efficiency Program, #061-000-00363-1, Department of Energy, for sale from Superintendent of Documents, U.S. Government Printing Office, Washington, DC 20402. $3.50.

Forests and Woodlands — Stored Energy for Our Use

By Lawrence D. Garrett

Our vast public and private forests represent a giant storehouse of energy. Daily they derive the necessary nutrients and water from the soil and energy from the sun to produce new stored wood energy via the photosynthetic process. Little energy is needed except where the natural process itself is being improved.

This natural forest process of energy production has many redeeming attributes. Most importantly, it is self-sustaining. Given that we take only the annual growth, the forest can remain a constant provider of our needs, including energy.

Where then are these forests of energy? How are they sustained for continued use? And, will it take more energy to sustain and improve them than they can provide?

Our forests of energy are everywhere we turn — from the rolling hardwood forests of New England, through the conifers of the high Rockies, to the pine-hardwood hamlets of our Southland. Let's look closer and see how they are used and perpetuated.

The North

Winters are cold in the North and especially in northern New England. Here is a part of our Nation where much of the population is crowded in large cities such as Detroit and Boston, and most of the energy used for heating is oil and gas. But in the small cities and towns, wood stoves are in vogue. omeowners and industry alike have turned to the woodlots and vast forests for energy.

In these predominantly hardwood forests, maple, beech, and birch are the preferred wood for fireplace, stove, and industrial boiler. Here, where wood has long been used for boiling maple sap and heating homes, the farm woodlot has always been recognized as an important source of energy.

In fact, if you ask farmers in Aniwa, Wisc., or Fairfax, Vt., they will tell you the coming generations

---

LAWRENCE D. GARRETT *is Project Leader for Multi-resource Analysis and Management Research, Rocky Mountain Forest & Range Experiment Station, USDA, Flagstaff, Ariz.*

Wood to heat homes is one of the many ways our forests contribute to the energy needs of the United States.

G. LAVRIS

will be using their woodlots for a long time to make maple syrup and heat their homes. Of course, they'll tell you that if you're smart, you'll always be two years ahead on your wood.

Every farmer knows seasoned wood is the best. Even if you let it dry only one year the moisture content will drop, from about 35 to 50 percent down to about 20 to 30 percent, and give you 10 percent more heat and a more even burning fire.

Rockies, Northwest

They don't call the western forests woodlots. If you ever stand in Wolf Creek Pass, Colorado, looking west across the San Juan National Forest, you will know why. Timber reigns here. Every day enough logs leave the forests of western Oregon, Washington, Montana, and Idaho to build a small city. But for every tree that is taken out, there is a lot of wood left on the ground — wood that can make pulp chips, flakeboard, and fuelwood.

Trees are big here, and homeowners, farmers, and people in forest industry and Federal and State forestry are making those trees fit many needs. Heating homes is one of them. Just arrive on a Friday afternoon in September to a U.S. Forest Service timber sale on the Mt. Hood National Forest in Oregon. You may pass several trucks loaded with logs, but you will also pass a lot of homeowners with ¼ to 1 cord of firewood in their cars or trucks.

Douglas fir, larch, and ponderosa pine are the species most used for firewood. However, the locals in Colorado, Montana, Oregon, or Washington will tell you to get oak for the most heat per truckload. It is not as available, but a cord of it will give almost one third again as much heat as a cord of larch or fir.

Southwest

In the Southwest, water is scarce and timber growth more restricted than in other regions. Yet it is here that Indians long ago held an appreciation for wood as fuel.

The forests of pinyon-juniper and ponderosa pine are widespread on vast holdings of public lands. Ponderosa pine is an important species to the region's wood products industry. The slow growing pinyon pine, Utah and alligator juniper forests are important producers of nuts, cover for wildlife and domestic cattle, as well as critical elements in water production.

Use for firewood is increasing at a rapid rate in the pinyon-juniper forests, causing concern to public forest managers. A typical acre of pinyon-juniper forest will only produce 1/20th to 1/10th cord growth of wood per year and because of its size and quality has little value as a wood product. However, it is a favored fuelwood, as its resins produce a hot fire. To prevent overuse of the pinyon juniper forests, forest managers are developing energy sources from the tops and limbs of harvested ponderosa pines.

Central U.S. and Southeast

Upland hardwoods of the Central United States and pine-hardwood forests of the Southeast have long been a source of wood for both cooking and heating. These forests are some of the most productive in the Nation.

Oak, hickory and ash are prized firewood. They produce one to three cords of wood per acre per year in bole wood (logs) and tree tops. Much of the tops are not suited for other products but well suited for fuelwood. Homeowners of the Appalachian Highlands and Southeast have long been aware of their value as fuel. Even in the shadow of the largest coal-producing area in the United States, homeowners have traditionally used wood for cooking and heating.

Wood Replaced in Short Time

With such an increased interest in wood for energy nationwide, you might think it will become exhausted like oil or gas and then not be available. Or, equally as bad, necessary efforts to grow or regrow a plentiful supply will not be energy or cost efficient.

Forests are like coal, oil, and gas in that they represent a hydro-carbon substance which when ignited in the presence of oxygen, produces great heat. However, while replenishing coal and oil would take millions of years, wood can be replaced in a short time frame and with minimal energy requirements. Its replacement requires seeding or planting new trees and culturing them to some degree until maturity.

Today, forests and woodlots are regenerated or reproduced by both natural and artificial means. In a naturally regenerated forest, people do not spread or plant seeds or plant seedlings, but leave the dispersal and germination of seeds to nature. A forest regenerated artificially is one in which humans replant by broadcast seeding or planting of seedlings.

Most of our forests and woodlots are regenerated naturally, a process that requires little or no energy from people. Nature provides for millions of seeds to fall on each acre so that through a natural selection process, less than 100 seedlings grow and mature on an acre as adult trees.

Natural regeneration is not always successful. Bare soils left after a wildfire has ravaged a forest are not immediately conducive to seed germination. Dry areas of the Southwest and wet areas of the Southeast pose such difficult conditions for regeneration that decades can pass before good germination conditions coincide with good seed crops.

Artificial regeneration can be effective in reproducing forests where natural regeneration is slow, produces poor results, or creates unwanted forest types. This is widely practiced in the South and used throughout the United States. It is expensive compared to natural regeneration, and requires more energy.

Energy requirements for artificial regeneration depend upon the methods used. They include broadcast reseeding using aircraft, planting seedlings with machines, hand planting of seedlings, and hand or machine planting of containerized seedlings.

Tree Farm Plantings

Thousands of privately owned farm acres are planted annually to tree farms, by hand planting or with mechanized planting machines. Additional thousands of acres are planted by forest industry and by public organizations such as the U.S. Forest Service.

Although artificially regenerated stands require more energy for each tree surviving to maturity, this additional input is returned from increased growth. With genetically improved growing stock, an acre can be made to yield ¼ ton more wood per acre per year, thus partially justifying the planting effort.

After establishment, much of our forests are managed to improve tree growth and quality. These improvement practices, whether on small farm woodlots, large industrial forests or public forests, increase the amount of wood grown on each acre. Further, the fact that more wood is grown partially offsets the additional energy requirements.

The extent to which forests are managed depends on many factors including the owner's objectives, condition of the land, and economics.

Some public land is designated wilderness with no timber cutting permitted.

Growth on some lands is so low it offers no economic or energy return from managed treatments. The best lands can yield a positive return on investment from large increases in timber growth.

Public forest lands provide the best example of the complete range of intensity and diversity of management. They are managed for interests of the public at large. As such, some areas will be designated only for recreation or endangered wildlife, with no additional use allowed. Most forest areas are managed for multiple use, producing timber products such as lumber and fuelwood while providing wildlife, recreation, and water as well.

These public forests are managed with extremely low energy inputs as related to the amount of energy received from wood produced.

Fuelwood for Homes

In many States, special use legislation has been enacted to encourage and improve the harvest of fuelwood. Special harvests are managed to insure removal of cull, dead, and undesirable species. This improves growth and quality of the remaining trees which will be used for products.

Many U.S. Forest Service and State forest lands nationwide now have special management programs directed at producing fuelwood. These public agencies contract with loggers to remove overmature, cull, dead and undesirable species to special landings where homeowners can cut the wood into short lengths to load in their personal cars and trucks.

Most private woodland owners culture their woodlots using intermediate cuttings and/or harvests. These cuttings serve several purposes including thinning of unwanted trees, fire prevention, insect and disease control, and increased growth of young vigorous trees.

In completing these intermediate cuttings from

a 30-acre woodlot of average quality timber, about 12 to 16 cords of material can be realized annually for wood product sales and/or fuelwood. The total amount of energy required to grow and remove this material is equivalent to only 1/20th to 1/10th of a cord, or said differently, over 100 times as much energy is produced than consumed.

Industrial forests, especially in the Southeast and Northwest, practice more intensive culture. Here regeneration may be effected naturally, or through aerial seeding and/or ground planting of genetically improved stock. Forests are thinned at small sizes to improve growth and quality. Fire control roads which also help in harvesting are installed. When needed, aerial spraying is done to reduce insect and disease populations or their risk. Intermediate harvest cuttings also may be made in some species, while others are clearcut at maturity.

It is estimated that energy inputs into industries' most intensive cultured pine forests of the Southeast represent less than 1/30th the wood energy equivalents derived at harvest. Although as much as 1/10th of a cord per acre per year of energy equivalents is involved in growing some of these forests, over 3 cords of bole and tops can be produced.

Total energy inputs into the process of growing forests are low, since much of our forests receive relatively limited management and still are effective producers of wood products and energy. More management raises energy inputs, but the increased growth offsets many of these inputs.

To test the potential of intensive management, "energy forests" are being studied. Energy forests could make use of lands not needed for agricultural crops or used for other purposes.

Genetically improved species adapted to specific areas can be planted and cultivated like agricultural crops in short 4- to 12-year growth periods.

Energy intensive practices such as insect and disease control, cultivation, irrigation, and fertilization are applied to insure survival and rapid growth. The material is then harvested. Regrowth comes from root sprouts. This type of reproduction is called "coppice" and can be repeated as many as six times from the same roots. Growth is fast because sprouts grow from the existing root system. Harvesting can be done with mechanized equipment similar to corn or hay harvesters.

Even in these highly cultured energy plantations, such species as eucalyptus, sycamore, red alder, cottonwood, and willow can produce 10 to 20 times the amount of energy required for their production.

Potentials for Energy

To understand the relationship between the potential of forests for energy production, energy inputs required to gain that production, and total energy requirements of our Nation requires expanding our view of energy.

Take first the U.S. total energy needs of 75 quads (quadrillion Btus) *each year*, of which each quad would equal 50 million cords of wood. To satisfy our energy appetite completely from our forests would require complete removal of all the forests in less than seven years. A more efficient approach is to concentrate energy use from trees and areas of forests where there is limited demand for other uses, and energy requirements for growth and harvest are low.

Wise management of forests for energy would concentrate wood energy use in rural and agricultural communities where local use of wood energy could be as high as 25 percent of a community's total energy requirements. In so doing the harvested forest growth could easily offset the entire energy requirements for its growth, harvest, and transport to users.

Our Nation's forests grow much more wood each year than we take from them in the form of logs, pulpwood, poles, chips, etc. In fact, as much as 6½ to 8½ extra quad equivalents of energy is grown but not used. This material occurs in growth on quality trees, small saplings, and weed trees that are left standing, in treetops, limbs, and damaged logs left after harvest, and in cull and dead timber not taken in harvest operations. Using most of this potential would not reduce our forests and in many cases would produce greater growth.

Total energy required each year for planting, fertilizing, thinning, fire, and disease control, and management of forests is estimated at .003 quad. With an input requirement of only .003 quad and potential outputs of 6.5 quads, the energy efficiency ratio of producing wood energy from the forests is 2,000 to 1 (6.5/.003). Of course the ratio could range from over 2,500 to 1 in unmanaged forests to 5 or 10 to 1 in highly cultured energy plantations.

An additional .292 quads would be needed to harvest and transport the 6.5 quads of wood to the many places of use in rural America. Adding all requirements for growth, harvest and transport of 6.5 quads of energy from the forests, total energy used is only .295 of a quad (.003 + .292). That is, for every quad of wood energy grown, harvested and delivered, approximately .046 quads are used, most of which occurs in harvest and transport.

If only 4 quads of the wood energy potential of our forests were to be used annually, it would contribute 5 percent to our total energy needs. And, it would require only .003 quad for growth and .184 quad for harvest.

There is opportunity then to increase our use of wood products for energy. This can be accomplished by increased wise use of existing farm woodlots, industrial and public forests, and possible establishment of biomass plantations. Greater use of trees now being harvested should reduce the total input into derived products, since the total products received will be increasing with small boosts in energy inputs.

Forested areas must be maintained if we are to have suitable quality and quantity of clean air and water. As such, the wisest management would be to maximize the total use of these forests, deriving not only benefits of water retention, clean air, noise abatement, wildlife, recreation, and timber products, but *energy* as well.

Further Reading:

The Warmth of Woodfires, Information Bulletin 150, Cooperative Extension Service, Mailing Room, 7 Research Park, Cornell University, Ithaca, NY 14850. $1.25.

Forest Processing And Energy Savings

By John F. White

Through its early stages of development, this country relied heavily on the forest and its multiple resources for the bare essentials of survival. Timberlands provided fuel and shelter and, to a degree, food. Wildlife served as food and clothing. Water, stored and slowly released by the forest, offered avenues for travel and later a convenient source of power as the Nation moved toward industrialization.

There was a seemingly inexhaustible supply of timber in most regions. So much wood was available that it actually got in the way. Thus wood not needed for shelter, implements, or fuel was destroyed to make room for development of agricultural activities.

Agricultural success eventually reduced demands on the forest for food and clothing. However, our dependence on wood for shelter and fuel was to continue and grow with the country's increasing population.

For a long time wood was the only significant source of fuel. And as late as 1875 it still accounted for 75 percent of U.S. fuel needs. Energy from wood that year is estimated to have amounted to about 3 quads, or about 3 quadrillion Btu's — about twice the amount of energy derived from wood these days.

The availability and low cost of coal, oil, and natural gas eventually decreased the significance of wood as a fuel except for localized or unusual situations.

Renewable Resource

Despite heavy use in the past, 70 percent of the Nation's original forest land remains in forest cover today. The fact that some forest areas are still productive after being cut four or five times demonstrates a renewability that makes forests unique among the major natural resources. Renewability not only holds promise of a future supply but also an opportunity for significant improvements through good management.

When there seemed no end to the supply, some logging and processing of wood products was waste-

JOHN F. WHITE *is Forest Products Utilization Specialist, State and Private Forestry, Forest Service.*

ful. Only prime logs of desired species were removed from the forests, leaving the remnants to rot. Undesirable and poorly formed trees were left to make up the next forest and propagate future stands. This pattern of cutting, called "high grading," has led to millions of acres of low quality timber today. These consequences should encourage more careful planning in the future.

Integrated marketing — where multiple products are removed from forests during single or closely timed harvests — has resulted in higher levels of use. When sawlogs, veneer logs, poles, piling and pulpwood are all, or in any combination, supplied from a single sale, higher monetary and volume yields are more likely.

A developing market for fuelwood, either in solid form or as chips made from logging slash, promises to complete a full array of marketing options. That slash — made up of limbs, tops, and broken pieces of trees — has been difficult to market in the past because it contains a high percentage of bark which is not normally acceptable in the pulp chip market. Bark, however, has about the same heat value as wood, and poses little problem when included in fuel chips.

Both short and long term benefits stem from using logging slash as fuelwood. Short range benefits involve producing energy from a formerly unused material, helping the industry and the Nation achieve a more favorable energy balance.

Long range benefits will be felt when subsequent harvests are scheduled on these stands. A better job of cleaning up logging areas will make it possible to assure a healthy new crop of trees and to control undesirable species.

Dead and dying trees — victims of fire, insects, disease or natural catastrophe — offer similar possibiliities. Rapid removal of this timber will hasten return of the land to productivity.

Building Qualities of Wood

Of all the conventional materials used for housing and construction, wood is the most energy efficient. A tree has only to be logged, sawn into lumber, dried and processed through a planer mill to become a usable building material. This requires much less energy than alternative materials such as metals, concrete, and plastic. Steel, for instance, requires about eight times the amount of energy per ton of finished building material than wood.

Wood is a cellular material, a good natural insulator when dry and properly installed. Most building products manufactured from wood — such as plywood, flake board, particle board, and certainly insulation board — retain that insulating quality in place.

A dual benefit is thus achieved when wood materials are used in construction. First, energy is conserved in manufacturing and processing. Second, energy is saved eventually in heating the completed structure.

Use of manufacturing byproducts to produce energy further improves the overall energy situation.

A marketing decision by a landowner or forest manager normally begins the sequence of events that results in delivering finished wood products to consumers. Ideally, where public or industry owned timber is involved, timing those selling decisions is prescheduled in an organized forest management plan.

Planning forest operations, including sales, makes it possible to take long range land management objectives into consideration, as well as current timber market conditions.

If a mature stand of timber is to be totally removed, steps should be taken to insure regeneration of the next stand. If a partial cut is to be made, it is important to assure proper condition and composition of the residual stand after harvest. In either case a complete plan includes consideration for wildlife habitat and watershed.

Planning Aid for Private Landowner

Forest management planning should not be reserved for public and industry owned land. Management plan assistance is available and highly recommended to private landowners. Private landowners can have management plans developed for them by consulting foresters, or industry or public agency service foresters.

Recommended language for sales contracts, including performance specifications, can be helpful to private landowners not familiar with the terms or technical aspects of timber sales and utilization. Descriptions of the sizes, species, volumes and appropriate measurement scales for the timber to be sold — as well as logging road specifications and harvesting systems to be permitted or excluded — are important elements of sales contracts.

When multiple products such as sawlogs, veneer logs, or pulpwood are to be removed in single or closely timed operations, accurate descriptions of each product and operation are needed. The increasing impact of fuelwood marketing also makes it desirable to assign salvage rights to logging slash.

Following a decision to market standing timber,

and after an offer to purchase is accepted, harvesting begins. If a logging road network does not already exist, maps, photographs and land surveys may be used to set one up to fit contract specifications. Large clearings adjacent to the road are also planned for logging equipment and loading trucks.

From stump to truck the tree goes through four separate processes: felling, bucking, skidding, and loading. Although some mechanical felling and bucking systems are now being used, these operations are normally done by individuals with chainsaws.

Overhead Cables, and Copters

Skidding and loading are highly mechanized and energy intensive. In very rough terrain, overhead cable systems partly or completely lift logs from the ground. Helicopters are sometime used where the land is too steep or the soil too fragile for roadbulding.

On flat to moderately steep terrain, rubber tired skidders and tractors move the logs. Motorized feller-buncher equipment that shears the tree at ground line, rather than sawing, is becoming more common in flatland logging. One version shears the lateral roots below ground and pulls the tree up with the main part of its taproot intact. This is part of the developing technology that makes possible more complete use of forest resources.

Computers are also part of the new technology. An ability to model individual tree stems and to simulate various bucking patterns by computer has led to development of the Improved Harvesting Program (IHP) by the Forest Service-USDA. Cooperating State forestry specialists can acurately describe the operating efficiency of ongoing logging operations, leading to better practices.

A national potential improvement in yield of 4 to 6 percent in logging is estimated. Many operations have exceeded that, and increased their proportion of high value log lengths also.

Logs Head for the Mills

Most potential gains relate to better control of stump height, less breakage in felling, and better accuracy in bucking logs to length. Transportation of more accurately cut logs to mills reduces fuel consumption per unit.

Logs from the forest are usually directed straight to primary processing units such as sawmills or veneer mills. Some timber, however, passes through a concentration yard that separates high grade specialty items and logs of low potential. Presorting items such as poles, piling, house logs, and pulpwood logs improves wood utilization and permits smoother running plants.

Significant improvement potentials are in the veneer and sawmill industries. A trend toward smaller logs in both industries is accompanied with an increasing risk of loss of correct processing $ecisions are not made.

Small logs incorrectly loaded in a veneer lathe significantly increase loss to roundup waste compared to larger logs more common in past years. Electronic scanning devices in lathe charging equipment improve veneer yields overall, and increase the percentage of more desirable lengths.

Sawmill industry response to increasing numbers of small logs has been the design of single pass sawing equipment to minimize movement of any raw material in the reverse direction. Compared to large mills that used to saw 200 to 400 logs per shift, small log sawing systems today can process 3,000 individual logs in the same time.

Incorrect processing decisions on small logs in a sawmill can be costly. A computer based simulated sawing program, developed at the Forest Products Laboratory in Madison, Wisc., has been the base for most of the new technology in sawmilling. This program makes it possible to maximize lumber yield from logs after they have been accurately scanned and located on the processing equipment.

The Sawmill Improvement Program, using that computer simulation, makes it possible to compare actual mill practices with other simulated practices.

As a result, many mills increased their conversion efficiency by quality control and process control. Improved lumber manufacturing precision makes it possible to reduce the thickness of wood required for each stock thickness of lumber.

Thousands of Secondary Processors

Secondary Processing plants that use lumber, veneer and other primary wood products number in the tens of thousands. They range from planer mills, plywood plants and furniture factories to cabinet manufacturers and specialty shops.

Throughout the industry, efforts to improve yields and increase productivity are meeting with success. Several programs designed for hardwood dimension plants and furniture rough mills are available through consulting engineers and public agencies. A common characteristic is the ability to systematically calculate the best grade mix of lumber to purchase for required volumes of dimension parts.

Lumber and veneer drying are the largest energy consuming segments of the solid wood products industry. Drying is thus a prime target of improvement efforts. Fortunately the same planning that improved yields at sawmills can improve dry kiln operation.

Thinner, more uniform manufactured lumber takes up less space when stacked in a kiln and increases its capacity. Reduced amounts of "oversized" lumber saves energy which otherwise would be used to dry wood that would end up as planer shavings, not usable lumber.

Special drying techniques to "equalize" moisture content of different boards in a kiln charge are required less frequently when lumber of more uniform thickness is dried. Overall, the greatest energy savings in solid wood production will be at the dry kilns.

Logging Slash May Help Ease Energy Bash

Tremendous volumes of logging slash are expected to be a major source of energy independence within the wood industries. Other processing residues such as bark and chips will continue to contribute to energy productivity. However, some of those residues are the raw material base for other secondary processing operations such as particle board, flake board, and other reconstituted wood based materials.

Wholesale shifts from oil and natural gas fuels to wood will undoubtedly trigger some pricing shifts in the wood residue market.

Large volume markets for roundwood as residential and industrial fuel use will also create new levels of competition. The wood pulp industry has traditionally been the major user of the largest volumes of roundwood that were not acceptable to other wood using industries. It now is about 45 to 50 percent self sufficient in energy. Significant gains in yield and energy conservation are also close at hand in paper manufacturing.

Exciting developments are taking place within the wood using industries. Increasing interest in wood for fuel should make it possible to support timber stand improvement and improve future forest productivity. At the same time we must recognize the risk of overcutting the forests and therefore plan carefully to sustain our forest productivity.

Farm Machinery Ideas That Save Energy

By P. D. Bloome, I. W. Grevis-James, L. K. Jones, and D. G. Batchelder

Between 1960 and 1980, production agriculture experienced many changes in farm tractors and other machinery. Most were due to farmers' desires to reduce time and labor requirements for field operations. Wider implements and more powerful tractors became available and were bought by farmers.

The most powerful farm tractor available in the United States in 1960 produced about 85 horsepower—a figure which represents the average farm tractor in 1980. Tractors with 300 horsepower are available today.

Demand for ever more powerful tractors led to the four-wheel drive concept. Four-wheel drive tractors generally have higher tractive efficiencies, allowing them to convert fuel into drawbar horsepower more efficiently than two-wheel drive tractors. They also have greater flotation, which makes earlier working of damp soil possible.

During the rapid rise in engine horsepower, tractor weight did not increase as much. With lower weight-to-horsepower ratios, faster field speeds are needed to use available power. Lighter weight also limits torque loads imposed on the drive train.

In 1960, tractors fueled with gasoline and LP gas were used nearly exclusively. While diesel engines are more expensive than gasoline or LP engines, they are also more efficient converters of petroleum to mechanical energy. Besides, diesel fuel contains more energy per gallon than gasoline or LP gas, and its price has historically been lower. To reduce orerating costs, farmers today have almost completely converted their purchases to diesel powered machinery.

Rapidly rising energy costs have brought major pressures to bear on production agriculture. Farmers have watched diesel fuel prices climb past $1 per gallon, whereas diesel fuel for farm tractors sold at 16 cents a gallon as late as 1970. Of even greater concern are actual and potential shortages of fuel during critical farm seasons. These problems

PETER D. BLOOME, *Ian W. Grevis-James, L. Ken Jones, and David G. Batchelder are with the Agricultural Engineering Department, Oklahoma State University.*

326-621 O - 80 - 9 : QL 2

resulted in major efforts to reduce fuel expenses and eliminate fuel availability uncertainties.

Energy factors must be considered in selecting, operating, and maintaining farm machinery. The greatest scope for reducing energy consumption of farm machinery lies with the operation of tractors and tillage implements.

4 Key Steps in Selecting Equipment

Selecting implements and tractors involves these steps: 1) what crops are planned and acreages of each to be grown, 2) types of tillage and cultivation tools to be used, 3) implement widths to ensure timely completion of each field operation, and 4) power requirements for tractors established by widths and speeds of the implements and appropriate soil characteristics.

Selecting tillage implements depends on the type of farming desired. A farmer who prefers a clean tilled seedbed will probably select a moldboard plow as the primary tool. If the farmer wishes to leave a certain amount of crop residue on the surface, then a chisel plow or offset disk is more appropriate.

Each tillage operation requires a certain amount of energy. Energy needed for primary tillage operations with three implements are shown in the table.

Average Energy Consumption, Primary Tillage Operations

Implement	Energy Required (HP-HRS. Per Acre)
Moldboard plow (7″ deep)	23.5
Chisel plow	16.0
Heavy Offset Disk	13.8

Moldboard plowing consumes more energy than disking or chiseling. For minimum energy use, select a tillage system that uses implements with low energy requirements. However, energy is not the only basis for selecting implements. Leaving the desired amount of crop residue on the surface, forming a proper seedbed, and controlling weeds are also important.

A vital step in machinery selection is determining implement widths. Required widths depends on expected field efficiency, length of time available for each field operation (timeliness), and speed of travel through the field.

Field efficiency accounts for time spent in turning, repairing breakdowns, making adjustments, refueling, etc., and for overlap of implement width. It is expressed as the actual field work rate divided by the theoretical work rate, and normally varies from about 70 to 85 percent for most field operations.

Timeliness is the ability to perform a field operation both at the proper time and during a short period. It is most important during critical planting and harvest seasons. Agronomic research has shown considerable yield benefit from early planting of corn, soybeans and other crops. Timely and rapid harvest will avoid the field losses that can occur with a single storm.

Farmers Right on Timeliness

Engineers and economists have generally placed less value on timeliness than farmers, but continuing trends have shown farmers to be more correct.

High speed tillage with contemporary implements requires more fuel per acre than tillage at slower speeds, as illustrated. Therefore, operating costs for fuel rise as field speed increases. At the same time, fixed costs are reduced at higher field speeds since narrower implements can be used to produce the same work rate.

A compromise is needed between high energy costs and reduced fixed costs of higher tillage speeds. Solution to this dilemma is being sought in the design of tools with lower energy requirements.

A final step calls for selecting tractors to provide the power output demanded by the implements previously chosen. Comparative test data is needed to pick a fuel efficient tractor with the required drawbar horsepower output. Tractor fuel economy is expressed as horsepower-hours per gallon of fuel. Tractors with high fuel economies convert fuel to power more efficiently.

Tractor Test Operation

The Agricultural Engineering Department at the University of Nebraska has operated a tractor testing facility since 1920. All tractor models offered for sale in Nebraska must be tested at this facility. Test reports of individual tractors and annual summaries can be obtained by writing to the Department of Agricultural Engineering, University of Nebraska, Lincoln, NE 68503. Farmers use Nebraska test results to select tractors in the same way car buyers use EPA mileage ratings.

Nebraska Tractor Tests show tractors vary markedly in ability to convert fuel into power. Of tractors tested during 1979, there was a 23 percent difference between best and worst fuel economies at maximum PTO power.

If Nebraska Test results are graded according to fuel economy and the rankings of the PTO and drawbar tests are compared, considerable differences between the two rankings are seen. A tractor's performance in the field is affected not only by its engine efficiency, but by its weight-to-power ratio, distribution of its weight, number of drive wheels, and soil characteristics. Each of these factors affects tractor fuel economy. During the 1980's, farmers will become more familiar with all factors affecting fuel economy.

Fuel Economy Better at High Engine Load

Tractor engines have better fuel economy at higher engine loads. Fuel economy at full PTO power is about 30 percent higher than at 50 percent PTO power.

When engine loading is not high, fuel economy can be improved by reduced throttle operation using a higher gear, provided care is taken to avoid overloading the engine. This improvement is possible since typical diesel engines give their best fuel economy at about 2/3 rated power and 2/3 rated speed.

The fuel-saving potential of reduced throttle operation is shown in each Nebraska test. Since 1968, several hundred test runs — at about half full load with reduced throttle setting — have shown average fuel savings of 27 percent.

Many farmers are finding that even with relatively heavy loads, substantial fuel savings are available through throttling back. The graph illustrates improvement in fuel economy possible with heavy loading and reduced throttle operation.

Tractor operators are faced with complex decisions in deciding how to operate their equipment for high output with good fuel economy. In the near future they will have electronic assistance in making these decisions.

Performance monitoring is the key to improved tractor/implement operation. Monitors will measure and display important variables that affect operation and performance of the tractor and equipment.

Illustrated is the type of monitor console expected on future tractor models. By referring to information displayed on the console, the operator can immediately see effects of any changes in gears, throttle setting, ballasting, tillage depth, tire changes, etc. The operator then can make the changes that result in best fuel economy or working rate.

The next step beyond performance monitoring is automatic control feedback. Microcomputers can be used to automatically select gears and set governors for best performance or fuel economy. Microprocessors will also monitor oil pressure, coolant temperature, exhaust temperature, and other factors important to tractor operation.

Performance-monitoring equipment will also help the farmer make better machinery selection decisions. Farmers will accumulate information unique to their tractors, implements, farming system, and soils. This information will provide the basis for future decisions in selecting tractors and implements.

In terms of saving both energy and money, good maintenance makes good sense. Well maintained equipment runs more efficiently, is less likely to break down at a critical time, and lasts longer.

Thorough maintenance of tractors, especially engines, ensures maximum use of each gallon of fuel consumed. Both internal and external engine components require attention. This means all adjustments and clearances must be kept strictly within their specified range.

A tractor performance monitor for the future.

Fuel System Component Checking

Fuel system components, including turbochargers, must be checked by qualified mechanics at the first sign of improper operation. Faulty fuel injectors of pumps can dramatically increase the quantity of fuel used by the engine.

Blocked air filters can reduce engine output and increase fuel consumption up to 25 percent. It is vital to change filters at correct time intervals. Air precleaners must also be inspected and cleaned regularly. If precleaners are neglected, the more expensive main filter will quickly become blocked.

In the future, performance-monitoring equipment will indicate the need for maintenance. A drop in power output or a decrease in fuel economy will remind the operator of the need to perform routine inspection and maintenance work.

Further Reading:

Choosing a Tractor Using the Nebraska Tractor Tests, FS-16, Cooperative Extension Service, Cornell University, Distribution Center, 7 Research Park, Ithaca, NY 14850. 20¢.

Fundmentals of Machine Operation-Machinery Management, John Deere and Company, Distribution Service Center, Department SP, 1400 3rd Avenue, Moline, IL 61265. $8.25.

Tractor Test Data, MS-418, Cooperative Extension Service, Distribution Center, Umberger Hall, Kansas State University, Manhattan, KS 66506. 35¢.

Cheaper Ways to Move Irrigation Water

By M. E. Jensen and E. G. Kruse

Cropland irrigated in the United States has steadily increased, especially during the past decade. Major droughts like that in 1974 stimulated this growth.

Irrigation enables farmers to grow higher-value crops and reduces production uncertainties from year to year caused by variations in rainfall. Irrigated farms produce about 27 percent of agricultural products, yet irrigated cropland represents only 18 percent of the harvested cropland.

Most of the growth in irrigated land during the past five years occurred in the Central and Southern Great Plains, the subhumid States of Minnesota, Missouri, and Wisconsin, and the humid States of Georgia and Mississippi.

Rapid expansion of irrigation occurred when energy was cheap and rapidly available. Costly energy is expected to slow the growth of irrigation and significantly affect irrigation practices.

Much of the growth in irrigated land was due to installation of sprinkler irrigation systems, especially center pivot systems. Many surface irrigation systems have been converted to sprinklers, while the total irrigated area has remained relatively constant in areas such as the Pacific Northwest and the Central Mountain States.

Sprinkler irrigation also enables farmers to irrigate land that could not be economically irrigated by surface methods. Little labor is required, especially for the center pivot systems. Where tall crops like corn are not grown, side-roll sprinklers have become very popular.

The irrigation equipment industry also provided a major impetus to the growth of sprinkler irrigation because commercial equipment was readily available and service centers were established throughout irrigated areas. A new system can be installed and operating within weeks after it is ordered.

In 1974, only about 15 percent of irrigated land was irrigated with sprinklers, but by 1979 this pro-

MARVIN E. JENSEN *is National Research Program Leader, Water Management, Science and Education Administration-Agricultural Research (SEA-AR), Beltsville, Md.* E. G. Kruse *is Agricultural Engineer, SEA-AR, Fort Collins, Colo.*

portion had increased to over 30 percent. Sprinkler irrigation expanded most rapidly when energy was readily available and relatively cheap.

Sprinkler Effect on Energy Use

Conversion to a sprinkler system caused little change in energy use where high pumping lifts were involved because the pipeline distribution system and better water control required less water to be pumped. However, where pumping lifts were small, the pressure needed for sprinkler irrigation greatly increased energy requirements. Pumping lift is the vertical distance water must be lifted from the source to the point of discharge.

Energy required to lift water is directly proportional to the lift involved. Applying water under pressure is equivalent to lifting it an additional distance. For example, applying water at a pressure of 345 kilopascals (kPa) (50 pounds per square inch, psi) is equivalent to lifting the water an additional 35.2 meters (m) (115 ft.). Similarly, applying water at a pressure of 517 and 862 kPa (75 psi and 125 psi) is equivalent to lifting the water 52.7 and 87.9 m (173 and 288 ft.), respectively.

Equivalent Lift Associated With Applying Water Under Pressure*

Pressure		Equivalent Lift	
kPa	(psi)	m	(ft.)
172	25	17.6	58
345	50	35.2	115
517	75	52.7	173
689	100	70.3	231
862	125	87.9	288

*1 pound per square inch (psi) = 6.89 kilopascals (kPa) and 1 psi is equivalent to a pressure head of 0.70 meter (m) o2 2.31 feet (ft.).

Lower pressures (170 to 345 kPa) typically have been used with hand move and side-roll sprinkler laterals. Medium pressures (520 to 690 kPa) have been used on the center pivot sprinkler systems, although many newer systems now are operated at lower pressures. The highest pressures (over 860 kPa) are required for traveling and stationary hydraulic gun sprinklers, which are used mainly in subhumid and humid areas of the United States.

About a fourth of the crop production energy used in the United States is for irrigation. Since only 18 percent of the harvested cropland is irrigated, it is readily apparent that the average energy input per unit of irrigated land is substantially greater than the energy input to nonirrigated land.

Highest energy inputs for irrigation are in the Northwest — where pumping lifts from the Columbia and Snake Rivers are high and nearly half the cropland is sprinkler irrigated — and in the arid Southwest and southern High Plains where pumping lifts are high and large amounts of water are used.

In Arizona, where more than half the irrigation water is obtained from deep groundwater aquifers, about 90 percent of the crop production energy is used for pumping. A groundwater aquifer is a geological formation that transmits water in sufficient quantity to supply wells or springs.

In the High Plains of Texas, over 60 percent of energy used for producing corn is for pumping water. Irrigation and nitrogen fertilizer account for 85 percent of the energy input. Irrigated corn in the High Plains requires about 2½ times more energy than corn produced in the Corn Belt — mainly because of irrigation and some additional nitrogen fertilizer.

In pump-irrigated areas, energy-related inputs may make up 55 percent of all variable production costs, with about half of these for irrigation pumping.

Increases in energy costs have a greater impact on production costs in irrigated areas than in nonirrigated areas. If energy costs rise, you can expect a drop in the area of irrigated cropland, or a change to higher-value crops, where the pumping lifts are extremely high and low-valued farm crops are currently produced.

Annual energy required to pump water for various total dynamic heads and various depths of water applied are summarized in the second table. Total dynamic head is the sum of the distance water is lifted (pumping lift), friction losses in the pump system, and the pressure head at the pump discharge. An electric-powered pumping plant is assumed with an overall efficiency of 70 percent and an irrigation system that enables crops to use 75 percent of the water pumped. The quantity of energy required is expressed in kilowatt-hours per hectare (kWh/ha).

If a diesel-powered pumping plant were used with an overall pumping plant efficiency of 19 percent, about 1 liter of diesel fuel would be required for each 2.9 kWh (1 gallon/11 kWh) of electricity. With a natural gas-powered pumping plant with an overall efficiency of 15 pecent, about 28 cubic meters (1,000 cubic ft.) of natural gas would be required for each 63 kWh. (If the efficiency of fossil fuel electric generating plants and losses in the transmission lines are considered, overall efficiencies for the various power sources would be more nearly alike.)

Annual Energy Required for Pumping Water

Total dynamic head		Net depth of water applied[1]			
		100 mm (4 in.)	200 mm (8 in.)	400 mm (16 in.)	800 mm (32 in.)
m	(ft)	kilowatt-hours/hectare[2,3,4]			
5	(16)	26	52	104	207
10	(33)	52	104	207	414
20	(66)	104	207	414	829
40	(131)	207	414	829	1,658
80	(262)	414	829	1,658	3,316
160	(525)	829	1,658	3,316	6,632
320	(1,050)	1,658	3,316	6,632	13,263

[1]Assuming an electric-powered pumping plant efficiency of 70 percent and an irrigation efficiency of 75 percent (Net depth is 75 percent of that pumped).
[2]For the equivalent depth of water, the kilowatt-hours per acre is 0.4 of the values shown (1 hectare = 2.471 acres).
[3]For diesel-powered pumping plants with a pumping plant efficiency of 19 percent, about 1 gallon of diesel fuel would be required for each 11 kWh of electricity used for pumping.
[4]For natural gas-powered pumping plants with a pumping plant efficiency of 15 percent, about 1,000 cubic feet of gas would be required for each 63 kWh of electricity used for pumping.

For example, in the second table if the total dynamic head is 80 m (262 ft.), which is fairly typical of pump irrigation in some areas of the Great Plains, and if water equivalent to a depth of 400 millimeters (mm) (16 in.) is pumped, the energy required would be 1,658 kWh/ha (671 kWh/acre). If a diesel-powered pumping plant were used, about 570 liters (150 gallons) of fuel would be required, and 745 cubic meters (26,300 cubic ft.) of natural gas would be required for a natural gas-powered unit.

Currently, the lowest cost fuel is natural gas where it can be obtained, but its price also is expected to increase substantially in the future.

How to Reduce Water Applied

There is a direct relationship between the quantity of water pumped and energy use and pumping costs. Therefore, pumping costs can be reduced proportionately to the reduction in irrigation water applied, except where large demand charges are required for electric motors.

The normal management objective is to reduce the amount of water to near the net irrigation requirement to avoid plant water stress and significant reductions in crop yields. To accomplish this, an irrigation system capable of high efficiencies (80 to 90 percent) must be used and the system managed to achieve these high efficiencies. A system with a high potential efficiency may, through poor management, be operated at much lower efficiency.

Pumping Lift and Pressure Head

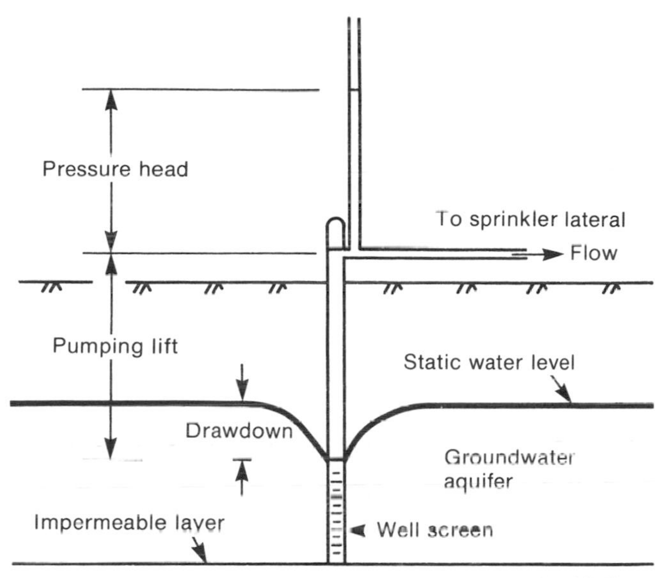

Total dynamic head = pumping lift + pressure head + friction

You can reduce pumping costs by cutting out unnecessary irrigations. Many recent field experiments show that one or more irrigations applied after the soft dough stage on grain crops have little or no effect on crop yield or quality. Yet many farmers continue to apply this last irrigation because of historic practices and the assumption that grain may shrivel if the crop is not kept well watered until harvest. Local and regional experimental data are available as a guide to reducing the amount of water applied near the end of the growing season or to establish the optimum date of the last irrigation.

Similarly, recent studies on sugarbeets in Idaho showed that after a thorough irrigation Aug. 1 on a soil that contains at least 200 millimeters (mm) (8 in.) of available soil water, there is essentially no benefit to irrigating again until just before harvest to make it easier to harvest the sugarbeet roots. In extremely dry years, an additional light irrigation about Sept. 1 may be needed to produce normal yields of sugar. Yet, farmers frequently keep sugarbeets well watered in August and early September, producing excessive top growth.

If energy costs continue to rise, many farmers in semiarid areas will switch from full to limited irrigation. With limited irrigation, timing becomes very important for maximum net benefit.

Soil moisture must be available at critical stages of growth, such as the silking stage for corn and the flowering stage for most grain crops. In Kansas, one irrigation applied just before the silking stage on corn, the flowering stage on soybeans, or the heading stage on small grains can bring the greatest return per unit of water applied.

In Kansas the largest 3-year average corn yield with a single irrigation was obtained when corn was irrigated during the early silk emergence stage. Irrigating at that time increased the yields by 2,820 to 2,950 kg/ha (45-47 bu/ac) over that not irrigated.

Grain sorghum, on the other hand, is not as sensitive to the timing of a single irrigation.

Applying a single irrigation too late in the season has little effect on yield. For example, corn irrigated once late in the season at the blister stage produced the smallest increase over the nonirrigated treatment.

Similar responses to limited irrigation on corn and grain sorghum have been obtained in the High Plains of Texas. Information on limited irrigation is available through the Extension Service or county agents in most irrigated areas of the Grain Plains.

Computerize Scheduling

Scientific irrigation scheduling is an effective management tool to reduce water applications for either full or limited irrigation. Computerized scheduling and the use of soil moisture detection devices can be very effective. Studies in the Benedict area of Nebraska in 1975 showed the amount of irrigation water typically pumped during an irrigation season could be reduced 50 percent or more without adversely affecting corn yields.

Near Crook, Colo., in 1977, irrigator Bill Condon applied water with his center pivot sprinklers on the basis of a computerized irrigation scheduling program. His seasonal irrigation application averaged 530 mm (20.9 in.). Neighboring farmers applied 730 mm (28.7 in.) to similar soils.

Condon's corn yielded 11,300 kg/ha (180 bu/ac). His peak yield of 15,190,kg/ha (242 bu/ac) was the high for a test plot in Colorado that year. On the neighboring farms, yields averaged near 9,415 kg/ha (150 bu/ac). Scientific irrigation scheduling permitted a 27 percent reduction in the energy requirement for pumping.

Another way to reduce irrigation water pumped is to modify tillage and management practices so as to reduce rainfall runoff from sloping fields. In the Southern High Plains of Texas, for example, furrow damming devices are being used to create basins, thereby essentially eliminating runoff.

Energy consumption and costs can be cut by improving the efficiency of pumping units. In some cases this can be done by adjustment or maintenance, and in other cases by replacing pump components. Many irrigation pumps are operating at 50 percent or less efficiency when attainable efficiency is near 75 percent. Pump efficiency tests are often provided without charge by utility companies and sometimes by the Extension Service.

Pump maintenance or improvement may bring substantial savings in both energy and energy costs. However, additional capital improvement costs for maintenance or replacement of the pump must be considered.

The potential savings in energy can be estimated with the following equation:

Potential percentage reduction in annual energy use and costs = $(1 - E_e/E_a)100$ where E_e = the existing pumping plant efficiency and E_a = the attainable efficiency.

For example, if an electric-powered pump is operating at 50 percent efficiency and the attainable efficiency is 70 percent, the potential percentage reduction in energy use and cost will be:

Potential reduction = $(1 - 50/70)100 = 29$ percent.

Efficiency of electrical powered pumps is determined mainly by the pump, while efficiency of pumps powered with natural gas or diesel engines is determined by both efficiency of the engine and efficiency of the pump.

Measuring discharge of irrigation well. Rate of flow from well is one variable needed to determine the pumping plant efficiency.

Farmer Acts, Saves 27% Energy Use

After considering the potential reduction in energy costs, the irrigator can consider the probable return on his investment, if needed repairs or replacement of pumping system components are made. For example, one Colorado farmer had a pump that was operating at a 47 percent plant efficiency in 1976. During that year, he used about 146,000 kWh. After he had the pump pulled and repaired in 1977, he used 40,000 fewer kWh, a reduction of 27 percent.

Recent studies show that 30 to 50 percent of total energy expended in pumping water could be saved through better water management and more efficient deep well pumps, irrigation power plants, and wells. Inefficient well screens, or improper well development, cause the water level inside the well casing to be significantly lower than that just outside the well while pumping. These head losses through well screens or gravel packs increase pumping lift unnecessarily.

In Nebraska, performance standards have been developed for well designed and maintained pumping plants. These standards indicate the amount of energy — electricity, diesel, propane, or natural gas — required to pump water for a sprinkler or a surface irrigation system.

The Nebraska studies show many irrigation pumping plants operate significantly below potential performance standards. Adjustments alone could increase their performance and reduce energy use by about 13 percent.

Normally, when water is pumped from groundwater sources, the lift involved cannt be changed significantly, except where well efficiency can be improved. However, when water is pumped from rivers, there often are alternatives for reducing pumping costs. On some projects, arrangements can be made to divert water further upstream and allow the water to flow to the irrigated area by gravity, instead of pumping directly from the river.

When energy costs were extremely low, upstream diversion by gravity may not have been economically feasible. This situation changed as energy costs rose. Conversion to gravity diversion may involve a major construction program, and land acquisition or easements. Such conversions cannot be done on a short-term basis.

Return Flow System Can Be Effective

An indirect but effective way of reducing pumping lift and costs with furrow irrigation is to use a return flow or reuse system. A small reservoir captures surface runoff. A pump-back system delivers this water to irrigate new land or to supplement the flow of water from the well during the start of each subsequent irrigation set.

Pumping lift from the surface reservoir is usually only a small fraction of that from ground water. For example, if depth to the water table is about 30 m (100 ft.) and a surface reservoir lies from 3 to 5 m (10 to 15 ft.) below the upper end of the fields, energy needed to reuse tailwater may be only 15 to 20 percent of that required to pump groundwater.

In Nebraska, reuse pits have increased irrigation efficiency 15 percent. By adding a pit, some farmers can reduce pumping costs 25 percent and cut by about 20 percent the amount of time the deep wells are operated.

In some river valleys, sprinklers are operated using gravity pressure. Mountain streams are diverted into pipelines if there is sufficient drop to generate the pressure needed.

High pressure sprinkler irrigation systems can be converted to low pressure systems to reduce total dynamic head. However, merely renozzling a center pivot sprinkler system to permit applying water at a low pressure will not significantly reduce energy consumed unless the existing pumping plant is modified. Reducing pressure in the sprinkler system by partially closing the pump discharge valve does not reduce dynamic pumping head or energy required if the same amount of water is pumped.

When converting a center pivot system to a low pressure system, the water application rate increases because the same amount of water is usually applied over a smaller area. The higher application rate, even though for a shorter period of time, can result in significant runoff on fine-textured soils that have low infiltration rates. More water must be pumped to achieve the same net application, which reduces the benefits of lower pressure.

Contact your local Extension agent or a consulting engineer to determine if your system can be converted to lower pressure operation at a sufficient savings in energy, or energy costs reduced without changing pumps.

Conversion to Surface Irrigation

Another way to reduce pumping pressure is to convert from sprinklers to a modern, well-designed surface irrigation system. Such a system might include a closed pipe or a concrete-lined open channel distribution system, land leveling or smoothing, and a runoff reuse system. Energy use and costs can often be significantly cut in areas where efficient surface irrigation systems are practicable.

Many on-farm pipeline distribution systems were designed when energy costs were very low. Size of pipe was based on the pipe's expected lifetime and anticipated cost of pumping against friction losses in the pipeline. If energy costs continue to escalate, there may be opportunities to cut pumping costs by reassessing friction losses in the farm distribution system and possibly installing larger pipelines.

Drainage is essential in many humid areas, but irrigation is also needed because of sandy droughty soils. Instead of installing sprinklers, some farmers in the Southeastern Coastal Plains States are putting in subsurface drainage systems that also can be used to irrigate low-lying lands. During short periods with no rainfall, the outlet channel is checked to maintain a water table in the root zone to avoid plant stress and reduced yields. During extended drought periods, the system is reversed and water is pumped from a surface reservoir or a shallow well into the drain lines for subirrigation.

Because of the energy requirement for sprinklers, at locations where water is available by gravity flow there is interest in modernizing surface irrigation technology and making surface irrigation more efficient.

Land Leveling with Lasers

In Arizona, laser-controlled land levelers are being used to level 4- to 8-ha (10- to 20-acre) basins to within ± 10 to 15 mm (0.5 in.). With carefully managed water applications, very efficient irrigation can be achieved, comparable to that with sprinklers. No pumping energy is required as long as water can be delivered from streams or surface reservoirs by gravity.

In the Central Great Plains where irrigation pumps are electrically powered, the cost per kilowatt-hour is determined by the peak,demand that occurs on electrical substations during one hour or less sometime during the irrigation season.

Some utility companies routinely manage electrical load by shutting off irrigation pumps as electrical demand reaches specific levels. Savings in costs to the utilities are passed on to cooperating irrigators.

New studies are underway to combine irrigation scheduling based on soil moisture level and load management, so as to minimize possible effects on crop yields. Reliable methods are being developed to identify fields where soil moisture is adequate to prevent crop yield reductions if pumps are shut down for periods of several hours to several days.

Anything that can be done to improve or increase irrigation efficiency will generally save energy and reduce energy costs. Irrigation efficiency is improved by more uniform application of water, applying only that amount of water which can be retained within the root zone, and reducing seepage from unlined ditches, leakage from pipelines, and surface runoff.

In the long run, energy conservation must involve not only consideration of pumping energy, but all inputs of energy into the system.

Conversion to a sprinkler or a trickle system can, in some cases, reduce energy consumption and energy costs by providing better control of water and higher irrigation efficiencies. However, we need to consider the intrinsic energy used to manufacture and transport the aluminum, plastics, and other components of such systems.

Justification for using energy-intensive materials like aluminum is that aluminum often is manufactured with off-peak power, developed with stored water supplies that otherwise must be released to make room for flood flows. Also, aluminum can be recycled.

Alternative energy sources for irrigation pumping are being evaluated. Windpower is promising either to supplement energy input into wells powered electrically or by diesel engines, or as a free-standing power source for pumping water from return flow pits or from shallow groundwater sources. Currently, windpower assisted irrigation pumps are nearly economically feasible in windy areas of the High Plains of Texas, Oklahoma, and western Kansas.

Coal-fired steam powered irrigation pumping plants for large projects were evaluated several years ago and found not economical. However, if energy costs continue to rise, such plants may become economically feasible for some arid irrigated areas near coal resources.

Further Reading:

Colorado Pump Tests Show How to Make Big Dollars Savings, R. Ross, *Irrigation Age*, March 1978, pp. 9, 12, 16.

Comparing Costs of Conventional and Improved Irrigation Systems, D. E. Eisenhauer and P. E. Fischbach, *Irrigation Age*, 1977, 11(8): 36-37.

Efficiencies of an Automated Surface Irrigation System With and Without a Runoff Re-Use System, P. E. Fischbach and B. R. Somerhalder, *Transactions*, American Society of Agricultural Engineers, 1971, 14 (4):162-165.

Energy Inputs to Irrigation, J. C. Batty, S. N. Hamad, and J. Keller, 1974, Proceedings of Amer. Soc. of Civil Engineers, *Journal of Irrigation and Drainage Division*, 101(IRA): 293-307.

Energy . . . Is It the Achilles Heel for Irrigated Agriculture? L. F. Sheffield, *Irrigation Age,* September 1979, pp. 32-34, 43, 50.

Farmer Adjustments to Higher Energy Prices: The Case of Pump Irrigators, ERS-663, U.S. Department of Agriculture, Room 0054-S, Washington, DC 20250. Free.

Implications of Irrigation System Efficiencies, E. G. Kruse and D. F. Heermann, 1977, *Journal of Soil and Water Conservation,* 32(6):265-270.

Irrigation and U.S. Agriculture: Irrigation Pumping, 1974-1977, Agricultural Economic Report No. 436, U.S. Department of Agriculture, ESCS, Room 0054-S, Washington, DC 20250. Free.

Irrigation System Management for Reducing Peak Electrical Demands, L. E. Stetson, D. G. Watts, F. C. Corey, and I. D. Nelson, 1975, *Transactions,* American Society of Agricultural Engineers, 18(2):303-306, 311.

Level-Basin Irrigation: A Method for Conserving Water and Labor, 1979, Farmers' Bulletin No. 2261, U.S. Department of Agriculture, SEA Publications, Room 6009-S, Washington, DC 20250. Free.

Pumping Irrigation Requirements for Irrigation in California, Y. D. Knutson, R. G. Curley, E. B. Roberts, R. M. Hagan, and V. Cervinkaa, 1978, Special Publication 3215, Agricultural Sciences Publications, University of California, 1422 Harbour Way South, Richmond, CA 94804. Free.

Re-Use Pits: Cheapest Water on the Farm, J. G. White, 1978, *Irrigation Age,* Nov.-Dec., pp. 58, 62.

Scheduling Center Pivot Sprinkler Irrigation Systems for Corn Production in Eastern Colorado, D. F. Heermann, H. R. Haise, and R. H. Mickelson, 1976, *Transactions,* American Society of Agricultural Engineers, 19(2):284-287.

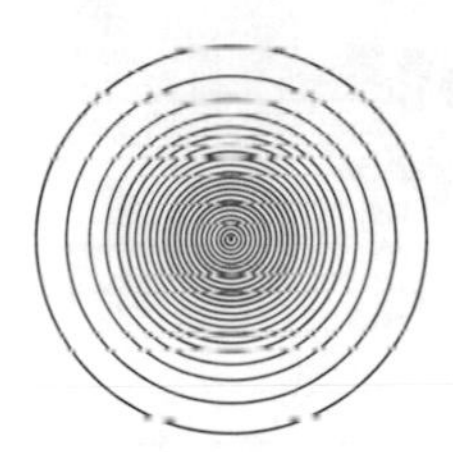

Section II

Family Living

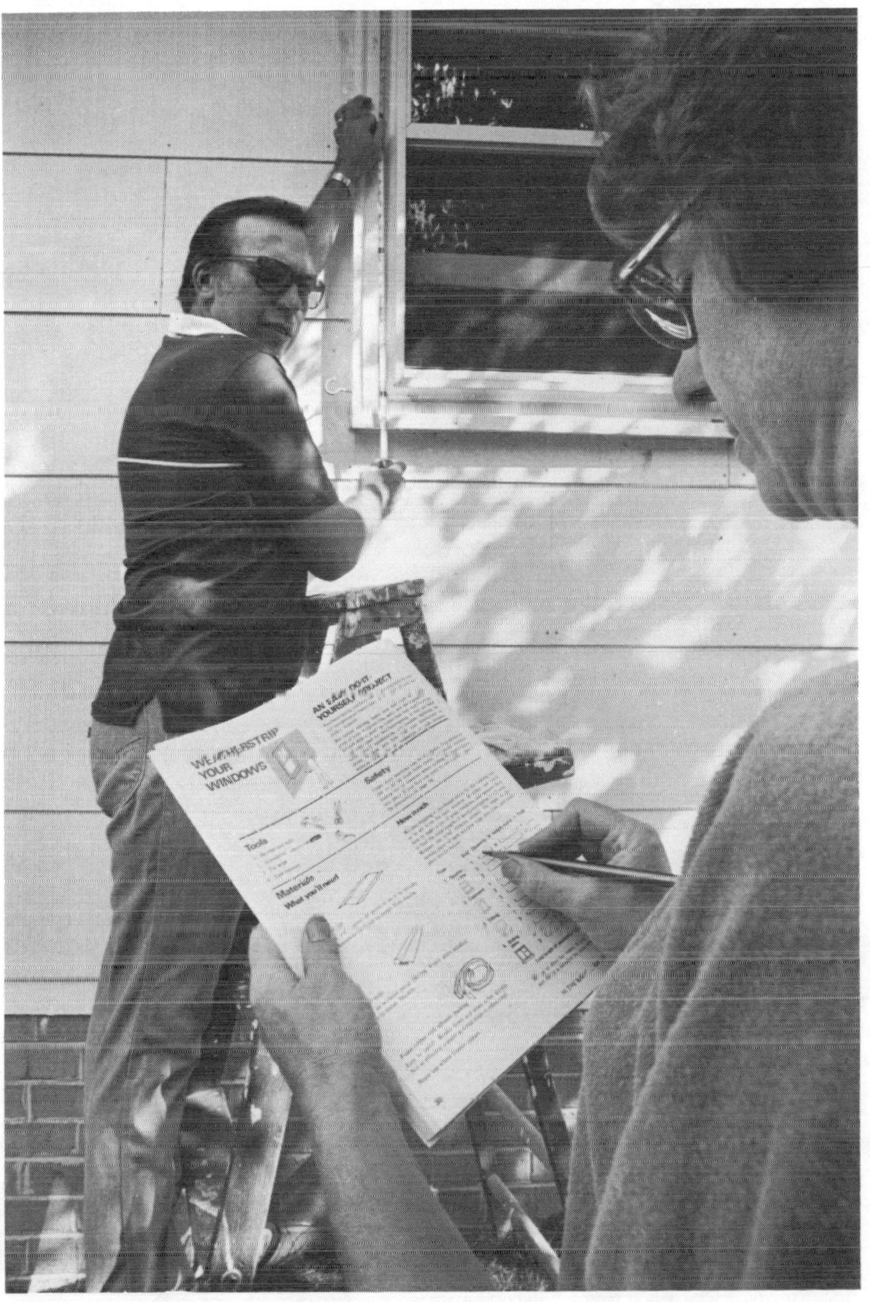

WM. CARNAHAN

A Family Checklist To Conserve Energy

By M. J. Hogan, D. Goss, W. W. Olson, B. L. Yust

The decade of the Eighties marks the beginning of an era of critical adjustments for many families. Increases in consumer prices and energy shortages are forcing families to make changes.

In general, families use energy directly for transportation, home heating and cooling, water heating, lighting, cooking and refrigerating appliances, clothing care, grooming, and recreation. In addition, energy is used for production and delivery of the goods and services families use. As the 20th Century winds down, we need thrift, conservation, and sharing of resources.

Families make decisions that not only affect their individual lifestyle but also the environment. The family and the environment are linked. The more energy we use from present nonrenewable sources, the more problems we create for ourselves and future generations.

Decisions families make such as where they live, number of children, and lifestyle influence their energy demands. Many of the following trends in the U.S. population have implications for energy use.

The number of households is increasing about twice as fast as the population because more people are choosing to live alone. This means, for example, more appliances to manufacture, more dwellings to build and maintain, and more space to heat and cool.

Better health care and improved living habits increase the lifespan. Since birth rates are decreasing, this results in an older population. Today about half the population is above 30 years of age. The over 30's tend to have more income and spend it for energy-intensive goods and services.

As more women are increasingly employed outside the home, they seek appliances, convenience foods and easy care clothing to replace home production of goods and services.

M. JANICE HOGAN is Associate Professor in the Family Social Science Department, University of Minnesota. Dorothy Goss is Associate Professor and Extension Specialist. Wanda W. Olson is Associate Professor and Extension Specialist. Becky L. Yust is an Instructor.

More people are choosing the suburbs as a place to live. Rural areas are growing faster than urban areas. The costs of travel to work, shopping and recreation become larger budget items as people leave the urban areas.

Sun Belt States of the South and West are growing in population more than other parts of the country. In these States, space cooling is a major energy cost.

Increased flow into the household of material goofs such as easy care fabrics, automatic washers and dryers, power lawnmowers, convenience foods, and automobiles has diminished the human energy expended for household maintenance and production.

Thermostat Tensions

As utility bills take a larger share of the family income, decisions about changing the thermostat may create tensions when family members choose between economy and comfort.

In a family with several cars, more than one TV, multiple bathrooms and a selection of stereo equipment, sharing and compromise are a choice — not a necessity. However, mass consumption within the family requires a continuous supply of resources, especially energy.

Operation of many of the small appliances may not decrease human energy use much, but it is a part of the daily choice pattern of our society.

Of course, not all families are alike in their consumption. Some families live frugally, even though they have enough income to do otherwise. They take pride in their efficient use of resources. On the other hand, some families live at a high consumption level with the help of consumer credit and always have needs or wants beyond their income.

The following cases illustrate that families are critical decision-makers and vary widely in how they choose to use their energy resources.

Family A. This family is a retired couple in their mid-sixties. They live in a 10-room single family house built in 1973 with a central heating system. It includes three bathrooms and four bedrooms — plenty of room for their grandchildren to visit during summers and vacations.

They own a travel trailer which they use in Arizona during the winter. They have two refrigerators, two ranges, three TV's (one is black and white), six clocks, three coffee pots, six power tools, three room air-conditioners, and four radios.

They use natural gas for space heating, clothes

dryer, water heater, and dehumidifier. They use gasoline for their lawnmower and two cars. They have worked hard all their lives and enjoy the fruits of their labor.

Family B. The family is headed by a farm couple in their forties. Family income last year was about $17,000. His father and mother spent their lives building the farm enterprise; they live across the road in the original homestead house. There are three children, 16, 12, 10 — the oldest child is from the wife's first marriage.

They live in a,three-bedroom wood frame house which was built when they were married in 1966. It is well built and has the following appliances: automatically defrosting refrigerator, freezer, clothes dryer, two TV sets, fry pan, toaster oven, dishwasher, and power lawnmower. They have a car, recreational vehicle, two snowmobiles, and a motor boat.

Mr. and Mrs. B are joint contributors to the farm enterprise; they share the work and expect their children to contribute their labor too. Mrs. B taught school the first year of their marriage and has considered seeking substitute teaching to supplement their income. The money would be used for a special holiday to the coast to visit friends and relatives.

Family C. The family is headed by a 28-year-old female. She has a 4-year-old child. They live in a large older home with a finished basement and attic. Natural gas is used as heating fuel. The house has no storm windows and needs weatherstripping, but the family head does not think she has skills or money needed to install these items.

This family has the following appliances: automatically defrosting refrigerator, range, microwave oven, three room air-conditioners, washer, electric clothes dryer, food freezer, and a dishwasher. It also has a color TV.

The mother works full-time on an assembly line. She commutes 18 miles to and from work. The child is cared for by a neighbor during the week. The family head feels she has too little time and too little money to provide the livestyle she desires.

Each of the families has made decisions that affect energy use, although they may be unaware of energy and environmental cost when making consumer decisions. New scientific breakthroughs may give us increased supplies of energy resources, but this alone will not solve the existing environmental problems. Families need to become more aware of energy and the environmental impact of their decisions.

Families can reduce energy use by careful management. An example of one family's experiences may provide ideas that can be adapted by other families.

The Browns began by adding insulation and storm windows to their older homes. They purchased and installed a device to adjust the thermostat in a four-setting pattern: higher in mornings and evenings when they are at home and lower in daytime and at night. They close off two bedrooms and a storage room during the heating season.

Plan to Add Wood Stove

They plan to add a wood-burning stove since they have wood available to cut. They reduced hot water consumption by lowering the water heater setting and changing bathing and laundering habits. They replaced two window air conditioners with fans.

Mr. Brown joined a carpool for commuting to work and the family sold the second car to reduce transportation costs. Now the family members plan and coordinate trips since only one car is available.

Growth of electricity consumption is well-documented. In 1970, the average U.S. home used 7,000 kWh, four times more electricity than in 1950. This growth in electricity use came during a time when the average number of people per household showed a slight decline, and the number of households and consumption per household increased.

Average annual electricity consumption for appliances reflects shifts to energy-intensive options. For example, families are using more hot water, have larger refrigerators, and many have installed air-conditioning.

Since 1973, energy prices for gasoline, heating oil, natural gas and electricity for household use have risen faster than the overall cost of living. And, energy prices will continue to spiral upward as long as we depend upon a nonrenewable and exhaustible fuel supply to meet our lifestyle patterns. As we lower demand for fuel by adapting our lifestyle and develop alternative sources of energy, prices probably will begin to stabilize.

Surveys indicate that almost everyone favors energy conservation, but not nearly as many practice conservation. For example, in one study over 50 percent of the families polled turn down their thermostats during the day, but only 15 percent turn them down to 60 degrees at night. Seventy-six percent of the people say they are willing to carpool but 69 percent report driving alone in their cars to work.

Indirect Use of Energy

Indirect energy — energy used for producing the goods and services we buy — accounts for over half the energy the average family consumes. About two-thirds of upper income families' energy is consumed indirectly in comparision to about one-third of the energy used indirectly by lower income families.

The higher the income, the more goods and services the family purchases. Thus, the higher the income, the greater the potential for reducing indirect energy consumption.

The consumer is an important decision-maker in our economy. About two-thirds of the goods and services produced in our market economy are ultimately consumed by families and individuals in the household sector. The amount of resources required is influenced by wants or goals.

The family links its members to a larger world. Social organizations such as the educational institutions, churches, and retail market groups all write guidelines which influence public policy about how the natural environment will be used. Major changes require many unfamiliar decisions; these decisions require information about products, processes, regulations, and codes.

Family members exchange ideas, attitudes, skills and competencies with others. Society depends upon the family to teach its members conservation habits, to transmit cultural values and goals, and to redefine quality of life. So we need to understand the mutual impact of consumer behavior on the social environment and the limits of the social environment upon family decision-making.

Our high consumption society depends on large amounts of energy for producing goods and delivering services. For example, energy is required for manufacturing material goods such as refrigerators, ranges, microwave ovens, trash compactors, hamburger cookers, and stereo equipment. While most small appliances do not need large amounts of energy to operate, they require energy for manufacturing.

Easy care fabrics, convenience foods and throwaway goods such as paper towels, plastic cups and disposable diapers have diminished the amount of household labor required; yet they require other energy for production.

Families may make different choices in housing, cars, vacations, gifts, food and clothing when they evaluate the energy costs of various options.

Life Cycle Cost of Appliances

For example, the choice of appliances needs to be made on life-cycle costs, not just the store price tag. An energy-efficient refrigerator may cost more initially, but over the life of the appliance the utility bills will likely more than offset the difference in price.

Many things are linked to water heating costs: standards of cleanliness, frequency and size of showers, baths, and choice of color for clothing.

When a family decides to conserve energy, it can explore many avenues of savings, considering both direct and indirect uses of energy. The following lists provides some examples:

Transportation

Direct Energy	*Indirect Energy*
Number & length of trips, including vacations	Need for one or more cars
Type of transportation i.e., public vs. private, air vs. rail	Need for recreational vehicle
Sharing of private transportation	Cost of manufacture of vehicle
Efficiency as miles/per gallon	Lifespan of vehicle

Housing

Temperature of space	Type of dwelling, i.e., single vs. multiple
Type of heating fuel	Size of home
Size of home/number of residences	Type of fuel & equipment
Number & location of windows and doors	Furnishings
Insulation, caulking, storm windows	Number of bathrooms & kitchen facilities

Household Activities

Direct Energy	*Indirect Energy*
Practices related to cooking & refrigerating	Number of appliances
Appliance efficiency	Amount of home production
Cleanliness standards for clothing and person	Amount and type of household goods purchased
Water heater efficiency	Degree of processing & packaging
Convenience features of appliances	
Size of appliances vs. use of capacity	
Gifts & family rituals	

The family can play a critical role in reducing the demand for energy by assessing its decisions. Opportunities to improve energy efficiency in our homes include insulating walls, ceilings and floors, adding storm windows, caulking and sealing to reduce air leakage, and adjusting shades and draperies.

We can reduce the amount of heated water we use. We can support and/or use mass transit and carpooling and reduce the miles traveled by the family car(s). We can organize, join and participate in community organizations to educate consumers and provide alternate energy-conserving systems. For example, we can promote bicycle paths and special privileges for carpools.

The family plays an important role in shaping the values and attitudes of its members. Through everyday experience, members learn practices that relate to more efficient resource use. Parents teach children and children teach parents a wide range of values and attitudes. Conflict may arise as family members have different wants for human support and/or compete for limited resources.

Together the family can discuss the issues of needs and wants. Answers to our problems will not be found by returning to the family of the past, where there was great reliance on the labor of all family members. Instead, our environmental problems will be solved by a new design that restructures our manufacturing system to maximize the desirable output of each consumer purchase.

We must also work for re-emergence of the values of conservation, sharing, and concern for the environment and other people. The way in which we experience and interpret the world will underlie our consumer choice and form patterns upon the earth.

In summary, we have the responsibility of making decisions which will reduce our energy consumption. By so doing, we have the opportunity to improve our quality of life.

Fifty Ways to Save Your Energy Dollars

By Mary E. Purchase

Many reasons are apparent for wanting to reduce the amount of energy used and the money spent for energy. These include

- the desire to conserve natural resources
- the wish to be independent of foreign suppliers
- the need to save money

Whatever the reason for decreasing energy consumption, there are many ways in which savings can be made.

First, you need to develop an attitude of conservation. You must want to save before much effort will be devoted to changing habits or seeking ways to use less energy. Management decisions should relate to the goals of conserving energy or reducing energy costs.

Much has been written about changing lifestyles. To some people, changing lifestyle to conserve energy means a reduction in the level of living. For them, conservation is interpreted as doing without. To others, it means finding ways to do things differently, more efficiently, but it does not necessarily mean making great sacrfices in their level of living.

Lifestyle of the family is potentially the most important means to conservation

Women's liberation from the drudgery of housework has gone hand in hand with the increased availability and increased consumption of energy in the home. Few people would elect to return to the time-consuming, hard, physical work of housekeeping. Instead, what is desired are the benefits of energy use, without waste.

Conserving energy can be made into a game to challenge all members of the family. Positive aspects of conservation can be emphasized. Feelings of success then will be associated with reduction in energy use, and the negative aspects of conservation can be minimized.

The Consumer Price Index (see first illustration) provides an easy means of showing changes in

MARY E. PURCHASE *is a Professor in the Department of Design and Environmental Analysis, New York State College of Human Ecology, Cornell University.*

prices that consumers pay. Note the rapid rise in the index, especially during the later part of the 1970's. The Consumer Price Index is influenced by and reflects the cost of energy.

The price per unit of several sources of energy is also given in the illustration. Note that the prices of energy were relatively stable during the 1960's. However, during the 1970's energy costs escalated much faster than costs in general.

If saving dollars is a goal for the household, conserving energy provides an effective means of achieving the goal. To the extent that market price is a signal to consumers, the rapid increases in the price of energy should indicate the growing importance of conserving energy.

On looking for ways to save energy, focus first on relatively large uses of energy. The pie chart illustration shows the division of the total energy used directly by consumers into categories.

Transportation accounts for nearly half the direct consumption of energy by individuals and families. The rapid increase in the cost of gasoline and the large percent of energy used for transportation are good reasons for the emphasis on conservation through selection and use of automobiles.

Space heating accounts for the next largest slice of the energy pie. Although needs for space heating vary considerably from one part of the country to another, areas that have the least need for heating

Prices of all goods and services are rising, but energy prices are increasing much more rapidly than prices in general. Petroleum products, especially gasoline, show the steepest climb.

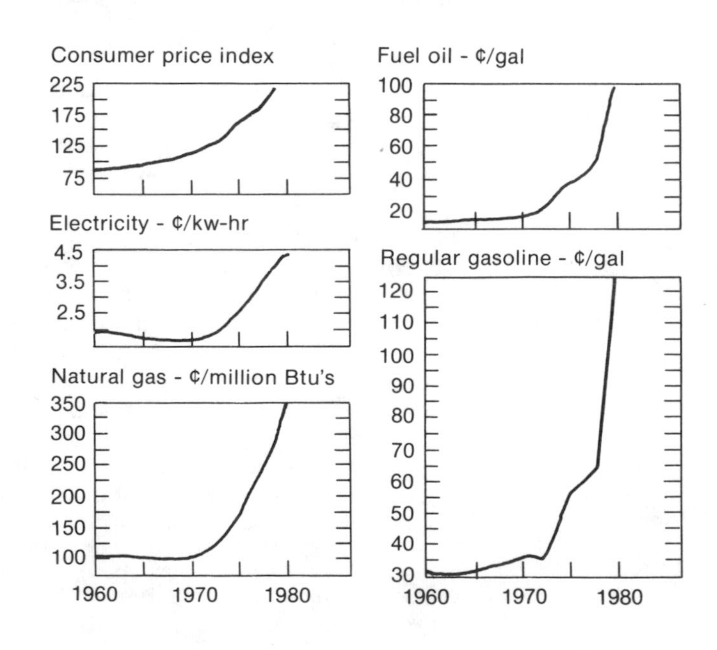

may have much higher than average needs for air-conditioning.

Heating water for bathing, clothes washing, dishwashing, and other purposes almost equals the total energy required for food preparation, food preservation, lighting, and home entertainment.

Transportation Nearly all the energy for transportation comes from petroleum, an increasingly scarce resource. Because nearly half of our oil is imported, its availability and price are determined in large part by others. Drastic efforts to reduce the use of petroleum products will decrease our dependence on foreign countries and help to control the cost of energy.

Transportation needs and alternatives differ greatly for urban, suburban, and rural dwellers. Mass transit is likely to be available in urban areas. For some suburbs, limited public transportation may be a possibility. In other suburban or sparcely populated areas, the automobile is the dominant form of conveyance.

Private means of transportation are depended on heavily in rural areas. No matter what alternatives are available, a very large fraction of the transportation energy is used by private autos.

Shifting to a smaller, lighter car with improved gas mileage will reduce the energy consumed and the cost of operation. Furthermore, controlling the number of miles that each car is driven will contribute to conservation. Carpooling, combining

Private transportation accounts for nearly half of the energy consumed directly by individuals and families. Space heating consumes another major portion. Individual appliances and lighting use small amounts in comparison.

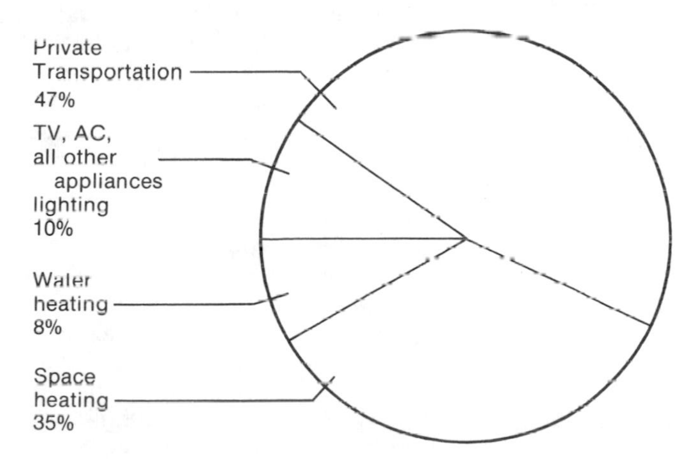

326-621 O - 80 - 11 : QL 2

trips, and use of public transportation are ways to reduce driving.

Perhaps a manager of transportation should be designated in each family. The manager could be aware of all the travel needs of the individual family members, and could plan use of the family car or suggest other means of meeting the transportation requirements.

Home Heating

Energy costs for space heating can be cut by shifting to less expensive energy and/or reducing heat losses.

If orientation of the house and location of the windows are suitable, the sun can be used to provide some of the energy for space heating. Where wood for fuel is available at low cost, its use to heat the house will help in cutting costs. For some situations, heat pumps or solar-assisted heat pumps will help control energy costs.

House design can contribute to energy saving. Houses with less outside surface require less energy for heating. That is, small houses rather than large ones, two-story houses rather than ranch style, and row houses or apartments rather than individual houses have lower heat losses because they have less outside surface through which heat is lost.

Landscaping can be planned to assist in reducing energy costs. Trees that act as a windbreak, and shrubbery near the house, help reduce heat losses.

Heat losses can also be reduced through insulation. The greatest savings are achieved by insulating the ceiling. Smaller benefits result from adding insulation to the walls and floor. Effectiveness of insulation is indicated by the R-value for the material, with higher numbers representing more effective insulation.

The value of insulation in reducing energy required can be calculated. An Extension agent, a representative of a utility company, or a building/insulating contractor can help estimate savings from the use of insulation in relation to its cost.

Control of air infiltration can reduce heat losses. Caulking around doors and windows is effective in stopping air leaks. Double glazing and storm doors and windows add another barrier to the passage of air and also reduce heat loss by conduction.

Close draperies or pull shades at night during the heating season, to reduce heat loss. During the day, open the ones on which the sun shines, to take advantage of solar energy. Operate exhaust fans as little as possible to avoid loss of warm air and excessive infiltration of cold air.

WM. CARNAHAN

When you lower the thermostat in cold weather, bundle up.

Lowering the thermostat during the heating season reduces the difference in temperature between the inside of the house and outdoors. When the indoor temperature is decreased, less heat is lost by conduction through the house walls and ceiling.

However, when the indoor temperature is reduced, you may need to change your manner of dressing. Sweaters, more layers of clothing, warmer clothing, heavy socks, warm shoes or slippers, and even a hat for indoors will contribute to comfort. Use of a lap robe or something similar will assist in conserving body heat.

Air-conditioning

To save on energy for air-conditioning, set the thermostat higher. Turn off the air-conditioner if no one will be at home. Use a timer if you wish to turn on the air-conditioner and cool the house before family members return at the end of the day.

For economy and comfort, cooling capacity of the air-conditioner should be matched to cooling needs. Your Extension agent, utility company representative, or an air-conditioner dealer can help determine your requirements.

A model that is slightly undersized is preferred to one that is greatly oversized. If the capacity is too large, the air-conditioner will cool the air and turn off, but it may not run long enough to reduce the humidity to a comfortable level. The result is clammy, cool air. Oversizing may be an increasing problem as capacity needs decrease because of higher thermostat settings and other conservation measures.

The efficiency of room air-conditioners is stated as the energy efficiency rating, or EER. Check the EER number on the energy label when you shop for an air-conditioner. EER values range from about 5 to 12, with higher numbers indicating greater efficiency and lower operating costs.

Many characteristics of a house that contribute to economy in heating in winter also decrease cooling requirements in summer. Insulation, especially in the ceiling, and double glazing help keep heat out.

Limit the operation of exhaust fans when the air-conditioner is in use.

Closing draperies or pulling shades on windows that face the sun also reduces the heat load. Trees that shade the house are very effective in limiting the energy required for cooling in summer.

For efficient operation, the condenser (the part of a room air-conditioner that extends outside the house) should be able to give off its heat readily. This means that if there is a choice, the condenser should not be placed in the sun, and air should circulate around and through it freely. The filter within the air-conditioner should be cleaned or replaced as needed.

Heating Water

Energy for water heating is used to raise the temperature of the water initially and to keep the water hot. To reduce the cost of heating water, look for ways to use a smaller volume of hot water and to use water at a lower temperature.

To minimize standby losses (energy to keep the water hot), choose a well-insulated water heater and insulate pipes that carry hot water long distances, especially through unheated space.

Reducing the thermostat setting on a water heater is an effective way to cut energy costs. Less energy is required to heat the water and, with a smaller temperature difference between the water in the tank and the air around the water heater, the standby losses are reduced.

When the hot water is at a lower temperature, less cold water is used to dilute it to provide water for bathing and other purposes.

Although showers have a reputation for using less water than baths, long showers can easily use more water than frugal baths. Concentrate on conservation whether in a shower or bath.

Other suggestions for using less hot water include 1) using warm or cold settings instead of hot for washing clothes, 2) rinsing clothes in cold water, 3) not letting hot water run constantly when washing and rinsing dishes, and 4) fixing leaky hot water faucets.

Because size of the water heater is one of the factors determining the amount of energy used for heating water, the size should be no larger than required to meet family needs.

Consider the various uses of hot water and the amount needed for each. For the hour in which the most hot water is needed, find the maximum number of gallons required by all of the uses for hot water. Choose a water heater that will supply (through storage and recovery) the volume of hot water needed for current requirements.

Think ahead also to consider changes in the family situation that would affect needs for hot water over the expected life of the water heater, perhaps ten years. Let both present and future needs influence the choice of size of water heater.

Turn off the water heater if hot water will not be needed for a period of days, as when the family is on vacation.

Laundry Equipment

Most of the energy for washing clothes is used to heat water. Therefore, to conserve energy in washing clothes, choose the lowest temperature for the wash water that will provide satisfactory cleaning.

In the past, hot water 140° F or above was recommended for washing some loads of clothes. Now, because thermostats on water heaters have been lowered, the hottest water available in many homes is 120° F — a temperature formerly considered to be only warm. When the warm setting on a washer is selected, the hot water is diluted by cold and the temperature is lowered further.

Temperature of water delivered on cold wash settings depends on the location in the country and the season of the year. The cold water temperature might vary from near 80° F in Southern States in summer to just above freezing in Northern States in winter.

If cleaning is not adequate when lower wash temperatures are used, consider increasing the cleaning by using more detergent, or a different detergent. If results are still not satisfactory, use a higher wash temperature. White fabrics and heavily soiled articles may need higher wash temperatures than other items to be laundered.

Washing in cold water below about 80° F is not recommended for good cleaning, but cold water can be used for all rinses. Slightly more energy will be used by a dryer if the clothes are cold when put into the dryer.

To economize on water, wash full loads, or use a small load setting on the washer if it is available. Washers with a suds-saver feature offer another means of conserving hot water.

Using a clothes dryer decreases the amount of human energy needed to care for clothing, but it does require other energy. Where outdoor drying facilities are available and the weather is favorable, consider line drying the clothes.

To minimize the energy needed for drying, extract as much water as possible before placing clothes in the dryer. Do not over-dry the clothes as that wastes energy. Use an automatic dryness sensor, or set the timer for the minimum time that might be required. Clean the lint filter regularly to allow a full flow of air and speed the drying.

Role of Kitchen Appliances

If wisely used, refrigerators and freezers may help save energy by reducing the number of trips by car to do grocery shopping.

The amount of energy for refrigeration depends on the defrost system, the total capacity as well as size of the freezer section of refrigerator-freezers, location of the freezer (top mount or side-by-side), other design features, effectiveness of the insulation, the ambient temperature, and use given the appliance by family members.

Manual defrost, available only on small refrigerators, requires the least energy. Partial automatic defrost, also called cycle defrost, provides frost-free operation of the fresh food section but requires that the freezer be defrosted manually; it is available on a mid-range of sizes of refrigerator-freezers.

Practically all large refrigerator-freezers have automatic defrost in both the fresh food and the freezer sections. The energy requirement is relatively great because of the large volume of refrigerated space as well as the type of defrost.

Refrigerators with the freezer section above the fresh food section generally use less energy than side-by-side refrigerators. This is partly because they are usually smaller in size and partly because, per unit volume, there is less freezer surface exposed to room conditions.

High efficiency models have improved insulation and other features to reduce the energy required and thus cut operating costs. Look for energy labels on refrigerators as you shop. Use the information to select a model that is economical to operate.

Locating refrigerators and freezers away from heat sources helps reduce the energy required. If possible, do not place these appliances next to a range or a built-in oven. Locate them where sun from a window will not fall on the surface. Be sure there is plenty of space for air circulation so heat given off by the refrigerator or freezer can be removed easily.

Check the fit of the door. Make sure the gasket is in good condition and forms a tight seal.

Because freezing ice requires a large amount of energy, use ice conservatively. If only one or two pieces are needed from an ice cube tray, do not throw away the others but save them for later use.

Similarly, creating frost from moisture in the air in the refrigerator requires energy, whether the frost accumulates and must be defrosted manually or is removed automatically. Therefore, covering food conserves energy as well as preventing dehydration of the food.

Limit the number of times the door is opened and the length of time it is open. Know what you want to get out or put away before you open the door. Keep foods in the refrigerator organized so that little time is spent hunting for items. Thaw frozen foods in the refrigerator; the thawing food can help keep the refrigerator cold.

Placing hot foods in the refrigerator seems wasteful. But for safety, foods should not be left at room temperature for long periods before refrigerating them.

If your refrigerator has a switch for the anti-sweat heater, turn it on only when the relative humidity in the room is high enough to cause the refrigerator to sweat around the door seal.

Cooks have many choices of appliances for preparing food — gas or electric ranges, top of the range or oven, microwave oven or a variety of small appliances.

Although electric ranges are likely to be more efficient than gas ranges in their use of energy within the home, the inefficiency of producing electricity generally makes the cost of cooking with an electric range higher than cooking with gas. Most decisions with regard to the choice of gas or electricity, however, are not based on cost but depend on other factors such as availability or personal preference.

Cooking on Top of the Range

Whether electricity or gas is used, cooking on top of the range is more efficient than food preparation in the oven. Start the foods cooking on high or medium high, but turn to a lower setting as soon as the cooking temperature is reached. Because rapid boiling does not cook the foods faster than a slow boil, choose the lowest setting that maintains the cooking process.

Choose an electric unit that fits the pan; do not use a pan smaller than the heated section of the unit. Adjust the flame of a gas burner so the flame does not extend beyond the bottom of the pan. Cover the pan with a tight fitting lid.

To increase efficiency of the oven, load it to capacity. A large quantity of food can be cooked with relatively little additional energy beyond what is needed to cook only one item.

Do not open the oven door needlessly. Instead of peeking to determine whether the food is done, set a timer for the appropriate cooking time.

Oven temperature can be lowered by 25° F when glass or glass ceramic pans are used for baking, because they absorb radiant heat better than metal pans. Baking at a lower temperature helps cut energy use.

If a small amount of food is being prepared, consider using a portable oven, an electric frying pan used as an oven, or a microwave oven, if one of these is available.

One-dish meals, whether cooked on top of the range, in an electric skillet, or in a slow cooker use less energy than meals in which several menu items are cooked separately.

Dishwashers present a special problem. For most uses in the home, water of 120° F is adequate, but for a dishwasher to clean satisfactorily, the water should be 140° F or above.

One way to provide this temperature for the small amount of water used in dishwashing is to set the thermostat on the water heater so all hot water for the household is at that temperature. Another way, one that would consume less energy, would be to choose a dishwasher that included a heater to raise the temperature of only the water within the dishwasher to 140° F.

To save energy, turn off the heater during the drying step.

Washing dishes by hand allows for great variation in the amount of hot water required. Some people wash or rinse dishes under constantly flowing hot water; they could save energy by turning off the water when it is not being used. If hotter water is desired for better sanitizing of dishes, use a teakettle or other utensil on the range to heat the water.

Whether washing dishes by hand or machine, you may find that dishes need not be washed after each meal.

Adjusting Our Lives To Stretch Energy

By Glenda M. Herman

"Use it up, wear it out, make it do, fix it up or do without." This World War II motto is just as appropriate today as it was 40 years ago. Many families are trying to cope with less energy and higher prices by "making do."

Now is the time to seriously examine current American values, attitudes, and behaviors toward energy use. Changing these values, attitudes, and behaviors to bring about a less energy-intensive lifestyle will take time and effort. Most people resist change, especially when it looks less appealing than what they presently have. Yet, a new way of life less dependent on energy may be not only necessary, but even allow us to develop a higher quality of living.

For several reasons, the energy conservation idea must take the lead. The first reason is time. In general, conservation can produce results more quickly than other energy options. The second reason is cost. Conservation costs less than developing other energy alternatives. And finally, the time for action has come. The American family can play a direct part in conservation.

In the simplest terms, conservation means the wise use of resources. We could eliminate a lot of waste and still not do without things we consider basic to our way of life. To conserve, we must understand the ways we use energy daily.

We use energy directly and indirectly. The major *direct* energy consumption methods are home heating and transportation. *Indirectly*, the consumer pays for fuel resources used by industry in production and shipping of goods, and for services provided by businesses. Some families have tried to control their direct energy uses.

Most families have felt the impact of rising fuel prices in the size of their utility bills. Adjusting the thermostat helped, but not a great deal (although this is still recommended). More efficient "direct" measures were needed: insulation, caulking,

---

GLENDA M. HERMAN *is extension Housing Specialist and Associate Professor, North Carolina Agricultural Extension Service.*

weatherstripping, storm windows, wrapping of water pipes, and having heating systems cleaned. Some families found it paid to invest in a new heating system, or adjust their house to take advantage of a free energy source — the sun.

Other families chose to cope with energy costs by changing cooking and refrigeration styles and equipment, turning down the water heater thermostat, reducing the frequency of baths or showers, exploring better ways to do the laundry, and even adjusting the way lighting and audio-visual equipment were used.

However, the American "romance" with the automobile continues. This has become a drive-in society: movies, banks, dry cleaners, liquor stores, fast-food restaurants, and even churches. The options people choose for their cars are also very costly to operate — air-conditioning, power steering, remote control windows and door locks. There is a lot of talk about organizing and supporting mass transit, carpooling, bicycling and changing driving habits, but do they actually happen? Americans have forgotten how to walk!

"Indirect" energy consumption is basically what's used to produce goods and services. All products available at the market place in some way required energy to manufacture, package, or deliver them. It is this *hidden* energy use that has been so long and easily ignored. Examples are numerous.

Small appliances may not require much direct energy to operate, but they do require a great deal of energy to manufacture. Too often these small appliances are non-repairable, and designed to be tossed out and replaced by newer models. Thus the term "planned obsolescence" evolved.

In the last 20 years, 2-income families have created a need for a revolution in kitchen equipment. Advances have been made in many time- and labor-saving appliances. But if these "labor-savers" begin to cost more in the way of direct and indirect energy, can their continued use be justified?

Each year the amount of energy used to produce, package and deliver food increases. Much of the food we consume reflects high energy costs of the food system.

American families could help control energy costs of food by growing food at home; reducing the use of processed, pre-packaged and convenience foods; and taking into consideration how energy-intensive some of our foods are. This might in turn lead to better diets and a reduction in the need for intensive exercise equipment.

Throw-Away Packaging

A startling example of high "indirect" energy use is packaging of products. Packaging was originally intended to protect and preserve contents. More recently, it has been used to substitute for labor. Self-service department stores and supermarkets use pre-packaged items not only to protect contents, but to speed turn-over, inform and attract buyers, and reduce the number of sales people.

We throw away huge amounts of packaging materials daily. Then, cities or communities must use additional energy to dispose of our garbage.

Demand for "convenience" increases. We ask for and get easy-care floor coverings, tiny calculators, convenience or quick foods, disposables of all types (paper cups and towels, diapers, pop bottles, razors, fountain pens), and gadgets to entertain or substitute for human imagination and energy.

Fabrics used for clothing and home furnishings require energy to produce. Consumers want easy-care, synthetic fibers — possibly not realizing that large amounts of petroleum were required to produce them.

Often direct and indirect energy uses are linked as in the cases of clothing and home furnishings. The choice of light-colored garments along with our standards of cleanliness are directly related to the amount of energy required to produce the garments, the amount of water needed to clean them, and the frequency of cleaning. Darker clothing worn longer could cut this energy use.

The current consumer preference in home furnishings is for large designs or patterns in sofa or chair fabric. Matching of these designs require more fabric. For example: a sofa covered with a plain fabric may use 12 yards while 22 yards of fabric may be needed to match a design. This is not only a waste of fabric, but of energy required to produce the material.

Some families have debated whether to buy a new sofa or have one recovered. Recycling of consumer goods is one way to save money and cut energy needed to produce new merchandise. Understanding these simple concepts can help you make wiser choices and save on energy costs.

The choice of housing is another major area where the average consumer can exert control. It takes thousands of gallons of petroleum products to build just one house. Costs per square foot of living space have increased rapidly in the past year. The choice of smaller houses or multi-family units, or certainly better measures to regulate heating and cooling costs, are necessary considerations of today's family.

A house designed or weatherized to be energy-efficient saves its owner in many ways, not the least of which is the direct use of fuel.

Many of the steps to make an existing house more energy-conserving can be done by the homeowner. It does not take much knowledge, skill or time to caulk a window, install weatherstripping, or change a furnace filter. It does take the *will* to do these things.

The family can play a critical role in reducing the demand for energy by re-assessing its living habits. As mentioned earlier, thermostat regulation is an important energy-conserving measure. Yet, people complain when the heat drops below 72° F. It takes a conscious act to go find an extra sweater, put another blanket on the bed, or wrap up in a quilt when reading or watching TV. But, these are ways to save.

The areas of recreational activities and selection of gifts are other ways. One of the most obvious changes taking place is reduction in the use of vans, motor homes, and campers for long distance travel. These eight-mile-per-gallon gas guzzlers are hard to justify.

"At Home" Types of Recreation

Many families are finding "at home" types of recreation can be fun and often less physically exhausting. However, the idea of adding expensive swimming pools or tennis courts is a false sense of savings. Both require great amounts of energy to produce and maintain. Perhaps a better idea would be a community project to fix up a local park or develop community facilities so all could enjoy.

When choosing gifts, consider the amount of energy used to produce the product, the amount of energy the product will use (electric hot dog cooker), and finally, whether the use warrants the energy costs. Most of our homes are full of energy-consuming appliances or toys that may be used only once or twice a year — a child's Christmas toy, for example. Many toys are powered by small disposable batteries, and may be used only a short time before they are discarded

As you and your family consider energy alternatives, try to look at both the direct and indirect use and costs of energy. This may mean more talking together to reach a solution. It may mean making some decided changes in the way your family lives. It will probably mean making some conscious changes in the way your family interacts.

Just how can an American family like yours learn to "live with less energy?" Consider the following steps.

1. **Change attitudes as to personal and family needs.**

This first step involves re-examining needs versus wants. Today a growing number of families are finding the value and necessity of a revised lifestyle which includes both "voluntary simplicity" and an "energy-conservation ethic."

Voluntary simplicity should not be confused with "back-to-nature" movements. Rather, it is a lifestyle which calls for self-determination, material simplicity, practicality in both working and living situations, and a way of doing more with less.

An energy-conservation ethic emphasizes conserving now to help provide energy resources for future generations.

The idea that "small is beautiful" may be a place to start. Smaller houses and automobiles would certainly decrease the direct and indirect use of fuel. Living with less does not mean giving up everything — but rather re-adjusting our lifestyles to less size, less "things."

2. **Substitute human energy for mechanical.**

There are many ways human energy can replace our dependence on fossil fuels.

Walk instead of ride. Air-dry clothes instead of using a clothes dryer. Turn some of your lawn into a garden and grow your own food instead of buying processed, packaged foods. Read a book instead of watching TV. And participate in sports — do not be just a spectator.

Not all these ideas are for everyone, but one or more may appeal to your family. Can you think of others?

The ideas of home production of goods and services, of learning to do many of the things about your house for yourself, of recycling items to a new use, or selecting multi-purpose products all call for the natural human intelligence and energy that Americans have always prided themselves on having in abundance.

3. **Adjust time schedules.**

Personal and family time schedules may need revision. Try to plan shopping trips to take care of several things at once.

Many utility companies are offering lowered rates for customers who will agree to make changes in the time of day they use power. Energy load management systems such as "peak load pricing" and "time-of-day rates" mean basically the same — dollar savings for energy savings. However, any adjustment in habits requires thought.

4. **Select more energy-efficient equipment.**

The purpose of the new appliance labels is to help you choose a more energy-efficient appliance. Some of these appliances may cost more initially, but are designed to have lower operating costs. Over a period of years, this should save you energy dollars.

Along with selecting more energy-efficient equipment, we must learn to use equipment better. Why buy an energy-efficient refrigerator and then stand in front of its open door to plan the evening meal?

Apply these same ideas to other products. What is the point of buying an energy-conserving car unless you also reduce the number and frequency of stop-and-go shopping trips, the speed you drive, and make more effort to keep the car in good working order?

5. **Search out reliable information.**

The concern for energy-saving measures has caused many new businesses to spring up around the country. For the most part, these are good additions to the market place, offering services and products which can help with energy conservation. Examples include insulation and solar companies.

However, as with any new technology, there can be a lack of knowledge and expertise on the part of some of these new business people. The unaware consumer can also be taken in by dishonest individuals out only to make a profit.

The amount of written information on energy is almost more than we can handle. Each day a new book comes out, magazine articles are published, government reports are produced, and TV and radio refer to the energy situation.

How do you judge what is accurate and usable? One recommendation is, do not rely on just one source. Become as informed as possible. Talk with people who have tried new things. Get estimates and check references.

Some of the future sources of help for the consumer include: house doctors trained to analyze energy loss from buildings; Energy Extension Services or one-stop energy centers; the Agricultural or Cooperative Extension Services located in most counties throughout the country; and computers to regulate energy flow in buildings and homes.

Specialists of all types will be able to provide advice and how-to suggestions on ways to live with less energy. However, in the end, you must make the final choice and take an active part.

In summary, the six-letter word ENERGY has and will continue to affect every person in the United States and the world. Our images for the future are somewhat clouded now by uncertainty and the possibility of changes in our "comfortable" way of life. Yet the prospect of a slower pace of life, increased physical labor, and greater community togetherness could enrich American life.

The time for decisions is now. We must either curb our wants, or pay the price.

Further Reading:

Energy: Crisis and Opportunity, #85292, J. C. Penney Company, Inc., 1301 Avenue of the Americas, New York, NY 10019. $1.25

Focus on Energy and Housing, #5105-7, American Home Economics Association, 2010 Massachusetts Avenue, N.W., Washington, DC 20036. $5

In the Bank . . . Or Up the Chimney?, #023-000-00411-9, U.S. Department of Housing and Urban Development, for sale from Superintendent of Documents, U.S. Government Printing Office, Washington, DC 20402. $1.70.

Making a Small House Seem Much Bigger

By Joseph L. Wysocki

For the past three decades, new homes have been larger than homes previously built. The 2-bedroom, 1 bath, Cape Cod of the post-World War II era had 1,000 square feet or less. In the 1950's the popular style was the larger 3-bedroom ranch house, followed in the 1960's and 1970's by the 3- and 4-bedroom 2-story Colonial or bi-level, often with 2½ baths and a family room.

Along with more rooms, additional square footage, and larger landscaped lots, a number of amenities appeared — fully applianced kitchens, patios, fireplaces, air-conditioning, two-car garages, intercoms and so forth.

Today we have reached the point where the price of housing is soaring and surpassing increases in family incomes. It is becoming increasingly difficult for a family to purchase a home. Families are also confronted with other housing expenses: high interest rates on mortgages, mushrooming energy costs, increasing property taxes, maintenance and repair costs.

More families are spending over 30 percent of their income on housing. Predictions are that this percentage will continue to increase unless our housing expectations are modified. Living in less space often appears to be the only solution to the common need for affordable housing.

With housing getting more expensive and energy costs higher, American families may find their housing changing in the future as we see a halt to the trend of more square feet so evident in recent new construction.

Instead of the traditional 4 bedrooms, 2½ baths Colonial, families will need to consider other housing options such as smaller lots, more compact homes with multi-functional spaces, condominums, manufactured homes, duplexes, townhouses or other multi-unit structure types, all of which would be less expensive to obtain, heat and maintain.

Some predict that our homes, physically and

JOSEPH L. WYSOCKI *is Family Housing Specialist with The Pennsylvania State University.*

technologically, will change more over the next 20 years than in all the years of home building since the Egyptian era.

How to live in less space is a challenge facing more individuals and families. We must be careful that we don't sacrifice our human space needs and those of our children as we contemplate living closer together. How do you insure privacy and maintain individuality? As families shift to smaller housing, they must carefully evaluate their space wants and needs.

If, for example, a family needs a larger amount of land with its dwelling, it would have to consider the tradeoffs to make with other dwelling features.

More yard for a garden may mean giving up a bedroom or an extra bath, or some other space the family has wanted. If, on the other hand, a family wants all the appliances currently popular in the kitchen — microwave oven, dishwasher, trash compactor, crepemaker and the rest — the family must consider the cost of what it would have to sacrifice in terms of number of rooms or space, for example.

Living with less space in our home environment can be satisfying and enriching. However, careful attention must be given to selecting furnishings and a home so that space is not wasted but used wisely. The total amount of space and its divisions, the arrangement of rooms or areas, and flexibility in the use of space are all important considerations.

One Floor Level Living Areas More Flexible

If you are planning a new home, several basic design and use principles should be followed to make less space more functional and still private. Incorporating all living areas on one floor level increases flexibility so that rooms may be used for more than one purpose. Fewer rooms, fewer walled hallways, and carefully planned storage areas will make small housing seem larger.

Plan traffic areas and door arrangements so that rooms are not cut in half by traffic flow and doors. Too many ill-placed openings waste valuable wall and floor space. Plan the house with different heating zones so seldom used areas can be easily closed off by doors and not heated or cooled when unoccupied. This requires design coordination with the heating-cooling contractor.

Coordinate the house interior with the exterior living areas so that certain family activities can be held outdoors when weather permits.

Consider the following ideas in planning specific areas of your new house:

326-621 O - 80 - 12 : QL 2

Good traffic pattern. From the guests' entrance, traffic crosses only the end of the living room, or the corner of the kitchen. To reach the central hall from the service entrance, traffic goes through the utility room, not the kitchen.

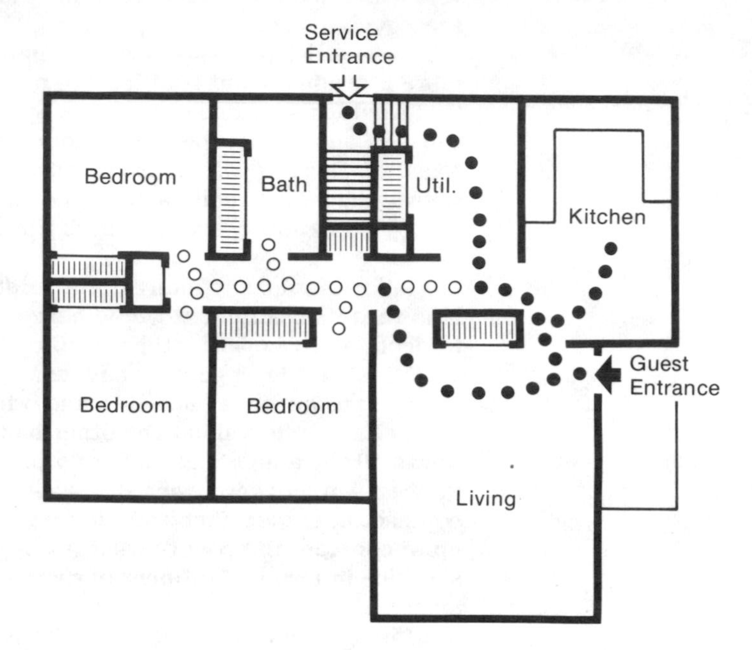

Good traffic pattern in a small house. The guest entrance may open directly into the living room, but it should be located so traffic goes across the end of the room.

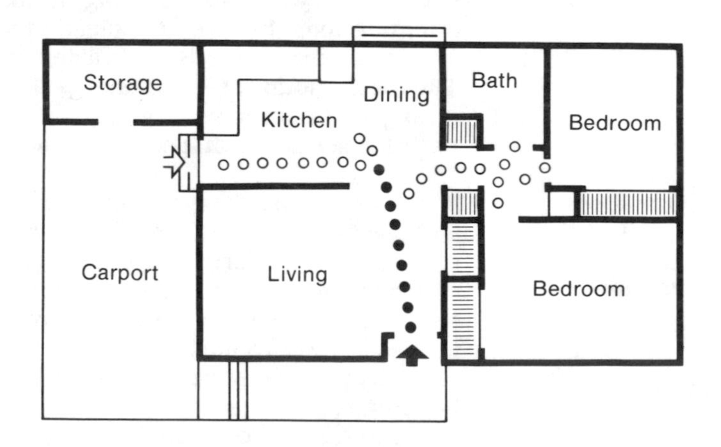

Kitchens, Work Areas. A reduction in the amount of space you build will result in considerable cost savings — particularly if these reductions are in the kitchen and bath areas.

A small, well-planned kitchen will be more efficient than a larger one that has appliances widely scattered. Eliminating less essential built-in appliances will lower costs and provide more storage space.

Consider using the soffit space above cabinets to store seldom used but needed items such as chafing dishes, baskets, large pots and bowls.

To cut expenses, laundry equipment may be located in kitchen or bath areas rather than in a separate room. Always try to minimize plumbing costs by locating kitchens, baths, and laundry near each other.

Dining Areas. For best space utilization, dining areas should be combined with other rooms such as the kitchen or living room. An eating area in or near the kitchen and living area — and large enough for family and guests — may eliminate the need for a separate, seldom-used dining room.

Sometimes one end of the living area can accommodate a dining table, especially a drop-leaf or folding type that can be folded when not in use, for the times a family may desire a more formal eating or buffet space.

If a dining table is free standing within another living space, the area around the table becomes a visual and usable part of the other space. Also, the table can be used for many activities other than dining.

Living Area. One living area or family room may be adequate to meet family needs, thus eliminating the need for a separate formal parlor. Some builders are calling this area the Great Room.

Be sure it is designed to accommodate several simultaneous activities and still preserve some privacy. Even in limited space, each family member needs an area for personal privacy.

Bedrooms. Bedrooms can be smaller when built-in units and closets are used effectively.

Children's bedrooms may double as play areas. If two or more children are to share a bedroom, consider letting them have the large master bedroom to accommodate their sleep, dressing, study, and play needs.

For adults, a master bedroom may double as a sitting room or study and desk area.

Baths. Avoid the all-in-one-room scheme for bathrooms. A compartmented bathroom that accommodates two or three people at the same time can eliminate the need for a second bathroom.

Making Space Seem Larger

If some areas of the home you are living in or about to move into seem overcrowded and other areas underused, reassess the use of space. Explore new and different ways of making space function better for your needs.

Some changes may require major remodeling or decorating, while others may be accommodated by rearranging furnishings or minimal purchases.

Major Changes. Consider changing an existing room or rooms to create an open "country kitchen" area for cooking, eating, family living, and informal entertainment.

Opening the kitchen in such a way allows the cook to join in conversations with family and guests, an arrangement that may improve both social occasions and the attitude of the cook.

However, do not remove any walls before consulting an engineer or contractor to determine which walls are load-bearing, since you could seriously affect the structure of your home. It isn't always necessary to completely remove a wall — you can add a feeling of space by piercing a wall with an opening.

You may want to incorporate a wood burning stove in this area.

Extend the amount of space you have by creating an outdoor private living space adjacent to the indoor living area. Even a small section of fence and a few shrubs can provide visual privacy in a small outdoor area.

Eliminating a small or awkward window in a room will gain additional wall space, and if the window faces north you also will lower heating bills. You probably will want to keep as many windows that face south as possible since you can capture passive heat on a southern exposure.

Before you permanently remove a window, cover the opening to see if you like the effect of less light and ventilation. If possible, adding a skylight to a room or hallway will open up the ceiling, let in light, make an interior space more usable, and give the area a spacious feeling.

Other ways to make existing space seem larger involve the converting of unused spaces in the home — attics, garages, porches and basements, — to year-round living space.

Don't eliminate storage space since luggage, lawn furniture, and other equipment must be kept somewhere.

You can build a loft in a high-ceiling room in such a way that you gain a whole new level of living, while the space below the loft remains as useful as ever.

Decor, Furniture Changes. Plan the decor for the entire home as a unit rather than each room separately, to create a feeling of spaciousness and continuity.

Carry wall and floor colors from room to room and change textures rather than colors. Blending simple window treatments with wall colors will make rooms seem larger.

Pale walls that reflect light tend to close you in less than dark walls that soak up light.

Modify a guest or extra bedroom to double as a study, TV room, sewing and/or hobby room. You can also adapt a bedroom and make it more multi-purpose by adding daybeds with bolsters instead of conventional beds. Or use trundle or bunk beds to save on floor space.

Select small-scaled furniture with simple lines, and multi-purpose pieces such as sofa beds or drop-leaf tables, when selecting or replacing furniture.

Avoid large, triple dressers and massive chests that require a lot of wall space and limit your furniture arrangement. Several small stacking chests will be more flexible for most needs.

Consider clustering items such as TV, stereo, bookshelves and storage cabinets in a wall unit to help eliminate clutter, increase floor space, and add interest to your room.

Place furniture against walls to leave as much space as possible in the center of the room. You can expand space visually by the use of mirrors — for example, on the long wall of a narrow room to make it appear wider. If possible, hang a mirror to reflect the outdoors.

In general, eliminate unnecessary household furnishings and bric-a-brac. Beautiful objects need space around them to be fully enjoyed. Remember that people need eye room as well as elbowroom.

To gain maximum use of limited storage space, compartmentalize your closet storage area. For example, children's clothes closets can usually have double clothing bars — one higher than the other.

Don't overlook the storage possibilities of doors and the floor area — such as under beds — as well as shelves. Inexpensive storage devices can be purchased or made from boxes to more effectively use whatever space you now have.

As our homes and communities become closer, more efficient and cohesive, we will experience a greater feeling of togetherness.

Smaller homes will require less upkeep, and permit a more leisurely lifestyle.

Success in living in less space can be assured if privacy is maintained. You don't need a lot of space for privacy. But in housing, privacy doesn't just happen — it must be consciously planned for all family members.

Careful choices concerning space arrangements in the home must be made. Every dwelling, every room has space waiting to be used. Sound design principles coupled with some creative imagination can do wonders to make limited space livable, inviting, and comfortable.

Further Reading:

A Welcome Home, Sperry & Hutchinson Co., 330 Madison Avenue, New York, NY 10017. 50¢.

Family Housing Handbook, MW-PS-16, Midwest Plan Service, 122 Davidson Hall, Iowa State University, Ames, IA 50011. $2.50.

Improving House and Grounds, J. L. Wysocki and J. R. Nuss, Correspondence Course 115, The Pennsylvania State University, University Park, PA 16802. $3.50 plus 50¢ postage and handling.

Low-Cost Energy Efficient Shelter, Eugene Eccli, Ed., Rodale Press, 33 E. Minor Street, Emmaus, Pa. 18049. $8.95 paperback, $12.95 hardback.

Planning A Home, Sarah Faulkner, Holt, Rhinehart & Winston, New York, NY $16.95.

Planning A Home Projects Manual, Karen Gustafson Bromberg, Holt, Rinehart & Winston, New York, NY $6.95.

Small Homes Council, University of Illinois at Urbana-Champaign, Champaign, IL 61820. Write for list of over 30 non-technical circulars on various phases of home planning and construction.

The Housing We Would Like, Mary Winter and Earl W. Morris, *Journal of Home Economics*, Vol. 69, No. 3, May 1977, pp. 7-10.

How to Save Energy Preparing Foods

By Fern E. Hunt

Consumers are key elements in national patterns and levels of energy usage, both directly in the energy they use and indirectly in the energy used to produce food, goods and services for them. Industries have learned that energy efficiency is worthwhile. For example, commercial canners report that changes in equipment to reduce heat wastes in food processing paid for themselves in as little as one year.

Energy conservation actions in individual households may have less dramatic results than in large scale manufacturing operations, but small amounts multiplied by millions of households can result in substantial savings overall.

Direct use of energy for food for the family includes gasoline for auto trips to buy food; electric power for refrigerating food; and gas, electricity or other fuel for cooking and for water heating for dishwashing. Consumers have control over their direct uses of energy.

From the consumer's standpoint, energy used to produce food and the appliances for food preparation in homes is **indirect** energy. Consumers have control to some extent over indirect energy usage by their purchasing decisions — for example, whether to buy dried, fresh, canned or frozen foods; what cooking appliances to buy; whether to buy beverages in glass or plastic bottles or aluminum cans.

Careful management in use of a car for shopping trips and in use of appliances that burn fuel (such as gas, wood, or coal) results in corresponding savings in fuel.

Saving energy in use of electricity is somewhat more complex. Use of only the amount of fuel or electric power needed and avoiding wasteful practices are desirable in any case.

Avoiding heavy usage of high wattage electric equipment at times of day when the demand on the local utility company for power is highest helps to reduce the amount of scarce fuels the utility

FERN E. HUNT *is professor of Home Economics, School of Home Economics, The Ohio State University and Ohio Agricultural Research and Development Center.*

company must use to assure uninterrupted, stable power service. In rural areas, demand tends to be highest in late afternoons and early evenings, especially during winter months, at about the time dinner preparation and dishwashing are generally being done.

Energy use in the food system in the United States is estimated to account for 12 to 17 percent of total U.S. energy consumption. Of that amount, about 2.9 percent goes for agricultural production of food, 4.8 percent for food processing, 4.3 percent for home preparation of food, 2.8 percent for quantity food service operations, 0.5 percent for wholesale trade, and 0.8 percent for retailing.

Farm Production Input Vs. Output

For farm production of food, energy inputs for each unit of output varies with the type of food. One way to evaluate the return on energy investment in food production is to compare yield of energy (calories) and protein (grams) from foods in relation to units of cultural energy; that is, energy used in crop production.

Field crops such as oats, soybeans and wheat require relatively low amounts of cultural energy per unit of production. Deciduous fruits are intermediate. Vegetables and small fruits are the most energy intensive of the plant crops because of difference in cultivation, pest control, and harvesting requirements.

Production of meat animals and related animal products, on the other hand, is considerably more energy intensive than the growing of plants because animals must feed on plant materials and are not efficient in converting what they eat to energy or body mass.

Yield of protein from soybeans is fairly high per unit of cultural energy. Grains (wheat, oats, corn) yield lower amounts of protein per unit of energy input. Animal protein is highly energy intensive. Protein yield from legumes per unit of energy used in production is estimated at about 60 times greater than from beef or pork and 15 times greater than from chicken. Differences in quality of protein from different sources are not accounted for in such estimates.

If Americans obtained their food energy and protein entirely from grains and legumes, energy costs of food production for human consumption might be reduced to some extent.

This kind of analysis, however, overlooks at least three major factors: 1) the importance of other nutrients essential for human growth and health which are supplied in fruits, vegetables and animal products; 2) low acceptance of vegetarian diets; and 3) energy costs of converting such foods as soybeans to edible forms having familiar textures, appearance and flavors.

The more precooking and processing, special packaging and refrigeration a food requires, the higher the energy input is. For example, average energy requirements for slaughter of beef and pork are estimated at 910 and 1,750 Btu per pound of live weight, respectively. But processing (such as making weiners, bologna, smoked ham and bacon) increases energy costs by 5 to 10 times, adding as much as 7,000 Btu (more than 2 kilowatt-hours) per pound processed. It should be mentioned here that, with processing, some increase in carcass utilization is possible.

Although processing adds greatly to the energy required in production of meat, some of the products are consumed without further heating. In such cases, energy input in home preparation of the food is lessened and the extra energy used in production may tend to be equalized in the food chain from farm to table.

Fruits, vegetables, fruit and vegetable juices, and tomato sauces and catsup make up the bulk of food processed in the canning industry. In the making of catsup and tomato sauces, a major factor in energy use is the amount of water removed by evaporation. Sterilization by processing with steam is the major energy user in canning operations.

Energy requirements for commercial canning of tomatoes, fruits and vegetables in 1974 were calculated at about 1,600, 1,800 and 2,150 Btu per pound of fresh weight, respectively. Vegetables require longer processing than fruit and tomatoes to assure sterilization, and the longer food must be processed, the more energy is required.

The amount of energy required for sterilization in canning is affected not only by composition and acidity of the food but also by container size and shape. The food industry is searching for ways to reduce energy costs, including possibilities offered by new types of containers.

Food pouches made of a layer of aluminum foil sandwiched between two layers of heat-resistant plastic film are among container innovations considered by food canners.

The flat package permits more rapid heat transfer to food throughout the package than is possible in the cylindrical can. Shorter processing times are then needed and the fresh flavor and texture of foods are reported to be retained well. Further, the pouches can be stored at room temperature.

An important drawback to the pouch is that more energy is required to make the pouch than to heat sterilize the food it contains.

Alternatives to commercial food preservation are home canning and freezing. Information on energy requirements in home preservation of food is more limited than for commercial operations at present and more difficult to determine as well.

However, for canning 7 quarts of tomatoes by the water bath method, 2.43 kWh of electrical energy were estimated by one source to be needed to bring the water bath and jars of food to a boil and to process them for 45 minutes. The energy input for this part of the canning job would amount to about 545 Btu per pound of canned tomatoes.

Energy for manufacture of canning jars and equipment and for heating water to clean the jars and peel the tomatoes is not accounted for. These factors, coupled with inefficiencies of home equipment and homemakers' procedures, could easily amount to more energy than that needed for processing the food in an energy efficient commercial cannery.

Pressure canning fruits and vegetables by recommended procedures requires less energy than the water bath method because less time is required for heat processing. Perhaps more important, pressure canning helps assure safety of vegetables and low acid foods by permitting use of temperatures above 212° F.

Frozen foods, from the standpoint of total energy inputs from field to table, would be considered luxury foods. The initial energy costs of freezing alone are relatively low compared to energy costs of storage.

In general, about 0.1 kWh (314 Btu) of electrical energy is reported to be required to freeze a one-pound package of food and drop its temperature to 0° F. This figure does not include energy costs for preparing foods before freezing, such as the blanching of vegetables, nor for packaging materials.

Average energy consumption for food freezer operation per day — disregarding size, type and other factors — is reported to be about 3.3 kWh in cold months and 4.1 kWh in warm months. If a family kept 100 pounds of frozen food in the freezer on the average, the energy cost would amount to about 102 to 130 Btu per day per pound. The longer a package of food is held in the freezer, the higher would be the energy cost for its storage.

The Long Haul for Our Food

Much of our food is not locally grown and must be transported long distances. The average distance for moving food in the United States is reported to be 765 miles. Citrus fruits and juice, for example, are produced primarily in Florida and California and grains are grown and processed into animal feed, cereals and flour in the Midwest. Where the food is grown and processed in relation to where it is consumed affects transportation energy inputs correspondingly.

Two other important factors besides distance enter into energy consumption for food transportation: temperature requirements and weight. Refrigerated transport naturally requires more energy than nonrefrigerated, and the lower the temperature needed, the higher the energy input. As for weight, the lower the water content, the less transportation energy required. Thus less energy is required for hauling dried beans than canned baked beans or the like.

In some cases, energy inputs for producing and transporting foods over long distances may be less than for growing them locally. Production of vine-ripened tomatoes out of season is an example. As much as 40 times more energy may be required to grow tomatoes in northern greenhouses for local consumption than to truck field-grown tomatoes from Florida. No comparisons are made here of eating quality, nutrient content, or dollar costs.

The bulk of the food that families use is purchased. Food shopping trips generally require use of a car; consequently a part of transportation energy costs in households is chargeable to providing food for the family. Energy inputs for transportation are related to the energy efficiency of the auto, the distance of the residence from the shopping center, distances between stores shopped, and frequency of shopping trips.

In weekly trips with shopping for lowest prices in up to four food markets separated by a total distance of less than 5 miles, savings of as much as 14 percent have been reported over dollar costs of the same items purchased in a single store.

Energy for cooking in homes has been estimated at 1.1 percent of the total energy used in the United States. Most food preparation is done with the range, although American families own a number of portable appliances which can be used as substitutes for parts of the kitchen range — egg cookers, coffeemakers, countertop ovens, electric skillets, slow cookers and the like.

Some Cooks Great, Others Don't Rate

Work habits of the "cook" are a major factor in energy consumed in food preparation. Energy usage has been shown to vary by as much as 50 percent among women doing identical meal preparation tasks with the same kitchen range.

How can such variability among range users occur? With surface units on an electric range, 70 percent of the heat produced is estimated to go into the food in a utensil which fits and rests on the unit properly. The remainder of the energy goes to heat the element (10 percent) and losses to room air (20 percent). Additional losses can occur if utensils used are smaller than the heated area of the element and if heat settings are not appropriate for the cooking job.

As an example of the effect of heat settings on energy consumption with an electric range, consider the cooking of potatoes in a 2-quart covered saucepan. A 6-inch unit at the *high* setting would be used to quickly start the boiling. Once boiling has begun, the cooking temperature can be maintained with a *low* setting for about 20 minutes. If *medium low* is used instead, 100 percent more energy will be used than actually needed.

Use of a utensil with a fitted cover during cooking with water is worthwhile. The lid prevents loss of heat from the pan by evaporation. Six times more energy is required to change water to steam than to bring it to a boil. In addition, small amounts of cooking liquid can be used in a covered pan without burning food if heat settings are controlled, cooking time is shortened, and uniformity of cooking is improved. Further, nutrients and flavor of foods are conserved.

Range ovens are less efficient in energy use than surface units and burners. Only 14 percent of the heat produced during cooking in an electric range oven is estimated to enter the food. Of the remaining 86 percent of the energy, 46 percent goes for heating the oven lining, 25 percent is lost through oven walls and 15 percent is lost through the oven vent.

Efficiency of gas range ovens is poorer than for electric ranges. Only 6 percent of the heat produced is estimated to penetrate the food load, 20 percent heats the materials of the oven structure, 11 percent is lost through the oven walls, and 63 percent is lost through the vent. Greater movement of air through the gas oven than through electric ovens is needed in order to provide oxygen for the flame and to remove moisture vapor produced in combustion of the gas and evaporated from the food.

It should be pointed out in comparisons of gas

and electricity consumption that about 10,500 Btu input is required to produce and deliver one kilowatt-hour (3,413 Btu) of electric energy.

Keep That Oven Door Closed

With both electric and gas range ovens, door openings cause additional heat losses and further reduce the energy efficiency of the ovens. Suggestions to time oven cooking and to avoid frequent or lengthy door openings during oven uses should be heeded.

If basting of a food is necessary or items are added to food already cooking in the oven, the food might well be removed from the oven for attention in order to avoid wasting heat through prolonged opening of the door.

Heat losses in cooking contribute to the heat load and cost of home air-conditioning in summer. In winter, the wasted heat from cooking contributes toward home heating but is an inefficient method of comfort conditioning.

Planning food preparation to do several cooking jobs while the oven is heated improves efficiency in energy use. An oven meal when meat or a pie is to be cooked in the oven, for example, takes advantage of available heat.

Many foods lend themselves well to oven-cooking. Potatoes may be oven-cooked in several ways besides baking. Fruit and vegetables can be steamed in covered baking dishes. And a variety of desserts are appropriate choices for oven preparation.

The additional food load for an oven meal causes some increase in energy needed, but not nearly as much as reheating the oven a time or two or heating additional surface units to complete a meal.

Recipes requiring use of ovens often call for preheating. Some revision of traditional practices may be appropriate in view of claims that oven preheating wastes energy, that preheating may increase energy usage by as much as 25 percent or more, and that cold oven starts in modern ovens yield acceptable products.

Items that need to be cooked for half an hour or more and non-critical items such as roasts, baked potatoes and casseroles should not require a preheated oven unless an old model range is used in which the broiler unit comes on during preheating. With modern ranges, preheating occurs quickly, usually in less than 10 minutes, and some heating of foods occurs as the oven heats if preheating is eliminated. Quick-cooking items such as biscuits may require as much as 30 percent additional baking time in absence of preheating the oven in order to get desired browning and thorough cooking.

In comparisons of energy usage in cooking with portable appliances and conventional ranges, portable appliances usually are slightly more energy efficient. The differences are attributed to the smaller mass to be heated, lower wattage rating, and better contact between the food container and the heating element in the portable appliance than for a saucepan or skillet on a range.

In cooking jobs normally requiring long slow cooking, such as navy bean soup, a pressure saucepan on a conventional range may be more energy efficient than a covered saucepan or a slow cooker.

As much as 16 percent less energy may be required with the pressure saucepan than with the slow cooker, and 40 percent less energy with the pressure saucepan than with the regular saucepan. Percentages of savings vary greatly with cooking times involved.

Purchase of portable cooking appliances with the expectation of reducing the drain on U.S. energy resources may be counter-productive. Energy savings in use of the appliances may be small and involve very long payback periods. Further, energy required to produce the appliance may far exceed energy saved by its use. If portable appliances are owned or acquired for whatever reasons, however, they certainly should be used when possible.

With the microwave ovens, only 40 to 50 percent of the energy input is absorbed by food loads. This explains why a table model microwave oven may have a wattage input rating of 1,450 W and an output (cooking power) rating of only 650 W.

Less energy is generally required for cooking or heating small quantities of food in a microwave oven than with an electric range. For cooking complete family meals, however, a microwave oven does not use significantly less energy than an electric range when appropriate procedures are followed.

Dishwashers

Energy usage associated with food for the family doesn't stop with acquiring the food, storage, and cooking. Energy is used also in cleaning the dishes and cooking utensils. About 43 percent of American homes wired for electricity were equipped with mechanical dishwashers as of December, 1979.

Energy used in automatic dishwashing includes electricity for operating the motor and a heating element during the process. A typical dishwasher model on the market today requires about 0.6 kilowatt-hour of electrical energy each time it is used on a "regular" setting, including both wash and dry phases. The energy usage is cut about in half if the dishes are air-dried without heat.

Some dishwasher models have a heat/no heat drying option. Similar energy savings can be accomplished in older models by stopping the dishwasher operation after the last rinse and drain, leaving the door slightly ajar, and letting the dishes dry by evaporation.

Average energy usage per day in households for operation of mechanical dishwashers is about 0.4 kWh. Families are apparently drying dishes without heat or are waiting to wash them until they have a full dishwasher load.

Dishwashing water must be at least 140° F to effectively soften and remove fatty soils such as beef fat from surfaces of dishes and cookware and to cause water to evaporate during drying, particularly when the no-heat drying option is used.

For people who want clean dishes but also want the temperature of their household water supply lower than 140° F, dishwasher models are now available which will heat the water to the appropriate temperature after the dishwasher fills with water but before dishwashing action begins. Energy losses associated with storage of hot water in the household hot water system may thus be minimized, but use of the feature increases total time needed for dishwashing because of the initial delay while the water heats.

Use of hot or warm water to prerinse dishes before loading them into the dishwasher wastes energy. Most dishwashers are designed to thoroughly clean dishes with food materials simply shaken off orscraped lightly and not pre-rinsed.

Dishes washed mechanically and handled appropriately are generally more sanitary than those washed by hand unless particular care is given in the handwashing process. A procedure for bacterially clean dishes by hand includes scraping, washing in hot detergent solution (120° F), rinsing by pouring boiling water over them, and allowing them to air dry in a clean environment.

Hand washing of dishes may require as little as 2 gallons of water or much more per time, depending upon whether water at the faucet is allowed to run continuously throughout the dishwashing. At the least, 1 kWh of energy would be required to heat 2 gallons of cold tap water.

Mechanical dishwashers typically use 12 to 14 gallons of water, all of which is as hot as the household water heating system provides, for a complete cycle at the "regular" wash setting.

Heating 12 gallons of cold water to 150° F in order that the water entering the dishwasher may be at least 140° F requires about 3.2 kWh of electricity or 10.4 cubic feet of natural gas in winter, and 2.6 kWh or 8.5 cubic feet in summer in northern climates (assuming tap water temperatures of 40° F in winter and 60° F in summer). Thus 4 to 5 times more energy is required for heating water than for operating the dishwasher itself.

About the same amount of hot water is used in mechanical dishwashing, whether a few items or a full load is washed. More energy will be conserved by accumulating a full load before washing than by drying the dishes without heat.

Energy management in providing food for the family is a highly complex matter without easy answers. At present, much more information is needed in order for us to feel comfortable with our decisions about how to be good stewards of the resources available to us.

Managing Your Home To Save on Energy

By LaVerne Farmer

Every time you turn on a light, use a vacuum cleaner or do the laundry, you are using fuel. What can you do? A lot!

Even though your own contribution toward energy conservation may appear small, the combined efforts of millions of Americans can greatly reduce our total energy needs.

More than half the energy used in homes goes into heating and cooling. Here are a few suggestions you can use to be an "Energy Conservationist" and still maintain comfort in your home.

Smart Use of Space. Don't heat or cool rooms not in use. Close off areas of the house that are not needed.

In summer, it's easier to keep the lower level of your house cool than the upper level. If you have a choice, plan your living arrangements accordingly and cool only the rooms you need. The basement recreation room may also be used for sleeping during hot weather, reducing the need to cool bedrooms on upper levels.

Buy the cooling equipment with the smallest capacity for the space to be cooled. It's better to buy a slightly undersized unit than an oversized one. Energy-efficiency ratios (EER) are provided on window units. The higher the EER, the more efficient the air-conditioner.

Setting the Thermostat. Begin the heating season by setting the thermostat no higher than 65° F. If there are older people in the home the thermostat may need to be set at 70° F to prevent a drop in body temperature. Turn it lower at night or while you are away for extended periods.

During extremely cold weather, do not turn the thermostat so low that the heating system must labor to reach the 65° F temperature when you reset the thermostat.

You may wish to install a time-clock thermostat which will automatically set back the temperature to your nighttime setting and reset it to the daytime

LAVERNE FARMER *is Professor, Energy Coordination, for the University of Tennessee Cooperative Extension Service.*

326-621 O - 80 - 13 : QL 2

temperature before you get up in the morning.

Turning the thermostat several degrees higher than desired when you arrive home or awake in the morning does not speed the rate of heat delivery. It will, however, run the temperature higher than necessary and waste fuel.

Avoid the temptation to turn the thermostat higher if you feel chilly. Instead, put on additional clothing for warmth or move to a sunny spot in the house.

If the house becomes warmer than necessary, set the thermostat down rather than opening windows. In fact, you may be more comfortable if you set the thermostat several degrees lower while you are working (active) and then set it higher when you relax in the evening.

In summer run the air-conditioner only when and where you need cooling. Don't overcool. Set the thermostat no lower than 78° F.

A timer, to turn the air-conditioner on in advance of your arrival home, will let you come home to a cool house, yet save running the air-conditioner all day.

Before air-conditioning was invented, people opened up the house at night to let it fill with cool air. In the morning when the sun began to heat up things, the house was closed until evening. This practice may have some application in your home today.

Window Fans

During mild weather, use a fan instead of an air-conditioner. A window fan uses only a small fraction of the energy of air-conditioning units. If you have a window air-conditioner, you probably can use it to circulate air and still be comfortable without using the cooling unit.

When a window air-conditioner is running, close the registers from your heating system. This prevents cold air from escaping into the ductwork.

Use exhaust fans in kitchen and bathroom

Regular Setting

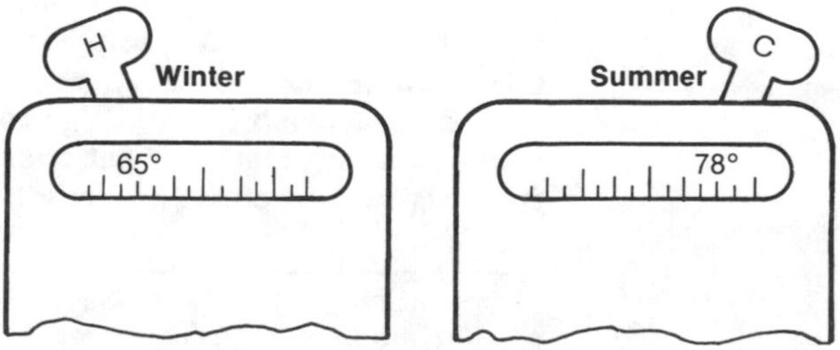

sparingly during cold weather. They remove warm air from the house. During hot weather, limit the use of exhaust fans while using the air-conditioner.

When the air-conditioning is not being used after the temperature has dropped in the evening, exhaust fans can help pull outside cooler air into the house. Remember to open a window on the opposite side of the house.

In summer, higher temperatures are easier to tolerate if the humidity level is lower than 60 percent. You may find that use of a dehumidifier improves the comfort level and requires less energy than running the air-conditioning. Conversely, increasing the humidity level during very cold weather will improve the comfort level.

In-and-Out Trips are No-No's

Needless opening of outside doors during cold weather lets lots of heat out and equal amounts of cold air in.

Remind all members of the family to close the door quickly as they enter or exit. Keep in-and-out trips to a minimum.

Be sure doors are closed properly. Doors left ajar drain heat rapidly.

A simple way to keep drafts from around windows and from under doors is to make "draft chasers" to place against the closed door or window. First use a tightly woven fabric to make a tubular casing 2 to 3 inches in diameter the width of the door. Then fill it with sand and you've got a "draft chaser."

If you have an attached garage, keep the doors closed. Always close the big door before opening the door into the house. If you have a door with a vestibule, use this entrance in cold and hot weather rather than doors opening directly into the living areas.

Keeping windows covered in cold weather helps you stay more comfortable, because you're curbing a major source of heat loss in most houses.

If you cover your windows with roller shades, they should be installed within the window frame, close to the glass, and fitted snugly on the sides.

Effective Draperies

Draperies are more effective when installed with a close-fitting cornice over the drapery, or close fitted to the ceiling to prevent air flow over the window. Lined draperies or draperies made of closely woven fabric are the most effective in reducing heat loss.

In winter, use shutters, shades, or draperies to reduce heat loss on the cold side of the house. On the sunny side, uncover windows to let in solar heat.

During the summer, keep out solar heat by covering windows when the sun strikes. Especially shade the east windows. When the sun shines strongly on them each morning, the house heats up. Next, cover west windows that are exposed to the afternoon sun. Even though the summer sun may not enter south windows directly, reflected heat may be a problem on the south side of the house.

Carpet for That Warm Feeling

Carpets are warmer to the touch and offer more insulation than wood, slate, or resilient floor coverings. The thicker the carpeting and padding, the greater the insulating quality. Carpets with fuzzy yarns that trap air have greater insulating qualities than carpets with smooth yarns.

BOBBE BAKER

During the colder months, draperies on sunny windows should be opened to let in solar heat. In the summer months they should be kept closed to keep out the heat.

In carpeted houses you feel warmer because less of your body heat is radiated to the floor. You can turn the thermostat lower and still be comfortable. Every degree you lower the thermostat will generally reduce your heating bill 2 or 3 percent.

However, if you choose between insulating under the floor of an unheated area or carpeting, remember that the insulation will be more effective.

Place furniture far enough away from radiators, registers, and cold air return vents to permit free circulation of heated or cooled air. You will be more comfortable during extremely cold weather if you sit away from windows and outside walls.

Chairs with closed arms and backs or closed upholstered chairs will help hold body heat so you will feel warmer.

If you are chilly when your thermostat is set at 65° F in winter, wear additional clothing. Several layers of clothing will be more comfortable than restrictive heavy garments.

During summer, the most comfortable garments are those of absorbent cotton, cotton blends, and linens. In cold weather, wool or woolen blends are effective for holding body heat.

Two lightweight blankets that trap the air between them keep you warmer and more comfort able than one heavy blanket.

Some people may prefer an electric blanket and sleep in a cold room. But they should keep regular blankets on hand in case of electrical power outages.

Periodically, clean radiators or heating/cooling registers and ductwork.

Filters in the hot air heating/cooling system should be cleaned or replaced regularly to keep the air moving freely. Check to see that the condenser unit of the central air-conditioning unit, located outside the house, does not become clogged with grass and leaves.

Clean windows to allow the maximum radiant heat to enter in cold weather. Shade them during hot periods.

Close fireplace dampers when the fireplace is not in use. If there is no damper, a plug can be made to fit inside the entry to the chimney.

Heating water for household and personal use accounts for about 15 percent of total energy used in the home. The average American family uses more than 26,000 gallons of hot water each year. The amount of energy needed to heat this water is more than that consumed by a family's refrigerator, freezer, clothes dryer, television, kitchen oven and range, and lights combined.

Water heaters not only use, but also waste, a substantial amount of energy. The most significant waster of energy in a water heater is caused by heat loss through the tank (standby loss). In a 50-gallon water heater, 14 percent of energy used to heat the water is lost as heat escapes through the tank.

Simply wrapping insulation around the outside jacket of the water heater tank can reduce this standby loss, and cut your annual water heating bill about 10 percent.

Do not apply supplementary insulation over controls or house wiring connection boxes and covers on these boxes.

Several times a year, drain a pail or two of water from the faucet near the bottom of the heater. This removes sediment and mineral deposits that accumulate in any water-holding container. Sediment build-up makes the water heater use more energy.

Locate your water heater as close as possible to the water users, such as the kitchen sink, dishwasher, bath, shower, and washing machine. If the thermostat setting of the water heater provides hot water temperatures in excess of your family's needs, energy is being wasted. For families with dishwashers, a 140° F setting is recommended; families without dishwashers should experiment with a 120° F setting.

You can cut your water heating bill even further by reducing the amount of hot water your family uses. The more cold water you use in place of hot water, the more energy and money you save. Here are a few tips for conserving hot water:

Hot-Water Appliances. Run your automatic dishwasher and clothes washer with full loads only. Use warm or cold wash temperatures in your clothes washer, when possible, and always rinse with cold water.

Showers Instead of Baths. Water-saving devices, such as "low-flow" showerheads and sink aerators, can reduce your hot water use significantly. In particular, a water-saving showerhead can greatly reduce your hot water use — while still providing a satisfying shower. An efficient showerhead can pay for itself in a matter of weeks.

Dripping Faucets. A faucet that leaks a drop a second wastes 650 gallons of water a year. In most cases, you can fix a dripping faucet simply by replacing the washer.

When doing dishes, wash the dishes first, then fill the sink with rinse water, or put rinse water in a pan. Allowing hot water to run continuously to rinse each dish, glass or utensil is wasteful.

Avoid allowing water to run continuously when shaving. Close the drain and fill the basin partially with water instead.

Use hot water during evening hours to ease the strain on the electric utility. Electrical demand is at its highest during the day, to meet the needs of commerce and industry. Some areas have reduced rates for energy use during evening hours.

Home appliances help save both energy and make household tasks much easier. Become thoroughly familiar with operation of your appliances. Always read the operating instructions in the use and care booklet before using a new appliance.

The key to the cost of operating cooking appliances is the way they are used. You can exert a great deal of control over energy consumption of the range, cooktops, or oven. First of all, use cooking appliances for their intended jobs.

Use the range for cooking. Using it for heat wastes a lot of energy since the range is not an efficient space heater. It is also dangerous!

The oven is not a dryer. It is not economical, and it can start a fire.

Small Appliances for Small Amount

When you cook small quantities, it is usually more economical to use small appliances rather than the range top or large oven. Toasters, waffle irons, skillets, grills, popcorn poppers, fondue pots, bean pots and coffeemakers consume less energy for their specialized jobs than the range. If you have both a small and large oven, use the small one whenever possible.

Preheating the oven is often unnecessary and

STAN GRIFFIN

A leaky faucet can waste hundreds of gallons of water a year. The Washington, D.C., Cooperative Extension Service held a workshop to show home owners how to repair faucets.

For gourmet cooks, there are many small appliances that can be most helpful in the kitchen. Many of them consume less energy for their specialized jobs than a range.

WM. CARNAHAN

may be a waste of energy. When preheating is required, such as when baking time is only a few minutes, avoid preheating for longer than 10 minutes. Do not preheat surface units. Put pots and pans on the range top before the heat is turned on to avoid wasting the heat.

If you are an oven peeker you waste energy. Every time the oven door is opened during operation, the oven temperature drops 25 to 50 degrees. A range with an oven door window might be a good investment for the "peek-a-boo" cook.

A Cooking Schedule

Energy-conscious cooks schedule and plan for the most efficient use of their appliances. Cooking several items at the same time and choosing cooking times carefully can conserve energy. Following are suggested ways in which cooking might be better planned and scheduled.

It is more practical to cook several dishes at once instead of reheating the oven a number of times during the day. Two or three dishes can be baked with little more energy than one. For example, if three dishes are to be cooked at similar temperatures (325°, 350° and 375°) pick the average temperature (350°) to cook all three.

Preparing multiple recipes for spaghetti sauce, soups, and stews that take a long time to cook can save energy. Then refrigerate or freeze for future use.

When baking or cooking foods with extended cooking times try to avoid "peak hours" (8-11 am and 4-8 pm are usually the peak hours).

Care of Appliances. Proper maintenance of cooking appliances is also important, not only to conserve energy but also for safety.

Keep heat reflection surfaces clean, especially reflectors below the heating element on top of the range and the entire oven.

A Steady Blue Burns True

For the most efficient use of fuel, gas burners should have a steady blue flame. A yellow flame means it needs attention.

Make sure the pilot on a gas range is properly adjusted. It may be using more fuel than necessary.

Have faulty switches, burners, and thermostats fixed promptly and professionally. Check the oven thermostat every six months with a thermometer.

Make sure oven door seals are tight and not leaking heated air.

Approximately 60 percent of the heat entering the refrigerator does so through the walls. Thus, the refrigerator and freezer should be located where heat infiltration can be kept to a minimum.

Both appliances should be located away from the sun; away from heat-producing appliances, specifically the range and dishwasher; away from the heating system, and where air can freely move over and away from the condenser coils.

Reduce the chance of heat leakage at the door by occasionally checking the gasket for a tighter fit and replacing when necessary.

Dirt and dust will trap heat and act as an insulator, which in turn prevents the flow of heat from the coils and thus requires more energy. Condenser coils should be cleaned regularly.

What's Watt on Lighting

Everyone can economize on energy use through efficient lighting. This doesn't mean walking around in the dark.

Lighting amounts to 3.5 percent of a home's total energy bill. By using efficient lighting and turning off unnecessary lights, you can save energy and dollars in a number of ways.

Energy can be saved by using lower wattage light bulbs in areas where minimum lighting is needed. Adjust the amount of light in a room with the use of three-way bulbs and dimmer switches. Fluorescent lights are more efficient than incandescent and should be used in areas where they are suitable.

A timer to turn lights on at night before you get home rather than leaving lights on while you are away saves your energy and dollars.

Use long-life incandescent bulbs only in hard-to-reach places. They are less efficient than ordinary light bulbs.

Keep light fixtures clean and use translucent lamp shades with white linings for greater efficiency. Take advantage of natural light by opening curtains and shades and keeping windows clean.

Personal Care and Grooming

Grooming involves the consumption of hot water, electricity and petroleum products. Although the quantity of energy consumed for one grooming process or beauty product may be small, when many pieces of equipment are involved — or when energy is wasted — the costs mount up.

Beauty aids and equipment commonly used for grooming include electric shaver, electric make-up mirror, electric manicure set, electric hair blower/dryer, and electric shoe buffer/polisher. In addition, bathroom or dressing area equipment may be in operation — lights, heater, ventilator, sun lamp, heat lamp, air-conditioner, dehumidifier, and iron for pressing clothes.

Some tips to aid you in saving energy while grooming are:

Equipment no longer in use should be turned off, disconnected and stored.

Electric equipment should be properly maintained. Check for faulty wiring, dials, thermostats, and seals, Keep equipment clean.

Use equipment only if necessary. For example, air dry hair when possible, line dry clothes when practical, select fabrics and garments that do not require ironing, brush your teeth "by hand" and polish your shoes "by hand." Organize your ironing and pressing so you can do several garments when the iron is heated.

Home entertainment — television and television games, radios, record players, CB radios, and tape decks — can be enjoyed in an energy-efficient way.

Often a radio, record player, or TV is left on when no one is listening or watching. That's not entertainment; it's wasting energy!

Learn to turn off equipment when you leave a room. Teach children that part of the privilege of using home entertainment equipment is turning it off when they are finished using it.

If you find yourself "listening" to a TV program that is also being broadcast on radio — a ballgame or political news conference, for example — switch to a small radio. Radios operate on one-sixth the energy of TV sets.

Money Saving Tips For Home Appliances

By Rebecca P. Lovingood

Household tasks of preparing and storing food or keeping clothing, furnishings, and the living environment clean and neat have changed little over the years. Although Cornell University researchers have found much the same time spent in home-making, household appliances certainly make those tasks easier.

For example, compare washing clothes with a washboard or wringer washer to using a modern automatic washer which only requires the user to select the proper controls for water temperature, wash time and speed after putting the clothes into the washing machine. Or contrast preparing food on a cookstove of your great-grandmother's day with cooking on a modern gas or electric range or microwave oven.

Household appliances represent an initial expense of several thousand dollars, usually the largest single household investment after the purchase of a house and an automobile. According to U.S. Department of Agriculture research, the life expectancy of new major appliances, or number of years of ownership by one household, ranges from 11 to 20 years.

Purchase prices are increasing as are costs of ownership, due in part to the cost of energy.

Besides the money involved, other factors must be weighed in making the decision to buy an appliance.

First off, what are your needs? Your family has its own set of needs and wants which must be weighed in developing a family spending plan.

Don't buy just to "Keep up with the Joneses." Whether to buy or not to buy; what to buy first; what to add later — these are questions your family must decide.

Consider YOUR OWN needs, wants and resources. Be sure you will be sold on the appliance a year from now.

REBECCA P. LOVINGOOD *is Associate Professor, Department of Management, Housing and Family Development, Virginia Polytechnic Institute and State University.*

Ask such questions as these, of yourself or others:

— What do we really want the appliances to do?
— How much are we willing to pay? Should we buy a new or used appliance?
— What are the desirable features of this equipment?
— Which features will be most desirable and which "nice to have" or not necessary?
— Will the appliance be easy and safe to use, especially by those likely to use it most frequently?
— Will it be easy to care for?
— Will the appliance be economical to operate and maintain?
— Will it fit into the space available for it in our home?

You can get information to help answer these and other questions from many sources — appliance salespeople or service representatives, Extension or utility home economists, or your friends.

Keep an equipment reference file for items such as Extension bulletins, magazine articles, catalog descriptions, advertisements, and other available materials. A trip to your local library or to exhibits at county fairs or home shows may be helpful. Using the telephone instead of the automobile to get information will save time, energy and money.

Make Sure There's Room

Every appliance requires space in your home. Before you start to shop, measure the space you have and the doors, windows, or stairways through which the appliance must be moved. Don't forget space for yourself, if you are to use your equipment with ease.

Check fuel, power, and water supplies of your home. Is your supply of fuel and power dependable and adequate? Will your present wiring system carry the equipment safely and satisfactorily? Will you need to have new wiring, or add new outlets?

Will this equipment cause water and disposal problems? Will you have enough water, and is the water pressure adequate? Is your septic tank large enough? Should you change your selection or modify these facilities?

Learn to read and "interpret" appliance labels and other point-of-purchase information. For example, frozen food can be stored much longer in the "true" freezer of a refrigerator-freezer than in the frozen food compartment of a household refrigerator.

A nameplate stamped into the appliance or inscribed on a separately affixed plate gives operating conditions of the appliance as well as the model number and manufacturer's name and location. Sometimes special operating instructions are given such as "Connect to wall outlet only" or "Dry only items washed in water."

Look for the Underwriters Laboratory (UL) symbol, which indicates an electrical appliance has been manufactured according to a set of standards approved for safety by UL. In existence for over 80 years, Underwriters Laboratory is a private organization to which manufacturers voluntarily submit products for examination and testing.

The American Gas Association (AGA) Laboratories' blue star emblem on a gas appliance signifies that the design and manufacture of the appliance comply with national safety standards for construction and performance.

Yellow and black EnergyGuide labels affixed to refrigerators, refrigerator-freezers, freezers, clothes washers, water heaters, dishwashers, room air-conditioners, and furnaces are meant to provide shoppers with energy information that will be useful in appliance selection.

EnergyGuide labels are required by law on any of these appliances manufactured after mid-May 1980. Information on the labels is based on laboratory tests approved by the Department of Energy, and

WM. CARNAHAN

Be a careful shopper when looking for appliances. Most major appliances manufactured after mid-May 1980, are required by law to have an EnergyGuide label affixed to them. Be sure to read that label.

varies in content, depending on the appliance.

Room air-conditioners have an energy efficiency rating based on the amount of output energy — Btu's of cooling — you get for a given amount of input energy measured in watt-hours. The higher the number, the more efficient the air-conditioner.

Furnaces Have Labels Too

Furnaces have generic labels with general energy information along with an energy factsheet developed by the manufacturer.

The remaining products have energy cost labels which show an estimated annual energy cost of operation based on estimated average use and a national average gas or electric rate.

Labels on clothes washers and dishwashers show estimated yearly energy costs when operated with water heated in an electric water heater or a gas water heater.

When comparing energy costs, be sure to compare costs for appliances of the same style and size. For example, operating a 19 cubic foot frost-free refrigerator-freezer quite likely would require more energy than operating a 16 cu. ft. cycle defrost model.

Be a careful shopper. Don't buy the first thing you see, but "shop the field." Get some idea of styles and models available. What brands are common in your community? After you have decided on a style and the features you want, make comparisons of the same piece in several shops to discover differences in brands or in prices from one shop to another.

Carry a notebook to record brand names and model numbers to assure comparison of exactly the same items in several shops. Note price, materials, and finishes; your estimate of quality of workmanship, size, and shape; plus any special features or qualities of the product.

All models of appliances are manufactured to meet certain basic standards of performance. That is, all ranges provide a source of heat for top surface cooking, for baking, and for broiling. Some models have added features which make those operations easier or more automatic.

Features do increase the purchase price. Some features are valuable "servants." Some are largely for "show." You may find certain features worth the price; your neighbor may not. But be sure the model you select has the features you want and will use.

Read the warranty carefully before you buy, and see that you understand the terms. It is your legal protection against poor workmanship and materials.

Full, Limited Warranties

Written warranties will be labeled "full" or "limited." Under a full warranty, the manufacturer promises either to repair a defective product within a reasonable time or period of usage without charge, or to give a refund or replacement if the product cannot be repaired. If any restrictions are placed on coverage, the warranty must be labeled as "limited."

Warranties mean nothing unless you report failures to the dealer or the manufacturer, whichever is specified. To speed processing of your complaint, be sure to include all the information requested on the warranty along with a specific description of the problem, your name, and complete address.

Is the manufacturer dependable? Over a period of years, has the manufacturer earned and kept a good reputation by producing quality equipment and carrying out terms of the guarantees?

Is your dealer well established in the community? Does the dealer have a reputation for standing behind the equipment? Do the salespersons understand the construction, installation, operation and care of each appliance? Do they help you select an appliance to fit your needs and pocketbook, or are they more interested in selling the most expensive model on the floor?

As appliances become more automatic, service gets more important. Is service available from the dealer who sells the appliance? Or is there an independent service agency that specializes in servicing the brand of appliance you have chosen? If you move to another community will you be able to get service?

Look for a service agency that has a reputation for promptness, dependability, and integrity.

Tips on Service Contracts

The service contracts sometimes offered by dealers are much like a term insurance policy — the holder benefits only if a problem develops that requires service. In deciding whether to buy a service contract, consider points such as:

- What is covered by the appliance warranty and for what period of time? Coverage of the service contract and the warranty may overlap.
- Does the contract cover the whole appliance or just a specific part?
- Are exclusions listed in the warranty or the contract? Some cover parts but not labor; repairs but not travel time; repairs done in the home but not in the service agency's shop.
- How many calls are covered? Who is responsible for unsatisfactory work? If you

find service unsatisfactory on the first call related to a problem, is the callback covered by the contract?

— If you move out of the area before expiration of the contract, can you get a refund in proportion to the time remaining on the contract?

— Does the contract guarantee prompt service? Service on weekends or after hours without extra charge?

— Is the cost of the service contract reasonable in relation to the probable cost of service that may be required? Contract prices generally increase as appliances get older.

There are many costs — of the equipment itself, of installation, of operation, and of upkeep. When considering costs, divide the original cost by the number of years you expect to use the equipment. This may help you decide if you want certain pieces of equipment, or certain features on that equipment.

When figuring cost of operation, think of the "servants" you buy for that cost. Your time and energy may be hard to evaluate in dollars but you might consider the other tasks or activities you prefer to be doing while the appliance handles routine, repetitive tasks such as dishwashing.

Consider also the cost of the time spent in learning to use the appliance and to keep it in good condition.

An instruction booklet giving full directions for operation and care should come with each piece of equipment. Read it carefully before you use the appliance. Keep it handy and refer to it often. Record the model number of the appliance, date of purchase, and dealer's name and telephone number in the booklet.

The manufacturer's recommendations for use and care of the appliance are intended to increase your satisfaction in using the appliance and to reduce the amount of service required. Many booklets contain a list of common problems and solutions or "things to check before you call the serviceman."

Send Complaint to MACAP

If you cannot get satisfactory resolution to a problem with a major appliance through the dealer or the manufacturer, write to the Major Appliance Consumer Action Panel. The address is: MACAP Complaint Exchange, 20 North Wacker Drive, Chicago, IL 60606.

MACAP professionals are specialists in consumer education and communication, and attempt to view a problem from all angles before making a recommendation about settlement.

Through labels on an appliance itself and in the instruction booklet, a manufacturer attempts to communicate the intended use of an appliance. Using the appliance for other purposes may cause service problems that will not be covered by the warranty, permanently damage the appliance, or be dangerous to the user.

Appliance users need to be aware of potential safety hazards in operating appliances. How would you rate on these points:

— Do you use the "one-hand rule" when connecting or disconnecting electrical appliances? That is, avoid holding on to two electrical appliances or an appliance and a water faucet (connection to ground) at the same time.
— Do you routinely check to see that the continuous burning pilots on gas appliances are burning? That the burners are lighting and operating correctly?
— Do you disconnect electrical appliances by pulling on the plug, not the cord?
— Do you keep flammable materials away from gas flames or hot electric units?
— Do you help children learn the potential hazards of appliances and teach them how to avoid accidents?

Appliance manufacturers are increasing the energy efficiency of their appliances. Gas ranges and clothes dryers are now available with "pilotless" ignition systems that eliminate the need for continuous burning pilots. Ranges, refrigerators, and freezers have increased amounts of insulation and operating components that are more energy-efficient.

Although microwave ovens use less energy in cooking some foods, the time saving may be greater than the energy saving in cooking large quantities.

However, even appliances designed with the greatest energy efficiency can become less efficient under certain conditions. For example, researchers at the National Bureau of Standards have found as much as a 50 percent difference in energy use among homemakers preparing exactly the same menus on identical ranges.

Tips for Energy Savers

Cooking: Range or Microwave

- Cook foods only as long as necessary; overcooking wastes energy *and* nutrients.
- If you have an electric range, learn to use the retained heat that remains in the electric oven or surface unit after the control has been turned off.

326-621 O - 80 - 14 : QL 2

- Cook an entire meal in the oven rather than using both oven and surface units or burners.
- Use portable appliances or the microwave oven when cooking small quantities of food.
- Cover pans when cooking.
- Use the HIGH heat setting only when necessary.
- Fit the pan size to the heat source.
- Preheat the oven no longer than necessary. For some foods, such as meats and casseroles, it is not necessary to preheat the oven at all. Broilers usually do not require preheating.

Refrigerator or Freezer

- Allow space around unit for good air circulation. Heat trapped around the appliance makes the cooling system operate less efficiently.
- Open the refrigerator or freezer door only when really necessary, especially during hot weather, and keep the door open no longer than required.
- If the refrigerator or freezer is not automatically defrosted, defrost the freezer coils before ice builds up to more than ¼ thick (about the thickness of a lead pencil).

Dishwashing

- Operate the automatic dishwasher with a full load to conserve hot water. Using a no-heat drying period is one way to use less energy, but the cost of heating the water to wash the dishes is several times greater than the cost of drying them.
- In hand dishwashing, wash a number of items, not just a few, with a sink full of hot, sudsy water. When rinsing, fill one half of a double-bowled sink with hot water for rinsing dishes rather than rinsing them under a running stream of hot water.
- Pre-rinsing dishes may not be necessary; if it is, use cold water rather than hot.

Laundering

- Wash and dry full loads or adjust water level to match size of load.
- Use warm wash, cold rinse water for most loads. For lightly soiled clothes, use cold wash (minimum 80° F) and rinse water; for heavily soiled clothes, hot wash, cold rinse.
- Remove as much water as possible from clothes in the washer by proper selection of speed and length of spin cycle. (Spinning water out takes less energy then evaporating it in the clothes dryer.)
- Avoid overdrying articles in the automatic dryer.

To sum up, major appliances represent a sizable investment and have a relatively long period of service in the household. Because of the increasing cost of energy, cost of operation is a factor to be considered in choosing and using appliances.

For satisfaction and economy, follow the guideposts in this chapter which recommend that you weigh your needs, ask questions, consider space and installation needs, read labels, shop the field, compare features, know the reputation of the manufacturer and dealer, consider service, count all the costs of ownership and operation, ask for and use the instruction booklet, use the appliance as the manufacturer intends and according to recommended safety practices, and be a good energy manager.

For additional information, contact your local Cooperative Extension agent.

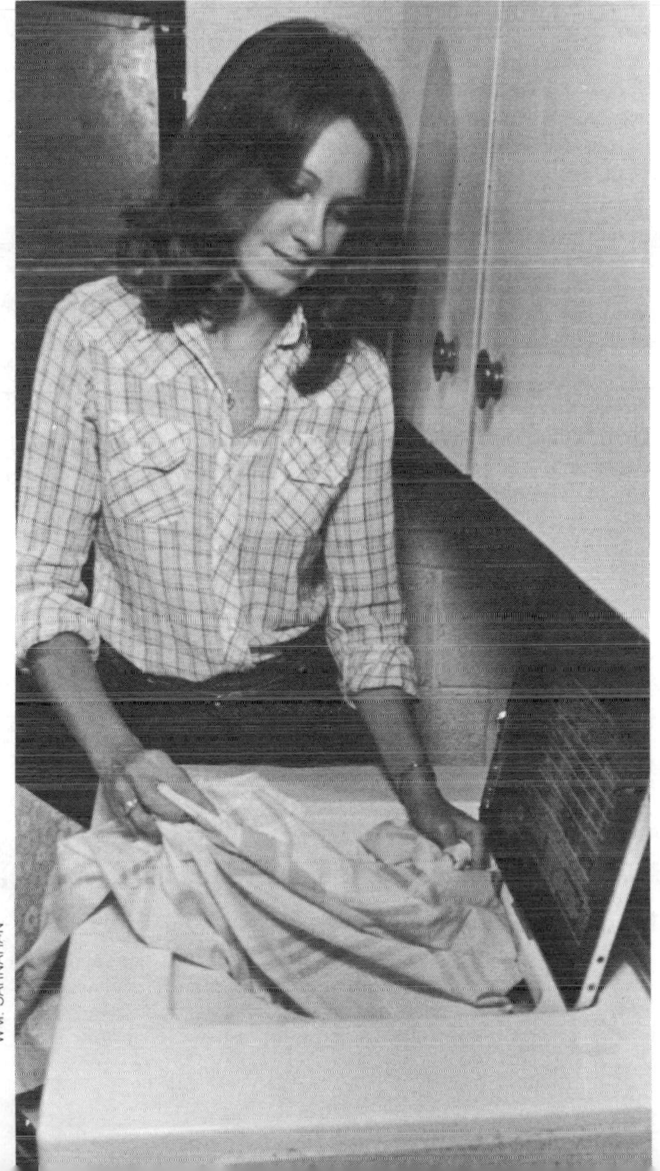

When laundering, wash and dry full loads or adjust water level to match the load size.

WM. CARNAHAN

The Energy Efficient Home of the Future

By James Buesing

Every day we make decisions which affect our homes and how we live in them. Many of these decisions concern our energy use: decisions about whether to suffer through sacrifice, to conserve by reducing waste, or to substitute the current fuel source for a less expensive and more reliable one.

Often these decisions are made with little thought as to their effectiveness or to other viable options. Many have been putting off the questions which need to be asked. "What does the future hold?" "How do I identify and decide among the options?" And finally, "What impact should future energy trends have on the decisions I make today?" These are the questions which will be dealt with here.

Here we are looking for trends that will affect the consumer. That is, what type of energy will be available, how reliable will it be, and how much will it cost?

Future electrical power will be generated with diversified energy sources. Centralized power plants will use coal, oil, natural gas, wood, wastes, nuclear, goethermal, wind, solar, gasification, and water.

The important thing for the consumer, however, is that electricity may be generated at home (onsite) or in the neighborhood. Utility companies may provide the financing to create onsite generating, thereby reducing their need for additional expensive, large-scale facilities.

Onsite generation can occur by using conventional fuels but also through the use of solar photovoltaic cells, wind generators, biogas conversion, etc.

These smaller generators may be tied into the larger power network. Power can then be bought, or sold to the utilities, depending on your demand. In addition there would be no need for expensive batteries to store the electricity for when the wind doesn't blow or the sun doesn't shine.

Storage may be desired but not necessary in the form of batteries. Power supplies may be intermit-

JAMES BUESING *is an Extension Specialist in Housing/ Interior Space, University of Wisconsin-Extension.*

tent due to any number of factors, such as storms, strikes, shortages, embargoes, or excess demand. Storage will probably be an inherent part of the equipment which uses the energy.

There is little doubt electricity will remain the dominant home energy source. But electricity is a second generation energy source. It must be generated by a primary fuel source such as coal, oil, gas, water, wood, waste, or nuclear.

Two-thirds of the potential energy of the primary fuel source is wasted through the generation and distribution processes in a large utility plant. In addition, much of the generating equipment sits idle just waiting for those few peak demand periods which may occur once or twice a year. Electricity cannot be practically stored at power plants; it must be generated when the consumers demand it.

Electricity Does the Job

Why then will electricity continue to be the dominant energy source? For three reasons:

1) It is the highest grade and most versatile energy source available. It is ideally suited to do work through the use of motors, it can provide light, and it can heat.

2) Electricity is the most universally available energy source already in almost every home. There is a tremendous national investment in the distribution system and in the equipment which uses it.

3) Electricity can be generated from any number of future energy sources, some more easily and safely than others.

Furnaces will contain enough mass,to store one day's to three days' heat, or this mass will be built into the home. Refrigerators will freeze fluids which can cool the food during power outages. Tools will come with portable battery packs.

Much of this technology is currently used on ships, which may run their generators only two hours per day. These steps will be made easier as more efficient equipment and conservation measures reduce the amount of energy required to accomplish the desired task. Onsite storage will also be used to assist the utilities in balancing their demands.

Cost of electrical generation is cheapest if all the generators are running at 100 percent capacity all the time, rather than sitting idle. Water heaters and furnaces will be controlled by the utilities and allowed to draw power only when there is a surplus. Storage in these units will still allow the consumer to draw heat upon demand.

While it is almost certain electricity will be generated to run equipment and lights, it is much more difficult to predict what energy sources might be available for heating. New homes will be designed and constructed so they have no need for a conventionally sized furnace.

Heating demand will be drastically reduced through heavy insulation, airtight construction, and earth sheltering. What little heat is needed will be supplied by direct solar gain (the sun's heat coming through the windows directly into the living space) and the heat given off by equipment, lights, and people.

Existing homes will not have these onsite advantages. They will have to make do by adopting conservation measures and using existing furnaces. Economics will dictate what changes to make in equipment and which conservation measures are called for. Comfort and security may dictate conservation measures beyond those considered economically feasible.

Some experts feel that by 1985-1990 all fuels will cost about the same in terms of the heat they can supply. But in the interim, significant savings may be realized by converting to a cheaper fuel source.

Actual costs of energy in the future are hard to compare to today's standards. Increased efficiency and conservation will allow for an equal or better lifestyle with just a fraction of the energy needed today.

If the cost of fuel doubles but your needs are cut in half, your budget costs remain the same. After the energy demand has been reduced as much as possible, then the energy price increases begin to erode the family budget. Even though energy prices will continue to rise faster than family incomes, reduced demand and onsite generation will help families offset energy price increases.

Energy Option Procedure

How do I identify and choose among options? There is a process by which we all make decisions. The three major steps are: 1) **Identify the situation.** What do I want to change? What is my current situation? 2) **Identify options.** How do I identify all the options available to me? and 3) **Select options.** How do I choose which option is best for me?

Identify Situation. When it comes to energy, the major objective is to reduce energy consumption. The motivations behind this goal, however, may be numerous. Research has shown that a desire for self-sufficiency follows closely behind economics as dominant factors influencing consumers' decisions. Concern for comfort and maintaining lifestyle are also mentioned.

Self-sufficiency means freedom from dependency on offsite energy sources. Can a habitable environment be maintained if all supplies are stopped? Can the structure be protected against freezing pipes? Can refrigerated foods be saved during a power outage? Can a productive, normal home life be maintained without outside fuels? What impact will rising energy costs have on your family's standard of living?

These are the concerns, but where do you begin? First, you must determine where you are now. What is your life situation and what is your energy consumption?

People who wish to save energy usually fall into one of the following life situations:

- Wish to stay in existing structure without investing in any major structural modifications, but still want to reduce energy expenditures and increase comfort.
- Wish to make changes in existing structure and minimize total energy use.
- Wish to buy an existing structure which is as energy efficient as possible or is most easily adapted to a minimum energy use structure.
- Wish to hire someone to design and build a new strucutre which is energy efficient.
- Wish to design and/or build their own energy efficient structure (do-it-yourselfers).

In addition to your personal life situation you must identify the existing local and regional energy situation. What are the local fuels, what is their projected future availability cost? This information can be obtained by talking with your utility company, utility commission, State energy office, or county Extension agent.

Local climate is a major factor contributing to energy use and potential conservation. What is the heating degree day figure? (A measure of winter temperatures used to calculate rate of fuel consumption.) It is available from your utility company or local weather station. Where are the predominant winds? How much sunshine is available for heating?

Conduct a survey of local resources. What is the status of design, engineering, and construction expertise and knowledge as it pertains to energy efficient designs? Is there access to alternative energy sources and the local expertise to assist you in using them, such as water, wind, solar, biogas, gasohol, conservation?

Also, identify local funding sources and their attitudes toward supporting alternative energy projects. How do the local building inspectors interpret the building codes and what direction do they give for energy conservation?

Finally, you must determine what your current energy use is compared to what it could be if all practical conservation measures were taken.

Home Energy Audit or Index

A free home energy audit will help give you a feel for where your house stands. Or, you may wish to obtain your home energy index. This is a means of measuring your home's fuel consumption, similar to miles per gallon for cars. Some utilities can supply this number or you can figure it yourself by using University of Wisconsin-Extension Bulletin E3031.

Identify Options. After you have identified your current situation, how can you determine what your options are?

Read the current materials on energy conservation and alternative energy sources. Get free estimates and audits wherever available; go to meetings and workshops; and talk to friends. Jot down any idea, regardless of its practicality. At this point the purpose is to generate ideas, not to evaluate them.

You can look at five different areas where energy conservation can occur:

1) *Self.* What changes or preparations can you make within yourself and those you live with?

2) *Source.* What can you do to best control the source and quality of your future energy?

3) *Site.* What can be done with the site to maximize natural energy forces and minimize energy waste?

4) *Structure.* What can be done with the structure to increase its energy efficiency and comfort?

5) *Equipment.* Finally, what can be done with selection of equipment for the home?

The type of energy conservation measures possible in each of these categories will depend on your life situation and the local resources and climate as previously mentioned.

Select an Option. After generating a wide variety of energy options, you must determine which are best suited to you. Weigh the options according to their financial merits; ease of implementation; and compatibility with your current lifestyle and values, that is, do you like the way it looks, will it make life more or less comfortable, will you gain more control over your energy situation.

What impact should future trends have on decisions I make today about my home and family?

Very briefly then, let us apply the trends and the

life situations to the five conservation areas. This exercise will help show the impact that future trends might have on decisions you are making today.

Self. Your feelings, attitudes and expectations will play a critical role in how you adapt to future trends. Adoption of an energy conserving lifestyle is the foundation of all other energy saving actions.

The need to feel self-sufficient will cause you to adapt more stringent conservation measures to reduce your dependency on energy. Your confidence in national energy supplies will determine how quickly alternatives are made available to consumers.

Source. We have already discussed the future trends in energy sources. They will involve more diversity in how electricity is generated and more onsite electrical generation. Many have turned to alternative fuels for heating. Wood is the most popular, but concern is growing over the Nation's wood supply and the potential pollution problems from large scale wood burning.

An onsite wood source should not be seen as free or as a substitute for conservation. Wood costs are running between $100 to $200 a full cord. Your wood could be supplying you with that income which then could be used to increase conservation and comfort in the home.

Many new energy efficient home designs will make greater use of internal heat given off by lights, equipment, and people as well as direct solar gain to heat the homes.

Site. The immediate site and the home's orientation to it can cut energy use in half. Site consideration should include plantings for shade and wind control. Prevailing winds will dictate winter sheltering and summer ventilations. Slopes can have an effect on air movement and temperatures.

Ideal House Faces South

Highest considerations should be given to how the sun moves across the site in relation to any shading which might occur. No matter how ideal the site, an improperly oriented home will negate most advantages. The ideal house should face south with as little exposure as possible to the east or west. Future home design and construction will be much more sensitive to proper orientation as a free method to reduce energy demands.

Structure. Design of the structure is the most important factor (besides climate) in determining your home energy consumption. New homes can be constructed so they require virtually no conventional energy for heating or cooling.

Super-insulated, almost airtight homes seem to be the most effective energy savers of all new home solutions. They use conventional building methods, require no sophisticated designers or engineers, and are less dependent on solar or other energy sources for heat.

Active solar, passive solar, and earth sheltered homes have all received much publicity in recent years but still require a skilled and qualified designer and/or engineer to make them work properly. In addition, the payback for their energy saving features is much slower than for the super-insulated homes.

If you are not building from scratch it is much more difficult to reduce all heating and cooling demands. All conventional conservation measures should be investigated.

You should consider an addition only after a thorough analysis of current space use. An efficiently designed small space will use less energy than a larger space.

If you plan an addition, try to maximize the amount of insulating and other conservation measures which can be done during construction. All efforts should be made to catch winter sun and summer breezes. This air may be circulated to other portions of the home.

In buying a new home, all the above should be considered when analyzing the home's future energy consumption. Sometimes it is better to buy a more rundown structure at a lower price and use the savings to modify it into an energy efficient home.

Equipment. As mentioned previously, most household equipment in the future will still run on electricity. Care should be taken to maintain existing equipment. When a replacement is needed, purchase the most energy efficient models. New energy labels will show the lifetime cost of running large appliances. These costs should be considered as well as the original purchase price.

Computerized controls and backup systems for intermittent outages will be appearing as options on future equipment. Alternatives may have to be considered for food storage and preparation in case of possible outages.

Since it is hard to predict what the energy sources and supplies will be in the next 25 years, today's decisions should center around solutions which reduce your need and use of energy. Suffering is not synonymous with conservation. Indeed, proper conservation measures should save you money, increase comfort and control in the home and finally, provide freedom from any temporary interruptions in energy supplies.

Further Reading:

Business Dealings With the Architect and the Contractor, A2.0, Small Homes Council, University of Illinois at Urbana-Champaign, 1 East St. Mary's Road, Champaign, IL 61820. 25¢.

How To Figure Heat Loss and Fuel Cost, A1844, University of Wisconsin-Extension Publications, Agricultural Bulletin Building, 1535 Observatory Drive, University of Wisconsin, Madison, WI 53706. 25¢.

Illinois Lo-Cal House, C2.3, Small Homes Council, University of Illinois at Urbana-Champaign, 1 East St., Mary's Road, Champaign, IL 61820. 25¢.

Is Your Home An Energy Waster? How To Calculate Your Home's Energy Index, E3031, University of Wisconsin-Extension Publications, Agricultural Bulletin Building, 1535 Obseratory Drive, University of Wisconsin, Madison, WI 53706. 10¢.

Living With the Energy Crisis, C1.5, Small Homes Council, University of Illinois at Urbana-Champaign, 1 East St. Mary's Road, Champaign, IL 61820. 25¢.

High Heating Costs: How to Cut Them

By Jerry O. Newman

Good grief! Ouch! What can I do? Expressions like these are frequent occurence as you and I confront costlier home heating costs.

Through the past half century of abundant petroleum supplies and low-energy costs, our desires have been fine tuned into habits and standards that are hard to compromise. So we are all looking for energy conservation practices and home operational procedures that will allow us to maintain the housing comfort we have learned to enjoy within an energy budget we can tolerate.

Some compromise in the present home heating standard will surely be necessary. But wise selection of a fuel and heating system, effective operational measures, and selected conservation practices will reduce your energy needs and thus the degree of compromise you must accept.

Because local prices vary so much and most fuel and heating systems are so related, their selection must be considered together rather than individually. If you are in an area where low cost fuels are available, fuel selection can be an effective means of controlling your home heating costs. But before you select a new system or replace an old system, determine both the initial and operating costs of available fuels and heating systems for the area.

Although conventional home heating systems that use convenient clean fuels will continue as the only selection for many families, alternate fuels and heating systems will play a role of greater importance for others.

Some homeowners alter their systems to improve efficiency and some alter them for conservation. An increasing number of families are supplementing or completely altering their home heating system to use readily available local renewable energy sources. But the economy of such systems vary considerably from location to location. So again it is important that you know as much as

---

JERRY O. NEWMAN *is Research Leader, Rural Housing Research Unit, Science and Education Administration, USDA, Clemson, S. Car.*

possible about all the systems and fuels available in your area.

Offsetting Fireplace Drawbacks

The conventional fireplace can be considered almost useless. To avoid smoking, large chimneys are required and they pull big volumes of hot air from the house through the firebox. The thick masonry firebox walls conduct heat slowly; thus energy transfer into the living area is limited.

If properly positioned, you can be cozy and comfortable even when room temperatures are cold, but the only significant energy contribution from the conventional fireplace is by radiation to those close to it. Quite often you are warmed on the front when facing the fire while your back stays cold.

Metal or glass doors on fireplaces contribute significantly to improved efficiency. They reduce the need for air flow from the living area through the chimney and thus the size of chimney needed. But when doors are used, you need to provide combustion air to the firebox through an auxiliary duct.

Both glass and metal doors block radiation from the firebox into the living area, so other methods of extracting energy must be incorporated.

Fireboxes with sheet metal walls and air spaces behind them transmit energy into the living area better than brick-lined fireboxes. Double wall metal fireboxes with air spaces between walls are commercially available and are good at extracting heat, especially when room air is circulated mechanically or naturally through the space. Recent studies in which heat exchangers were installed in the fireplace chimney were found effective in extracting heat from the escaping flue gases.

Stoves offer additional benefits that cannot be claimed by fireplaces, and for the most part are considered more effective. The wood stove firebox may be virtually air tight, built of heavy cast iron or plate steel, over which the operator has almost complete control, or it may be built of lightweight sheet metal into which air can easily flow and the operator has little control.

Free standing stoves emit energy readily. But blowers significantly improve performance because they disperse heat from the stove to a larger part of the house.

Stoves mounted in fireplaces are recessed into a pocket where only limited natural circulation is possible. Blowers generally are required to efficiently extract and distribute the heat.

Safety Tips for Stoves, Fireplaces

In all solid fuel systems, such as wood and coal, safety must be practiced. Radiant energy from fireboxes can ignite nearby wood, paper, or other flammables.

Generally a three-foot clearance is desirable between stove and wall, but special reflectors and guards can be installed if less clearance is available. Check with the manufacturer to find the recommended clearance for particular models. Also check the required clearance between stove and floor. Wood floor joists supporting concrete can be ignited by a hot fire on the concrete.

A nonflammable pad under your stove or in front of a fireplace is necessary to prevent hot coals from falling onto carpet, linoleum, or wood floors. Screens or glass doors should be closed when the fireplace is unattended, to prevent sparks and hot coals from being discharged. Always close and latch stove doors after tending the fire.

If you have small children, use a guard or double wall firebox to reduce the chances of direct contact and severe burns.

Install dampers, draft and air controls to prevent chimneys and fireboxes from overheating.

Chimneys and stovepipe are sources of potential hazards. To provide clearance between the stovepipe and combustible materials, vented thimbles or other spacers are needed when hot pipes pass through walls, ceilings, floors, or roofs. Stovepipe should always slope at least ¼-inch per foot upward as it moves away from the stove, to insure adequate draft and reduce the chances of smoking.

A ventilated thimble — a device permitting a stovepipe to pass safely through a combustible wall.

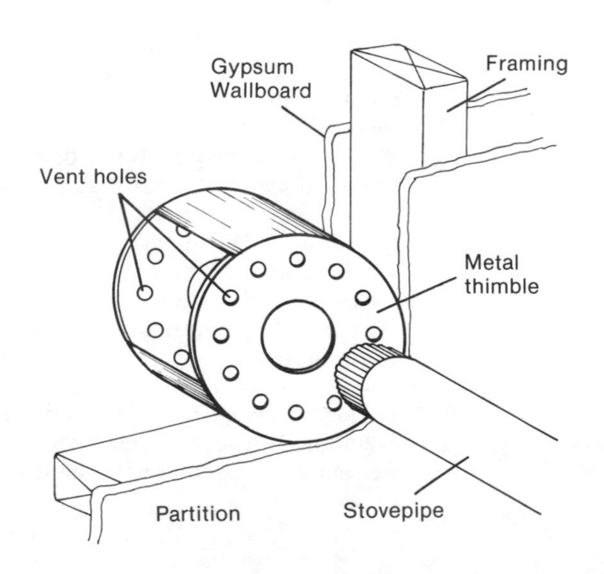

Smoke detectors with an alarm are highly recommended when stoves and fireplaces are used. Electric smoke detectors cost less than battery-powered detectors, but the battery-powered units will operate even if there is a power failure. Take care to avoid undetected battery failure which would inhibit operation of battery-powered units.

Check your insurance policy to make sure you are covered in event of fire damage. You may need to notify the company if you install a different type of primary heating system in your home.

In areas where supplies are available, wood and coal — two fuels from the past — are logical choices to be revived for home heating.

Damaged trees and waste wood products from the forest and wood processing plants are available at many locations.

Coal is not generally found as a waste product. Its higher energy concentration makes it more transportable than wood. But transportation remains a major cost which will control coal's economic value as a home heating fuel in most areas.

If you can tolerate fuels that produce residues, or are willing to put forth the extra effort required to operate the more labor-intense solid fuel systems, wood or coal may be your choice.

Heat Pumps Transfer Energy

Heat pumps made the scene many years ago but low cost energy and high installation costs caused homeowners to move toward the lower-cost, maintenance-free, resistance-type electric furnaces and baseboard units. Heat pumps can economically transfer energy from one medium to another, even from a low temperature medium.

The most common heat pumps transfer energy from outside air to the warmer house air, but swimming pools, wells, and the soil are sources of energy that can be utilized by a heat pump. Some heat pumps are being used to transmit solar energy collected in attics to the house heating system.

Heat pumps work best when the differential between the indoor temperatures and the heat source temperature is small, so they are more efficient when outside temperatures are moderate. Ordinarily, resistance-type electric heating elements are installed to aid the heat pump when outside temperatures are too cold.

Water and soil sources of energy are more stable than air energy sources, and are not likely to get as cold in the winter or as hot in the summer. The heat pump will therefore operate more efficiently on the average throughout the year when such energy sources are utilized.

Solar energy may be used to keep the temperature of heat sources like swimming pools or water tanks warm during winter, thus causing the heat pump to operate more efficiently. Heat pumps can be used to trap and utilize intermittently available energy sources, such as energy collected in attics or low temperature solar collectors.

Interest in alcohol as a source of energy for farm and family needs is growing rapidly. Farmers throughout the United States are installing alcohol-producing systems just to ensure themselves a supply of fuel and a market for their grain.

Many say alcohol is not an economical fuel; however, farmers will have alcohol to sell.

Solar Systems

The sun's energy is adequate to meet all our energy needs but it is not in a concentrated form like coal, gas, alcohol, or other conventional fuels that produce high temperatures, create violent reactions, and release vast amounts of energy. The most common heating equipment cannot use the lower temperature energy which the sun supplies naturally.

If you need high temperature energy from the sun, its rays must be collected from a large area and concentrated onto a small area. To be most effective the entire collector surface needs to be oriented perpendicular to the sun throughout the solar day, but sun-tracking equipment is expensive and is usually not cost effective.

Increased efforts are needed to develop applications for the low temperature energy the sun provides naturally. Development of systems for home heating are among the practical applications.

Solar systems for home heating can be classified in many ways. One way of classifying them is active or passive.

Passive systems are those in which the energy is collected and distributed by radiation, natural air or water currents, and other natural means and the energy is stored in structural or other massive materials. Active systems use blowers or pumps to collect and transfer the energy within the structure.

Most solar systems are partly active and partly passive and are called hybrids. They use pumps and blowers to complement the natural transfer of energy from point of collection to point of use.

Solar systems may be water or air, depending on the media used to collect and transfer energy. Water systems must be protected from leakage, freezing and corrosion, but large amounts of energy can be transported in a small volume of water.

Air, on the other hand, requires a large volume to transport even small amounts of energy. High blower operation costs result. One must therefore balance relative merits of the water and air solar systems.

Solar systems can be further classified as integrated or package units. Integrated systems are built into the house, and the collector becomes the wall, the roof, or other integrated parts of the structure.

Most package systems are manufactured offsite and are then attached (added on) to the house as a package. Manufacturing, shipping and warranties, along with middleman profits, are a few of the factors that make commercial package systems more expensive than integrated systems.

Rock beds, water tanks, and other massive materials are used for storing energy. Then they serve as a source of heat during periods when solar energy is not available.

Rock beds are generally used as the storage for air systems, but can work with water and other collection and transfer media. Likewise, water has been employed as the storage for liquid systems. However, some people are giving greater consideration to using water storage with other types of collection systems.

An increasing number of people are turning their attention to passive solar as a solution to their energy needs. Yet engineers and architects are not able to provide a pure passive solar system that will furnish uniform temperatures throughout the living area without excessive fluctuation or the use of excessive amounts of auxiliary energy. Pumps or blowers are required to make almost all solar systems effective, and more realistic combinations

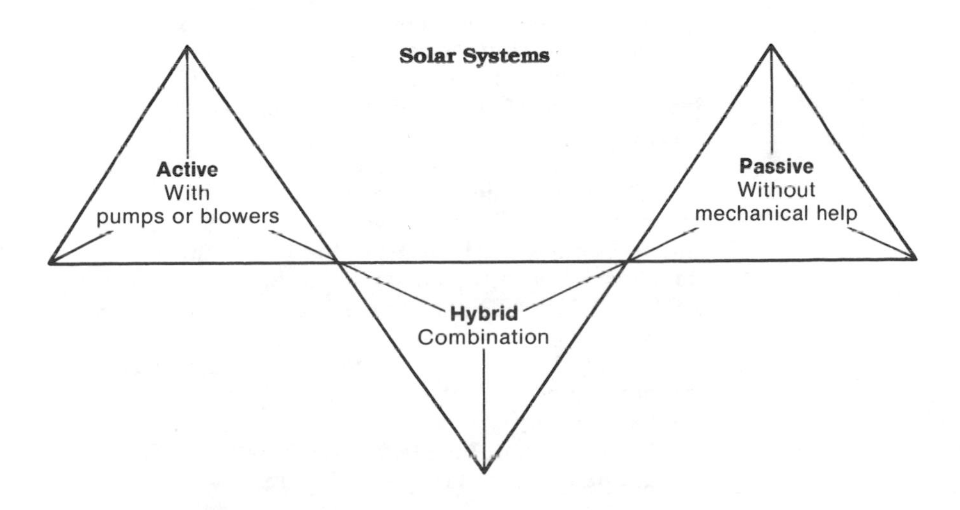

of the passive and active features (hybrid systems) are needed.

Zone or Room Control Over Temperature

The most commonly suggested method of conserving energy in the home has been to lower the thermostat setting in winter and to set it higher in summer.

An equally if not more effective way of reducing energy needs is to heat a selected portion of the house to a comfortable level, while allowing house temperatures elsewhere to fluctuate. Rooms with water pipes must be kept above freezing, and other specific factors may restrict the upper or lower temperature bounds in particular rooms or areas.

Individual room thermostats are an effective means of controlling rooms at the desired temperature, but with the exception of electric baseboard or wall units, few home systems are equipped with such controls. Therefore, homeowners may have to improvise to achieve zoned or individual room control.

For air type heating and cooling systems, you can damper or close off registers to individual rooms, or install dampers in the main ducts of one or several rooms. Properly installed valves in steam or hot water systems will control energy flow to selected rooms.

Separation of zones, especially upper and lower floor areas, can also be accomplished by doors which act as valves to control natural convection currents.

Inside air can be separated from outside air by a closed vestibule or "Air Stop" at all exterior doors.

Cooling Off Your Home

Proper ventilation of your house can reduce or eliminate the need for summer air-conditioning. You can use windows, doors (screened), and other natural ventilation, or electric fans. Natural ventilation may not be as cool as air-conditioning, but it may satisfy your needs at a cost you can afford.

Ventilate your living space in the evening and/or at night to gain the maximum benefit. Never ventilate when the house is cooler than outside temperatures. Trap cold night air by closing the house during the day. When house temperatures are increasing, open vents or windows near the ceiling to remove trapped hot air.

Ventilation fans are needed if evening breezes are not strong enough to move air through the house naturally.

Your attic can be a heat trap. In summer it should be ventilated by natural or mechanically induced air flow anytime it is hotter than outside temperatures.

A lot of air must pass through the attic cavity to effectively cool it. Frequently a combination of soffit, gable, or ridge vents are used to ventilate attics without a blower. Soffit and ridge vents are quite effective because the airflow path is short and the ridge vent exhausts at a higher elevation than the soffit opening, creating a strong natural draft.

Gable vent efficiency can be improved by locating a new house so prevailing winds flow through the attic cavity. However, when considering passive solar heat for the house, orientation of the house for the sun's heat may be more important.

Cyclone roof vents act as low-capacity turbines that use windpower from any direction to increase the airflow rate. Likewise, powered fans operated by a thermostat to reduce attic temperature levels usually cost less than the air conditioning expense saved.

Future Housing

Three integrated systems, designed and developed by USDA's Rural Housing Research Unit, show potential as single family dwellings: 1) The Solar Attic House, 2) The Solar Attic Retrofit, and 3) The Solar Earth Residence.

In the solar attic system, the attic of a house serves as a solar collector. Windows built into a south-sloping roof allow the sun's energy to pass into the attic cavity where it is absorbed by the attic walls, floor, and/or roof.

A properly constructed solar attic should be tightly sealed and well-insulated to decrease heat loss and aid in retaining heat after the sun sets. Such attics cool slowly and remain warmer than house temperatures for several hours after the sun goes down. Thus, the attic supplies energy to the house until attic temperatures drop below the house temperature during the night.

Of course, heat loss to the attic will generally occur during late night and early morning when attic temperatures have dropped below the house temperature. With the solar attic, one quite often finds a net heat gain of energy through the ceiling, compared to the net heat loss generally found in conventional houses.

The solar attic can be operated as a passive system without the use of auxiliary energy, when energy collected in the attic is conducted through the ceiling into the house with the ceiling acting as a radiant heater.

The solar attic becomes an active system if you

circulate air from the attic into the house or to an energy storage.

By making a solar attic active, you can control energy flow and distribution. Attic energy can be transported into the house earlier in the day and more quickly than by passive means.

Active attics will not be as hot during midday because much of the collected energy has been moved into the house or to storage earlier that day. Chances of overheating the attic or the living area are reduced with an active system because of increased control. And the stored energy available for use at night and on cloudy days reduces the need for auxiliary energy.

Most solar attics have a double attic cavity to control air flow. In addition, energy transfer through the ceiling during both the heating and cooling season is reduced.

Summer temperatures recorded in the lower cavity adjacent to the ceiling were 20 to 40 degrees cooler than those in conventional attics under the same ambient atmospheric conditions.

Tests conducted over an extended period have shown that 60 to 80 percent of house heating needs can be met by a properly sized, active solar attic collector with a simple crushed stone storage system. The system may be built into most new houses for 10 percent or less of the initial house cost. It is economical, effective, and needs only a minimum of low technology maintenance to keep it operating.

The solar collector does not need to be on the roof of a house. It can be attached to the south or near-south wall. It can also be located in an adjacent structure. However, both the rooftop and the south wall collector have worked, but to date a simple economical collector in an adjacent structure has not yet been demonstrated.

Solar Attic Retrofit

The solar attic can be adapted to both old and new houses. In new houses most of the factors can be controlled, but in existing houses roof slopes, orientation, and sunlight obstructions are generally fixed.

East, west, and south roof slopes can serve as window areas by cutting windows into the roof's surface. East-sloping roofs may not be effective if fog is a frequent winter morning problem, but west slopes can be effective and south or near-south slopes are more nearly ideal.

Attic ventilation must be kept low during the winter, and you must vent the attic or shade the glazed area to keep summer air-conditioning requirements to a minimum.

Preliminary tests conducted on a conventional residence retrofitted near Clemson, S.C., showed that glazing 10 percent of southwest-oriented, low-pitched roof provided energy for home heating on most sunny days and shortened the heating season by several weeks during the spring and fall.

Solar Earth House

The crust of the earth's surface provides an environment in which temperatures fluctuate much less than in the atmosphere. During summer the earth's crust acts as a massive solar collector that cools slowly during the winter months.

Tests have demonstrated that earth embankment does not insulate a house, but moderates the surrounding environment by capturing and storing energy that is attempting to move toward or away from the below-grade enclosure. Lightweight man-made insulation in addition to earth insulation has been found necessary to control heat loss through such earth-embanked walls.

Tests conducted on well-insulated earth-embanked houses shows they generally require only about half as much auxiliary energy as a similar house built above-grade. In moderate temperature zones, house temperatures generally remain above freezing without any auxiliary heating.

Some technical problems must be solved if we are to achieve economical heating and maintain comfortable temperatures in below-grade housing. Yet such physical problems are easily solved compared to the more complex social and psychological questions being asked.

The most economical system tested for single family heating has been an earth-insulated house combined with a solar attic system. Separately, both the solar attic and earth-insulated housing systems are effective. But the combination is a system that can be almost free of auxiliary energy needs in the South Carolina area except on successive cloudy days.

"Retreat Area" Solar House

A single family housing concept now under consideration, and ready for the drawing boards, is a passively heated house zoned with a "retreat area."

The basic house in which comfortable temperatures are maintained is quite small. The remainder of the house is a passively heated solar house in which temperatures are allowed to fluctuate as a function of outside temperatures and storage mass.

The Do's and Don'ts of Home Insulation

By Barbara J. Griffin

In your home, one key to cutting energy use lies in thorough insulation of ceilings, walls, floors, ducts, hot water pipes, and possibly the water heater. Caulking, weatherstripping, and installing storm windows and doors completes the job.

Since most homes were built before energy became a national concern, homes were seriously under-insulated if insulated at all. Heating and cooling systems were oversized in order to overpower structural deficiencies. Energy then was cheap and abundant.

Now homes are operated on expensive, questionably available energy. Oversized heating and cooling systems are guzzling our money and patience along with energy we do not really need to use. To stop some of this from happening, we need to weatherize our homes.

Where are you gaining heat and losing heat in your home? We can speak mostly in a general, though reasonably accurate manner. Certain additional investigations should be made by residents of Puerto Rico or Alaska, though following any of these instructions will be helpful there too.

Heat passes back and forth through the structure of your house. Insulation slows this process down and keeps warm and cool air where you want it when you need it.

BARBARA J. GRIFFIN *is Residential Housing Specialist in the Department of Agricultural Engineering at Clemson University.*

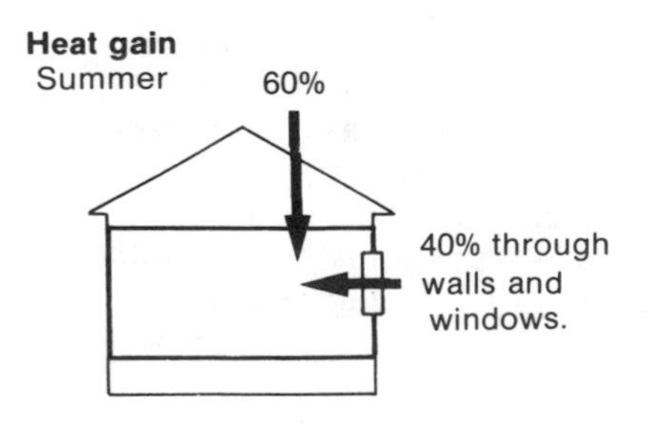

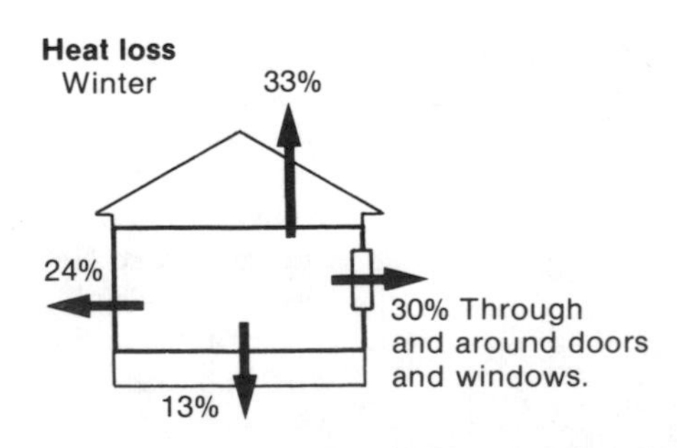

Summer heat gain is mostly through the ceiling, walls and windows as shown.

Winter heat loss occurs in the same places but also significantly through the floor.

Besides these gains and losses, a considerable amount occurs by infiltration through large and small cracks and holes. Air also comes into the home when doors are opened and closed as family members move in and out.

We need some air changes in the home to maintain a healthful environment. The goal of good weatherization is simply to slow down the process of unnecessary air changes, and control the heating and cooling to an adequate healthful level rather than the excessive level too often found today.

Insulation needed in ceiling, walls and floors depends upon where your house is located. Climate zones have been drawn on a map of the United States to enable you to determine these requirements easily.

The amount of insulation needed is expressed as an R-Value or an "R" followed by a number. The combination of numbers for ceilings (or attic floors), walls and floors is different, and each zone is different. You can determine basic requirements for your home by locating it on the map and simply reading the R-Value levels needed.

The R-Value of an insulating material is the most reliable indication of the job it can do for you when properly installed. This value indicates the material's ability to resist the flow of heat passing through it — the more resistance, the higher the R-Value, and the better job the material can do.

Some commonly used materials, the forms in which they are manufactured (batts, blankets, loose and blown-in fill), and the number of inches of thickness of each needed to achieve the R-Value required is contained in the table.

How much insulation do you need? Well, where do you live?

R-19/11/11
R-38/19/22
R-33/19/22
R-30/19/19
R-26/19/13
R-26/13/11

Note: R-38/19/22
Ceiling - R-38
Walls - R-19
Floors - R-22

Nominal R values for various thicknesses of insulation

	(inches of thickness)						
	Batts or blankets		Loose and blown fill				
R-Value	Glass Fiber	Rock Wool	Glass Fiber	Rock Wool	Cellulose Fiber	Vermiculite	Perlite
R-11	3½	3	5	4	3	5	4
R-13	4	3½	6	4½	3½	6	5
R-19	6	5	8½	6½	5	9	7
R-22	7	6	10	7½	6	10½	8
R-26	8	7	12	9	7	12½	9½
R-30	9½	8	13½	10	8	14	11
R-33	10½	9	15	11	9	15½	12
R-38	12	10½	17	13	10	18	14

Besides using the climate zone map to determine your insulation levels, consulting an energy supplier is a good idea. Many utilities recommend somewhat higher levels and may, in turn, give lower rates for homes with higher levels of insulation. Such a practice in your local community may save you energy and money, or at least balance out on the cost side while saving a little more on the energy side.

Batts, blankets, loose fill, blown-in and rigid boards are the main forms in which insulating materials are manufactured. Actual material content of the form may vary.

A particular material or form chosen should be used only for the purpose and place it was intended

Major Types of Insulation and Their Uses

Batts — glass fiber, rock wool

Where they're used to insulate:

unfinished attic floor
unfinished attic rafters
underside of floors
open sidewalls

Blankets — glass fiber, rock wool

Where they're used to insulate:

unfinished attic floor
unfinished attic rafters
underside of floors
open sidewalls

Foamed-in-place — expanded urethane

Where it's used to insulate:

— finished frame walls only

for. Inappropriate use, such as a fiberglass batt beneath a concrete slab, destroys effectiveness of the material (in this case by compacting it) and usually voids any manufacturer's warranty.

Each form of insulation has advantages and drawbacks, as follows:

Batts
- Do-it-yourself
- Easy to handle
- Fits standard joist and stud spacings
- More waste from cutting to fit

Blankets
- Do-it-yourself
- Less waste due to hand cutting of needed lengths
- Fits standard joists and stud spacings

Foamed In-Place Urea Formaldehyde (UF)
- For use in insulating existing walls
- Contractor installation only
- Improper installation may cause moisture problems in the home or discomfort or illness
- Shrinks after installation, lessening the R-Value in the process.

Urethane
- Specialized uses only
- Contractor installation only
- Only material for use on outside of roof of a mobile home. Must be sealed over for wear durability.
- Expensive
- High R-Value per inch of thickness

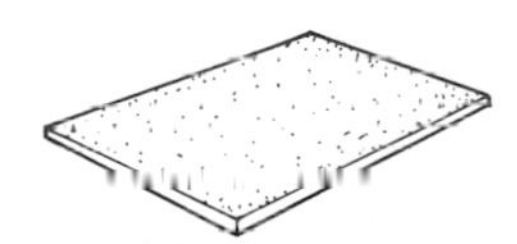

Rigid board—polystyrene (extruded), expanded urethane (preformed), glass fiber, polystrene (molded beads)

Where it's used to insulate:

exterior wall sheathing
floor slab perimeter
basement masonry walls

Loose fill (blown-in) — glass fiber, rock wool, cellulose

Where it's used to insulate:

unfinished attic floor
finished attic floor
finished frame walls
underside of floors

Loose fill (poured-in) — glass fiber, rock wool cellulose, vermiculite, perlite

Where it's used to insulate:

unfinished attic floor

Note: Care should be taken with these products to assure fire safety. Must be covered for fire safety.

Rigid Board	—High insulating value for thickness —Will not compact easily —Must be covered for fire safety
Blown-In Loose Fill	—For use in finished walls —Easy to use around obstructions and hard to reach spaces
Blown-In or Poured Loose Fill	—For attic floor —Easy to use —Do-it-yourself when poured —Follow instructions for recessed lighting, etc.

Qualities of materials to consider any time they are used in a residence are flamability or ability to support fire, ability to take up or hold water, and stability (Does it stay where you put it? Does it pack easily? Shrink?).

Moisture or Vapor Retarders

One last characteristic of insulating materials is impotant for the well-being of your home. Batts and blankets come with and without vapor retarders attached in the form of kraft paper, often sprayed with asphalt or layered with polyethylene, or foil. Rigid boards are impermeable, but loose fill often needs a vapor retarder added.

Vapor retarders have been most frequently referred to as vapor barriers. But in the true functioning of some of the materials we use, moisture vapor is simply slowed down in its rate of penetration and some small amount still passes through some materials.

A vapor retarder protects walls from condensation

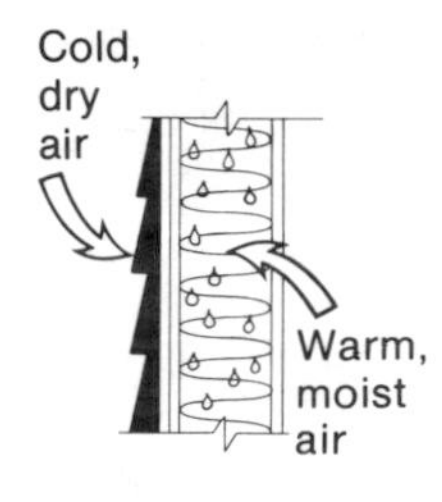

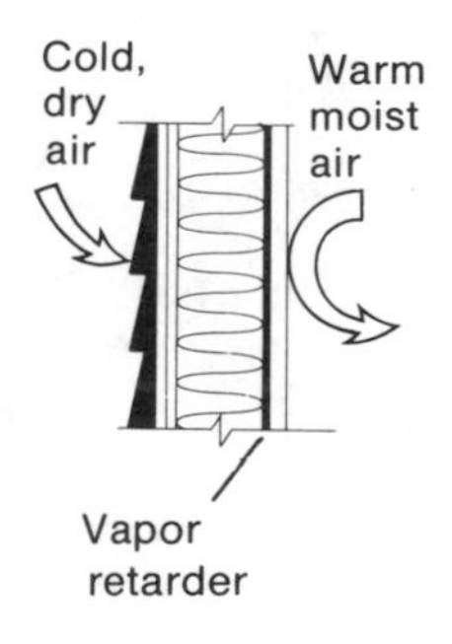

An acceptable effective moisture retarding material is any material with a perm rating less than 1. The rating is a measure of a material's permeability or characteristic of allowing moisture vapor to pass through.

Aluminum foil has a perm rating of 0, and if perfectly installed would allow no moisure vapor passage. Other materials in use have some permeability but are effective retarders.

Moisture vapor is generated in a surprisingly large quantity in our homes simply from breathing, certainly from bathing, and continuously throughout the day from clothes washing, dish washing and food preparation.

Moisture vapor behaves somewhat like heat. It passes *through* the structure of our homes and condenses or forms water drops when it hits a cold surface. To stop this from happening, in walls especially, vapor retarders are installed at the same time insulation is put in place. Vapor retarders are placed toward the winter heated space.

When you are seated in the living room, a vapor retarder would be beneath your feet just below subflooring, in the walls, just beneath the gypsum board or paneling, and most often overhead, just above the ceiling gypsum board or tile.

Besides vapor retarders, adequate and carefully controlled ventilation must be provided. Crawl spaces, as a minimum need a square foot of clear vent area for every 150 square feet of first floor space. Attics need about half that amount in a combination of low eave vents and high ridge area vents.

Exhaust fans inside the home and vented to the outside — operated in baths, laundries and kitchens at times of high moisture vapor production — aid the internal environment when excessive moisture conditions prevail.

Insulation you install may pay for itself in energy cost savings in 3 to 5 years or currently in about 9 percent higher resale value of your home if you plan to move soon. Income tax credits help, too, so there's no good argument for not saving energy and money by insulating. Loans are available if cash is not.

To Get Started

- Decide what form of insulation you want to use.
- Figure the square footage for ceilings, exterior walls and first floor (including floors over any unheated area such as carports). Joists and studs take up about 10 percent of the area, so you will be insulating about 90 percent of the area.
- Get an amount and cost estimate and an agreement about unused amounts if you buy all at one time.

Attic ventilation systems

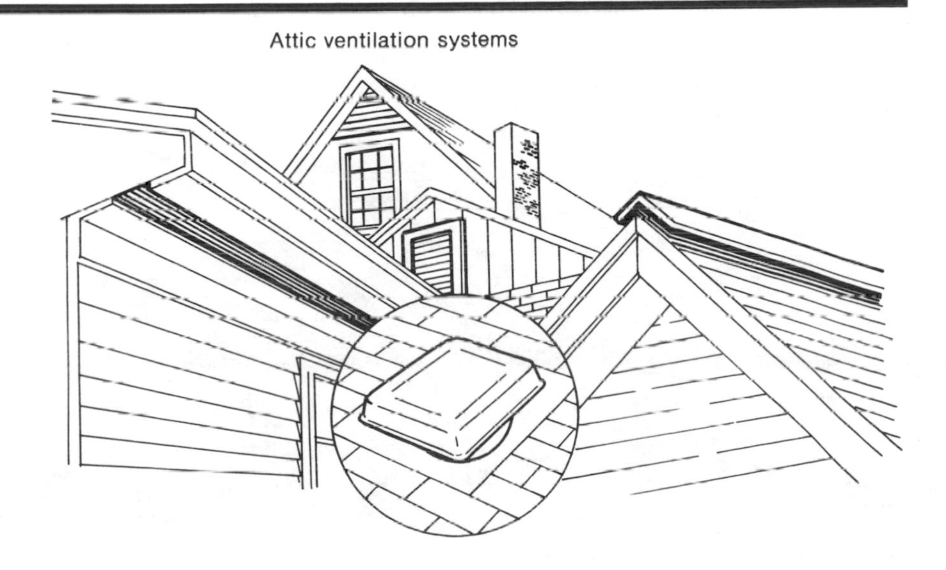

- Get an estimate for increasing attic ventilation, or adding a crawl space covering of 4-6 mil polyethylene if not already in place.
- Tools you need are a sharp knife or long-bladed scissors and a rigid straight edge (a board) if you decide on batts or blankets.
- You need a rake (bamboo is best) to evenly place poured loose-fill or to push batts and blankets into narrow spaces.
- Get some ¾" plywood to support your weight between joists. If you walk between joists in the attic, you will probably go through the ceiling to the rooms below.
- You need a portable light if the attic or crawl space is not lighted.
- Get some insulation supporters or wire for insulation installed in floors.
- Obtain a staple gun for fastening insulation in any unfinished walls.
- Wear clothes that fully cover you, including gloves. Cover your nose and mouth with a handkerchief, gauze or a dust mask to avoid breathing dust or small fibers.

What To Do and Not Do

- Read and follow manufacturer's instructions for appropriate uses and proper installation.
- Do not cover eave vents or block air passage space along the edge of the roof. Use a baffle if you are pouring in loose-fill or if the batt insulation is more than about 6 inches thick.
- Do not cover recessed lighting fixtures or exhaust fan motors. Box these off if you are pouring in loose-fill.

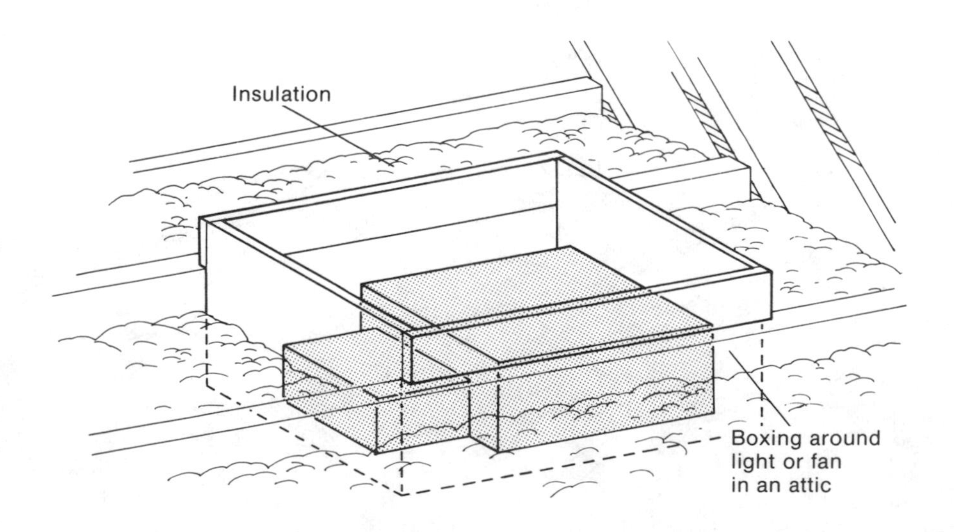

- Do not overlook any attic areas where there are heated spaces below.
- Push insulation as far as you can under floored areas of the attic.
- Never wear contact lenses when handling insulation.
- Work in the attic in the morning or on a cool cloudy day. Temperatures in attics can reach 140° F.
- Watch out for nails sticking through roof sheathing or sub-flooring.
- Take a cold shower when you finish. Cold water closes pores and washes off particles of insulation.

Uninsulated ceiling. Unroll *blankets*, or place *batts*, between attic joists. When you encounter wiring, slip the material under the wires. When you encounter bracing, cut the material and place it tightly above and below the bracing. Be sure the vapor retarder, if used, is placed downward toward the heated living area of the house.

Start from edges of the attic and work toward the center. This way, cutting most likely will occur where there is more headroom.

If you have chosen to pour in loose-fill insulation, simply pour the insulation from the bag into the space between joists to the thickness needed to give you the R-Value you need. Use the bamboo rake or a board to smooth the insulation to a uniform thickness.

Blown-in loose fill is done by a contractor with special pneumatic machinery, with much the same results as when loose fill is poured in.

Vapor retarders need to be added when pouring or blowing in loose fill. Plastic sheeting may be used, or the interior surface of the ceiling may be painted with special vapor-retarding paint or wallpapered with plastic-coated wallpaper.

Partially Insulated Ceiling. Use batts, blankets or loose fill to add insulation to get R-Values you need. Buy batts and blankets *without* attached vapor retarders. Otherwise knife-cut the retardant material about every foot, or tear it off. An added vapor retarder on top of existing insulation would trap moisture vapor.

These types of insulation may be used in any combination. First, determine what you have in the way of R-Values and vapor retarders. Then simply add a vapor retarder to the ceilings below if you need one and add insulation to the attic floor to achieve the full R-Value level you need.

Insulating Walls. Determine how much insulation you have, if any. Turn off the electricity and

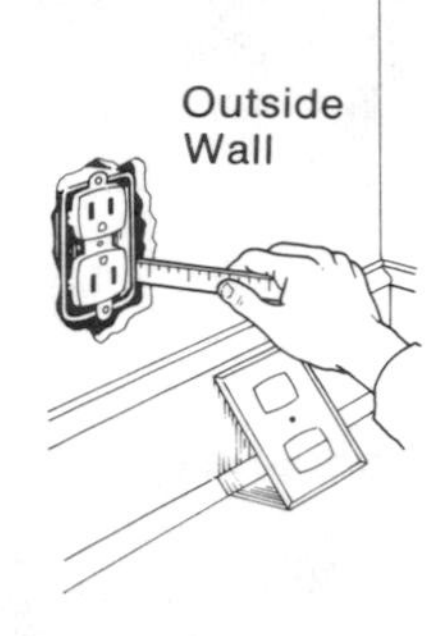

remove the cover of a convenience outlet or light switch plate located on an outside wall, to check.

If there is some insulation in the wall cavity, do not plan to add more. If there is none, the walls can be insulated by a contractor with special equipment to blow in or foam in place the material you select.

Holes about 2 inches in diameter are drilled in each wall cavity. The insulation is put in through the holes and the holes are then plugged with a pre-cut wooden plug. Where possible, holes are drilled from the outside.

A vapor retarder will have to be added to the inside surface of all outside walls in the form of two coats of oil based paint made especially for this purpose, or plastic or aluminum foil coated wallpaper.

The job is simpler and less costly when wall cavities are exposed, as when a house is under construction or complete remodeling is being done. Often studs are exposed in unfinished garages.

Blankets and batts with attached vapor retarders are used. The material is stapled in place.

If the vapor retarder is kraft paper, simply staple the flange of the material to the edge or face of the stud facing you inside the house. Two overlapping flanges can be stapled at once, spaced every 3 to 5 inches apart. Staple only the flange. Take care not to allow insulation to lap over on the stud face, creating a bulge that will show on the finished wall later.

If the vapor retarder is foil, staple the flange to the side of the stud facing you. This creates a 3/4-inch air space detween the foil and the finished wall installed later.

If the batts or blankets have no attached vapor retarder, press them into the wall cavity, compacting

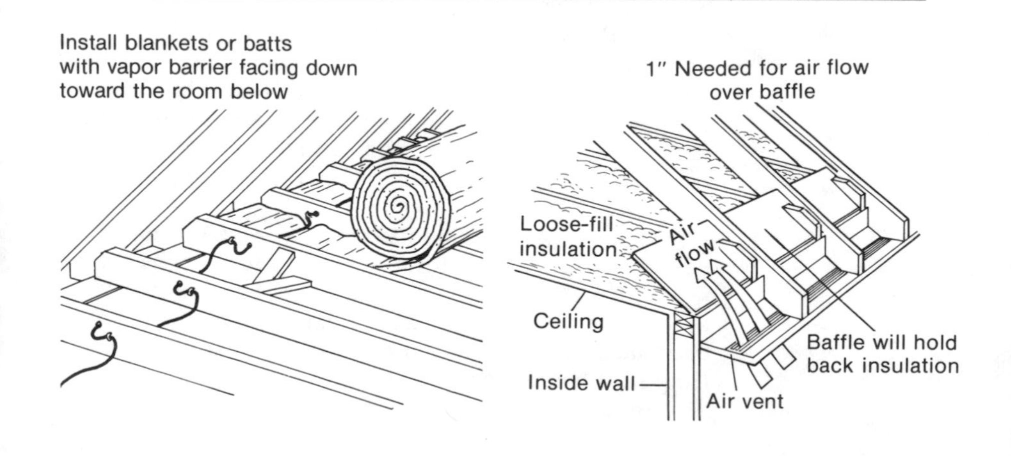

them as little as possible. Fill cracks around windows and doors and staple 6-mil polyethylene over the entire wall, including windows and doors. When finished, cut away the polyethylene from the openings. Cracks around openings (windows and doors) should be stuffed and covered with polyethylene when using the materials with attached vapor retarders.

Rigid insulating boards achieve higher R-Values and are installed on the outer side of the wall cavity in new and full remodeling jobs.

Insulating Ducts. Ducts passing through unconditioned space (not heated or cooled) must be insulated with special insulation manufactured for this purpose. Use the thicker type that is 2 inches thick with a vapor retarder attached.

Check joints in ducts first and tape them with duct tape if there is any looseness or spaces where ducts might leak. Wrap the ducts with the rolls of insulation with the vapor retarders to the outside this time. Seal the joints formed by wrapping with 2-inch-wide duct tape.

Insulating Floors. The most effective method of insulating floors is by installing batts or blankets between floor joists in unheated crawl spaces and basements. Buy insulation with a vapor retarder, preferably foil in this case, for better insulation of the air space formed. Place the batts as shown in the illustration, forming the insulation at the girder carefully in a well fitting manner.

Insulation supporters may be placed between joists every two to three feet to hold the material in place, but wire stapled to the bottom of joists does a better job. Work from outside to center, as in the attic. Staple a section of wire to the bottom of joists

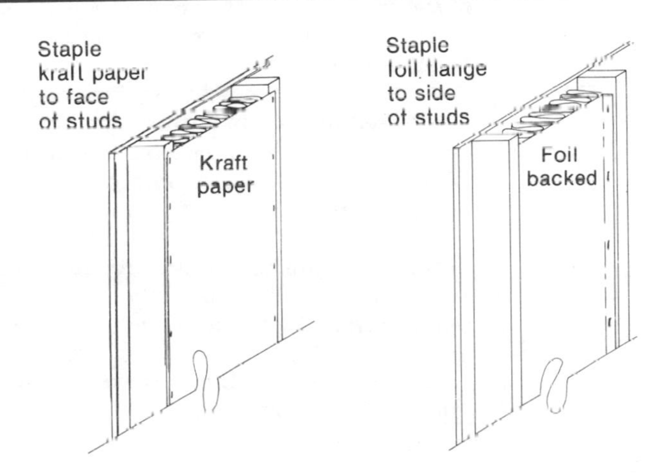

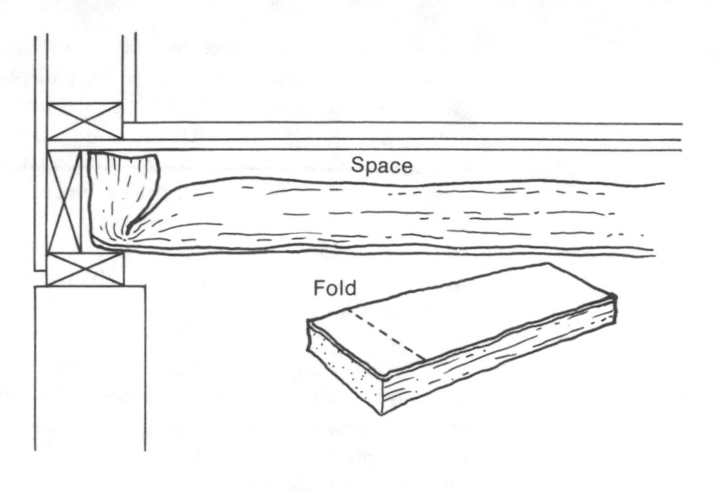

and slide batts in on top of the wire.

The house is now fully insulated but not yet fully weatherized. Two more steps complete the process —installing storm windows and doors, and weatherstripping and caulking.

Storm Windows. Several methods can be used to form an insulating dead air space of ½-inch to 4½-inch thickness. A minimum ½-inch of air space between parallel surfaces is required to provide insulating value. Less than ½ inch is acceptable only if air is evacuated from the space, forming a vacuum.

Polyethylene sealed over an existing window is an effective though short-term solution. Four to six mil polyethylene rolls or prepackaged kits with plastic sheets, tacks, strips (and instructions) can be used.

Prefabricated metal and wooden storm windows may be purchased. Metal storm windows usually have two or three tracks, are adjustable for summer ventilation, and have removable glass panels for cleaning.

Wooden storm windows are equally effective and preferred for use in extremely cold climates, since condensation and heat conduction is less with wood frames. Summer storage space is required and frames need repainting periodically.

Insulated glass in permanent windows is an excellent solution most often employed in new construction or remodeling. Two sheets of glass are placed in a single frame and the appearance is similar to single glazed windows. There are only two surfaces to clean. Breakage replacement costs are doubled, however.

Replacing Windows. Many homeowners are choosing to replace the single pane windows in their homes with a new double or triple glazed unit. This is a good solution.

Replacement windows come in both wood and metal. Some wooden ones may be covered with vinyl for maintenance purposes. But a metal replacement window should be used only if a thermal break has been built into the frame, and insulated or thermal glass is provided. Without a thermal break, heat will be rapidly conducted out of the house by the metal.

Storm doors are usually prefabricated metal, though wooden ones are sometimes used with equal effectiveness. Rigid frames, tempered safety glass or rigid nonbreakable plastic, automatic closing devices and strong safety springs are important considerations. Convertible screen/storm doors are available and popular.

Value will be added to your home with the installation of all types except plastic sheeting. Strength of frames, good quality, warranties, and repair service are important considerations. If you don't do the entire job at one time, do the side of the house facing the prevailing winter winds first, the north side second, and the south side last.

Weatherstripping comes in several forms and materials. Some are designed for use in one place and some are more durable than others. The chart covers commonly available types.

Weatherstripping

Form	*Installation/use*	*Notes*
Self-Adhesive Foam Tape	Apply to dry clean surfaces at room temperature by pressing in place on door and window jambs, stops or sashes	Resilient sponge rubber or vinyl on paper or vinyl backing, ⅜" to ¾" wide. Deteriorates when exposed to weather. May last only one season
Felt or Aluminum and Felt	Staple to wood or glue to metal stops, sills and sashes	Felt tears easily during use and is ineffective when wet
Vinyl	Tack, staple, screw or glue flange of tubeshaped strip to surfaces	Durable, easy to apply
Neoprene-Coated Sponge Rubber	Tack or staple to surfaces	Easy to install. More durable than uncoated material
Bronze Metal	Tack to door and casement window jambs	Durable, easy to install, not affected by moisture and temperature

326-621 O - 80 - 16 : QL 2

Caulking Cords	Press into place on any type surface	Comes in strips; easy to apply; pliable; durable, not affected by moisture
Fiberglass Strip	Various sizes with waterproof tape seals larger crack as around garage doors or may be wrapped around pipes for insulation	Durable
Waterproof Tape	Seals crack. Apply half on window sash and half on stops. Seals cracks by pressing to clean dry surfaces	Not affected by moisture
Air-Conditioner Weather Strip	Easy to install, rectangular polyfoam strip for sealing around window mounted units and window sashes	Low cost
Magnetic Vinyl	For steel door insulation	Durable

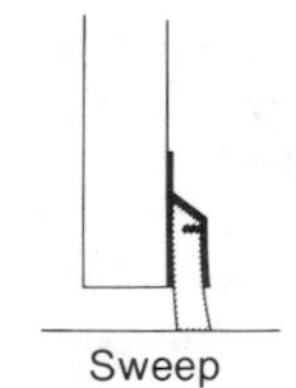
Sweep

Door Bottoms sometimes are fitted with as large as a ¼-inch crack left at the bottom. That is eqivalent to a 9-inch hole through your wall! Check this and use the best method to seal the crack, depending upon the size.

A brass plated strip fastened to felt or vinyl may be attached to the inside bottom of the door. An even threshold is required and level application is a little tricky to achieve. Other types of sweeps, even an automatically operated sweep, are available.

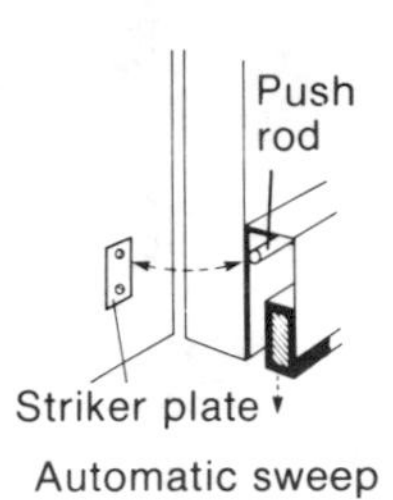

Automatic sweep

Thresholds may be improved to seal cracks. Replaceable vinyl bulb-shaped gaskets mounted in metal are effective when properly maintained. Combinations of door bottoms and thresholds are effective and longer wearing.

Caulking is the last material to be considered, but it may be the first used in the home. For a relatively small cost and time investment large savings are produced.

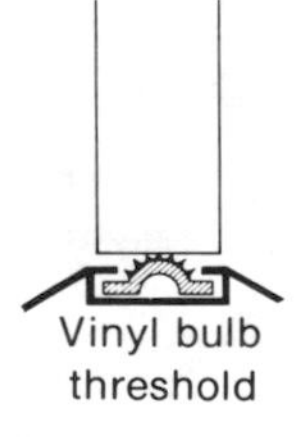
Vinyl bulb threshold

Caulking comes in toothpaste-size tubes and even 5-gallon buckets. But most often a caulking gun with a tube that fits it is best. The tubes have directions for use and suggested places where they work best.

There are a wide variety of products and prices. The less expensive may last only 3 to 5 years while the more expensive may last as long as 30 years. The chart lists characteristics of some materials.

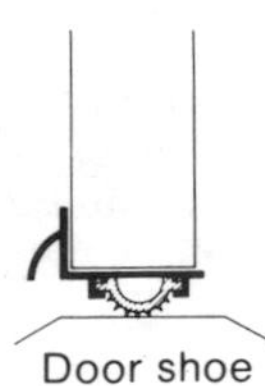
Door shoe

Something is available for sealing any crack or seam you find. Sealing exterior spaces reduces the entry of dirt and moisture as well as air. A firm, clean surface is always required for good application. The caulking job is a good detective job. Some places you should check around you house for cracks and seams are:

—joints between door frames and siding
—joints between window sills and siding
—joints between window frame and siding
—joints between window drip cap and siding
—inside corners of a house formed by siding
—joints where two things come together such as where steps and porches join the main part of the house
—joints where the chimney and siding come together
—around chimney and vent pipe flashings
—places where pipes, wires or vents pass through exterior walls

Caulk hair-line cracks as well as larger ones you find.

Priorities for the Job

Complete weatherization of a home may be done gradually rather than all in one big effort. Except for insulating finished walls, this is a do-it-yourself job for a homeowner in most cases.

The groupings below suggest an order to follow. The most effective steps are listed first with the less effective ones toward the end. This list is a general one that does not hold true for each home, since heat loss depends upon climate, construction of the house, the shape, wall area, window and door area, etc. But, in general, follow the groupings.

First	*Second*	*Last*
Insulate the Ceiling Weatherstrip and Caulk	Install Storm Windows and Doors Insulate Walls	Insulate Floors

A completely weatherized house will use up to half as much fuel as it used when not weatherized. These savings come every year and the comfort of residents is increased in the process.

There is a continued heat loss from completely weatherized homes. You have simply cut the rate of loss. Infiltration continues, certainly, as you open and close doors. And management of heated areas along with living habits of family residents are large factors in energy use. The basic fact remains that people are the users of energy— not houses or cars.

Besides infiltration of air into homes, windows and other glass areas are the big robbers. You can insulate a wall from a value of R-11 to R-24 more or less with little difficulty. But double glass gives you an R-Value of only about 2. Triple glass improves the R-Value to something approaching 3. Thus, windows are the big concern.

Most heat is lost through north-facing windows. About an equal, though smaller, amount is lost through east and west ones. South-facing windows, carefully managed, may break even or be of advantage in gain and loss measurements.

In new construction and in remodeling, window areas must be carefully weighed for value and function in providing your visual and psychological linkage with the world outside, needed natural ventilation, and continuous heat gain and loss. Placement and size to do the job must be carefully considered and weighed in value systems.

Control and management for best advantage becom lifestyle changes you need to make, perhaps first by temporarily sealing and covering some windows at night or when you are away or in unused rooms. And certainly you can operate thermally effective coverings—such as shades and draperies—as automatically as you brush your teeth each day. An awareness and lifestyle change will develop. A completely weatherized home is the important first step.

Further Reading:

Single copies of the following Agricultural Fact Sheets are available upon request to Utilization and Inquiries, Room 507-A, Office of Governmental and Public Affairs, U.S. Department of Agriculture, Washington, DC 20250.

AFS-2-3-1 How to Save money With Storm Doors and Windows. April 1978.

AFS-2-3-2 Save Heating and Cooling Dollars With Weatherstripping and Caulking. April 1978.

AFS-2-3-3 Tips on Financing Home Weatherization. April 1978.

AFS-2-3-4 Solving Moisture Problems With Vapor Barriers and Ventilation. May 1978.

AFS-2-3-5 Landscaping to Cut Fuel Costs. July 1978.

AFS-2-3-6 Weatherize Your Mobile Home to Keep Costs Down, Comfort Up. August 1978.

AFS-2-3-7 Keeping Home Heating and Cooling Equipment in Top Shape. August 1978.

AFS-2-3-8 How to Determine Your Insulation Needs. December 1978.

AFS-2-3-9 Home Management Tips to Cut Heating and Cooling Costs. November 1978.

AFS-2-3-10 How to Install Insulation for Ceilings. August 1979.

AFS-2-3-11 How to Install Insulation for Walls. August 1979.

Landscaping to Reduce Year-Round Energy Bills

By D. R. DeWalle and G. M. Heisler

Homeowners are becoming increasingly aware of the energy savings possible with landscaping. Through proper use of trees and shrubs, the natural terrain, and manmade structures, the climate around a home can be modified to reduce heat gains in summer and heat losses in winter. Reductions in energy use commonly are brought about by either protecting the house from the wind or shading the house from direct sunlight.

Although homeowners have intuitively used landscaping to save energy for many years, we are only beginning to realize the magnitude of the savings possible. Winter heating bills may be reduced as much as 15 percent, while summer cooling energy needs may be cut 50 percent or more.

Reductions in energy use for home heating and cooling translate into good economics for both the homeowner and the Nation. On the average in the United States, 63 percent of the total energy used in the home goes for space heating and 3 percent for air-conditioning.

Given rapidly rising energy costs, even a 10 percent energy savings can be significant to the homeowner. Such savings would be even more substantial in colder regions where a greater fraction of total energy use will be devoted to heating, and in hotter climates in centrally-cooled homes where more energy will be used for air-conditioning.

Energy use for home heating and cooling also represents about 8.5 percent of total national energy use. Thus reductions in home energy use will reduce total U.S. consumption and perhaps assist in cutting importation of foreign oil.

Purpose of this chapter is to discuss how landscaping can be used to achieve home energy conservation. The role of landscape vegetation will be emphasized, but advantage can also be taken of

DAVID R. DEWALLE *is Professor of Forestry, School of Forest Resources and Institute for Research on Land and Water Resources, The Pennsylvania State University, University Park, Pa.* Gordon M. Heisler *is Research Forest Meteorologist, Northeastern Forest Experiment Station, University Park.*

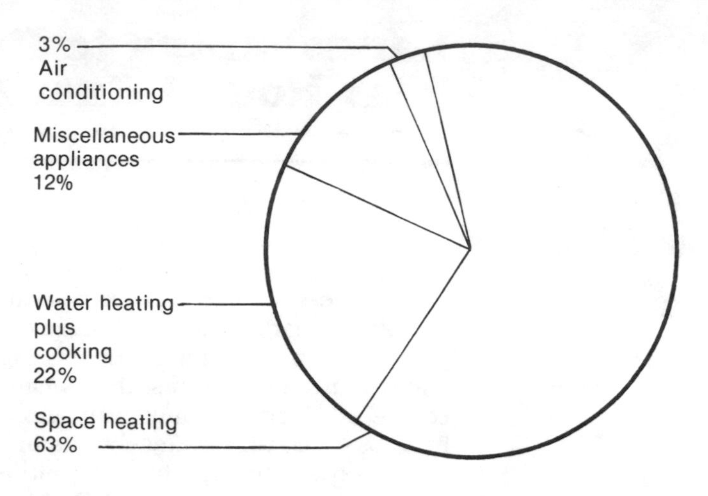

natural terrain and artificial structures around a home to modify climate and conserve energy.

Home Heat Exchange

To take full advantage of the effects of landscape vegetation, the ways in which homes gain or lose heat must be understood. Heat exchange in a home occurs through three major processes: air infiltration, heat conduction, and radiation transmission through windows.

The first mechanism, air infiltration, is the passage of outside air through cracks around doors and windows, porous materials, open doors and windows, and other openings. Outside air is forced or drawn through these openings into the home by pressure differences. These pressure differences are caused either by the force of the wind on the outside of the home or by temperature differences between inside and outside air.

Surfaces of the home facing the wind will experience increased air pressures as wind velocity increases, and air will enter the home through openings in these surfaces. Passage of air into the home will force an equal amount of interior air out of the home through openings in surfaces facing away from the wind.

Because warm air rises, temperature differences between inside and outside air will also create a natural circulation of air in the home. Warm interior air will rise and flow out of the home through openings near or at the top of the home, while at the same time outside air is drawn into the home through lower openings. This type of circulation has been referred to as the "chimney effect."

Air infiltration due to temperature differences and infiltration due to the wind frequently occur simultaneously. But the chimney effect often is most important in winter due to the large temperature differences between inside and outside air. When winds are high in winter, the combined effect of wind and temperature differences may result in very high air infiltration rates.

This combined effect of wind and temperature differences may cause air within a home to be completely changed as often as several times an hour. In winter, heat losses due to air infiltration may represent up to half the total losses by all methods on the windiest, coldest days.

For average home and weather conditions, from 20 to 33 percent of the heat loss in winter is by air infiltration. In summer, air infiltration is a minor component of heat exchange in cooler northern climates because of rather small differences between inside and outside temperatures. Conversely, in hot arid climates air exchanges in summer may be quite effective in increasing the heat load on a home.

Properly placed landscape vegetation can reduce air infiltration by reducing wind velocity in the vicinity of the home. The effect of landscape vegetation on air infiltration will depend on the extent to which wind pressure forces, rather than temperature difference forces, are causing air exchange.

Heat Transfer by Conduction

A second major way a home gains or loses heat is by conduction through materials from which the home is constructed. Heat conduction through solids is controlled by thermal conductivity of the building materials, thickness of the material, and surface area available for heat flow (for example, area of walls, floor, glass, or ceiling) and the temperature difference between the inner and outer surfaces of the material.

Thermal conductivity is a way of comparing the rate at which heat can be transferred through materials from the hotter to the cooler surface for a standard thickness, surface area, and temperature difference.

A layer of still air has the lowest rate of conductivity of materials commonly encountered in the home. Insulating materials are effective in reducing the rate of heat conduction because they entrap air within their pores.

Most walls and ceilings are composites of materials and are effective in reducing heat conduction by trapping air within or between the layers, even when the basic materials, such as metals, have a high thermal conductivity. Heat conduction through glass windows is rapid unless

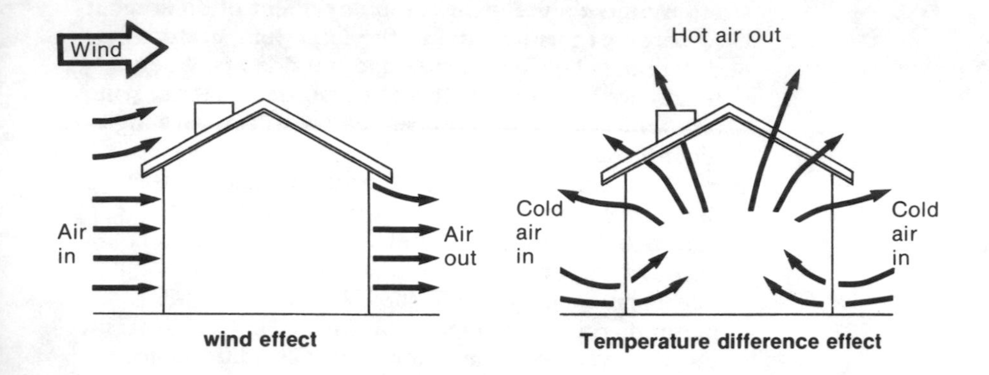

the double-pane type or storm window is used (with an air layer sandwiched between the panes).

Control of the temperature difference between inner and outer surfaces of walls, ceilings, and floors offers the best opportunity for reducing heat conduction.

The inner surface temperature is largely controlled by the interior air temperature. One way of conserving energy in winter is obviously to lower the interior temperature, reducing the difference in temperature between inside and outside surfaces.

The outer surface temperature of a home is controlled by outside air temperature, wind velocity, and solar radiation, as well as by the amount of heat being conducted through the material. Full sunlight can raise exterior surface temperatures to levels considerably above outside air temperatures, but this difference will be reduced somewhat at higher wind velocities.

Landscape vegetation can reduce the amount of sunlight reaching the outer surfaces of a home and thereby reduce the temperature difference between inner and outer building surfaces in summer, when heat is being conducted rapidly into the home. However, in winter, solar heating of the building's exterior surfaces can be beneficial in reducing rates of heat loss. Winter shade would interfere.

Heat conduction generally represents from 33 to 50 percent or more of the total heat exchange between a home and the surrounding environment.

A third and highly variable mechanism for heat transfer into homes is transmission of solar radiation through windows or other glazed surfaces. If sunlight is received perpendicular to a single-pane glass surface, up to 90 percent will be transmitted into the interior living space. However, sunlight will be increasingly reflected by the glass as the sunlight departs from the perpendicular.

One-Way Radiation

Radiation transmission through glass is essentially a one-way process. Radiation from the interior of the home has long wavelengths which are not easily transmitted by glass. Thus, short-wave radiant energy from the sun can pass in through the windows but long-wave radiation cannot be transmitted back out very well.

Obviously the size, position, and type of windows in a home relative to the position of the sun in summer and winter greatly influence the role of transmission in home heat exchange. Vegetation around a home also can influence radiation transmission by blocking sunlight from windows during midday, which is desirable in summer.

Since transmission and conduction of heat loss through windows are generally treated in combination, estimates of the role of transmission alone in heat transfer are not available.

Role Varies by Region

The role of landscape vegetation in conserving energy varies from region to region. In cooler, northern regions where most energy is consumed in winter heating, control of cold air infiltration is paramount.

Hotter, southern locations place more emphasis on use of shade to control heat conduction and summer air-conditioning. In southern zones where outside air temperatures regularly exceed interior temperature by 20° to 30° F or more (for example, with 90° to 100° outside air temperature), control of infiltrating hot air may also be important.

Regions of moderate climate calling for some winter heating and some summer cooling require landscaping which conserves energy year-round.

Before offering some specific hints for homeowners, let's review what is and isn't known about the effects of landscape vegetation.

When a home is air-conditioned, trees can save energy. In Alabama, results of one study in 1970 indicated that mobile homes receiving summer shade by trees had annual electric bills ranging from $45 to $100 less than bills for unshaded mobile homes. Differences in electric bills prevailed even when homes averaged only 20 percent of roof shade per day.

In Pennsylvania, energy required for air-conditioning a mobile home was estimated to be 75 percent less in a grove of tall deciduous trees than for an open, unshaded site. Sunlight received on the roof in the deciduous grove was only about one-tenth of that received in the open.

Vegetation arrangements which provide shade in summer may be detrimental in winter if solar heating of the home is interrupted. In a dense red pine forest in Pennsylvania, heating energy needs for a mobile home were 12 percent greater than at an unshaded site. Here reduced solar heating of the home offsets any benefit from reduced wind velocity caused by the trees. A home should not be located in a dense coniferous forest where winter heating needs are important.

Even a deciduous forest can provide considerable shade in winter. Leafless deciduous trees in winter may reduce the amount of sunlight reaching the roof of a home by more than a third. Consequently, energy consumption for heating a mobile home in one study was only reduced 8 percent even though the deciduous trees reduced wind velocities by 40 percent.

Windbreaks that are sufficiently far away from a building can reduce wind velocities without shading it. A windbreak is a single row or several rows of trees oriented perpendicular to the prevailing winds which will reduce impact of the wind. The windbreak is located upwind from the home at a distance which depends on maximum tree height. Windbreaks properly located on one side of a home can be expected to reduce average wind velocities by about 40 percent.

Air infiltration rates can be cut by reducing wind velocities with windbreaks. For example, the single row of white pine trees depicted in the sketch produced up to 50 percent reductions in air infiltration rates in a small mobile home.

Since air infiltration accounts for about one-third of total heat loss in winter in this mobile home, maximum energy savings for heating were about 1/3 x 1/2 or 17 percent. But considering that the winds blew from the preferred direction in winter only 65 percent of the time for this Pennsylvania site,

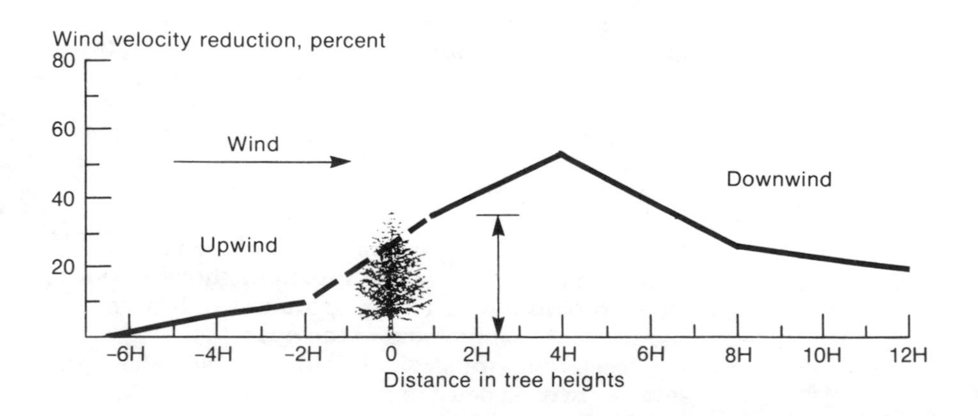

average heating energy savings in winter would be about 11 percent. A windbreak on several sides of this home would have helped immensely.

Another study of windbreaks in New Jersey showed that air infiltration rates in a townhouse could be reduced as much as 42 percent. Accounting for the fraction of heat loss due to air infiltration and the frequency of occurence of optimum wind directions produced an estimated average heating energy savings of 3 percent for this site.

Virtually nothing is known of the effects of windbreaks on air infiltration in summer and energy savings for summer cooling. Reduced wind velocity in summer should cut infiltration of hot outside air and reduce the energy required for cooling. However, reduced wind velocities in summer would carry away less heat from unshaded surfaces of the home and possibly permit greater rates of heat conduction into the home.

Research in the Great Plains indicated that up to 25 percent heating energy savings are possible using windbreaks. These results may not apply directly to Eastern States, where average wind velocities are considerably lower. In the East, average reductions are estimated to range from 3 to 15 percent.

Savings will depend upon the amount of reduction in wind velocity effected by the windbreak. Savings also will be greater for loosely constructed homes. It should be remembered, though, that windbreaks have almost no effect on air infiltration during calm days or when the wind blows from the wrong direction.

An optimum arrangement of trees for year-round energy conservation seems to be: windbreaks for reducing wind velocity in winter, accompanied by vegetation which shades the home in summer. Achieving this optimum arrangement depends on vegetation being already present on the property, and ownership of sufficient land.

Homes built on land formerly in forest very often have enough trees on the property to achieve the desired arrangement relatively quickly. However, when homes are built on cleared agricultural land, all or nearly all the necessary trees and shrubs must be planted.

Windbreaks — Windbreaks should be located upwind from the home in the direction of the prevailing wind.

In the East, the winter wind is primarily from a westerly direction. However, local topography and structures can channel the winds so that prevailing direction in the vicinity of the home can vary considerably. Observation of snowdrifts can be used to determine the prevailing direction around the home.

In hot, arid climates the direction of summer winds would also be important so the windbreak could be used to reduce infiltration of hot air.

Whatever wind direction prevails, the windbreak must be oriented perpendicular to this direction. The windbreak may have to extend along several edges of a property where wind direction is highly variable.

The windbreak should be located upwind from the home a distance depending upon tree height. The optimum distance for reducing air infiltration is about one to three times tree height. Remember, windbreaks can cause drifting of snow which can be a nuisance if a driveway is located between the trees and the home. Where possible, the rows of trees should extend 50 feet beyond the ends of the area being protected.

Limited lot size often necessitates reducing both the distance from the home and the length of the windbreak.

Where large areas of dense forest already occur upwind at the required distances, there is no need for planting additional windbreak trees. The effect of other upwind homes acting to slow the wind reduces, but does not eliminate, the need for a windbreak.

Windbreak trees grow to an effective height (say 15 feet for a single-story home) long before reaching their maximum height. If the windbreak is planted at 3H, where H is considered to be an effective height (for example, 15 feet), then the windbreak would still be within the recommended 1H to 3H zone when the trees grow to greater heights. Therefore, a rough rule of thumb is to plant windbreaks 40 to 50 feet upwind of a single-story home where possible.

Design and composition of the windbreak depend upon the space available on the property and upon the species and size of planting stock which can be obtained.

Where space is limited, a single row of conifers such as spruce trees is quite effective. However, up to five rows consisting of several evergreen species is much more effective. The outside rows — both upwind and downwind — should be trees with dense, low growth. The inside (core) rows should be faster, taller growing trees such as pine.

Assistance in planning and establishing your windbreak may be obtained from the County Extension Office and the local Conservation District Office. Lists of commercial nurseries selling tree planting stock and soil testing kits are available at County Extension Offices. Most commercial nurserymen offer advice on selection, planting, and care of trees.

Spacing in one, two, and three-row windbreaks should be 6 feet between trees. With four or more rows the spacing between trees should be 8 feet. Rows should be 10 to 12 feet apart, with trees planted in a staggered arrangement.

If there is enough space and quicker, partial, protection is desired, one or two rows of faster growing trees may be planted at least 15 feet upwind of the permanent windbreak. Fast-growing deciduous trees such as one of the poplars could be used for this purpose. These trees would be only a temporary planting and should be removed before they retard growth of the permanent planting.

Most windbreaks serve several other purposes. Visual screening is provided when trees become 5 to 6 feet in height. A well planned and properly maintained windbreak is esthetically pleasing to most people. A most important benefit from a living windbreak is wildlife. Birds and mammals are attracted to trees for protection and food.

Summer Shade — Summer shade is best provided by strategically located vegetation along the sunny borders of the home. The location of shading vegetation varies with the direction that the surface of the home faces.

Walls facing generally to the east or west should be protected since these surfaces receive considerable direct sunlight in the morning and afternoon when the summer sun is low in the sky. Shade should also be provided for south-facing roof surfaces which receive the most direct sunlight during midday when the sun is higher in the sky.

House walls facing either in an easterly or westerly direction can be shaded with clumps of vegetation. Deciduous or evergreen vegetation which

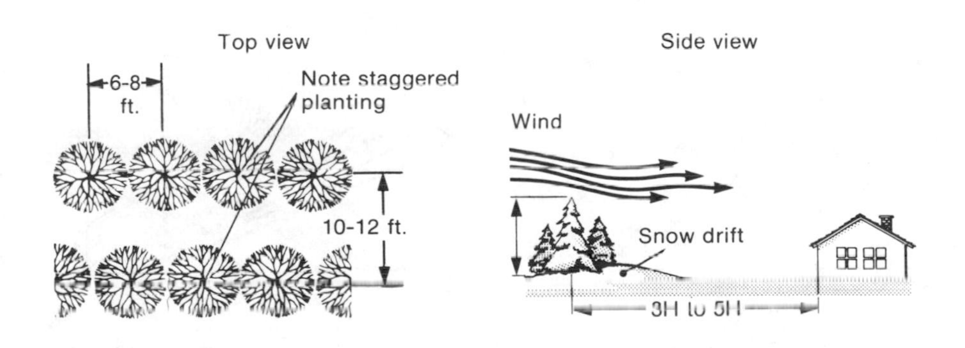

reaches a height great enough to shade the wall may be used.

Conifers which hold the foliage year-round may be preferred if winter winds also come from an easterly or westerly direction. This vegetation could provide summer shade for the walls and winter protection from the force of the wind. Although the planting may not fully substitute for a windbreak, such conifers planted near the home may also trap a warm layer of air against the home and help insulate the wall in winter.

Shrubs and small trees planted very near the home, or perhaps ivy, could be used to shade the walls, but shade for the roof requires taller vegetation.

South-facing roof surfaces would be shaded in summer by several deciduous trees. Location of shade trees depends upon the height and shape of the tree crown, elevation of the sun in the sky above the horizon, and height of the roof.

Securing shade for south-facing roof surfaces in summer generally depends upon having overhanging tree crowns. Trees which do not overhang the roof will not cast much shade on the roof during midday in summer due to the high position of the sun in the sky. Thus shade trees should be planted as close to the home as practical based upon other considerations. If tall shade trees which form a closed canopy over the roof can be preserved on a wooded lot during construction, this would be ideal.

In winter, leafless deciduous trees should not significantly shade the roof of the home. Typically the sun in winter during midday is less than 45

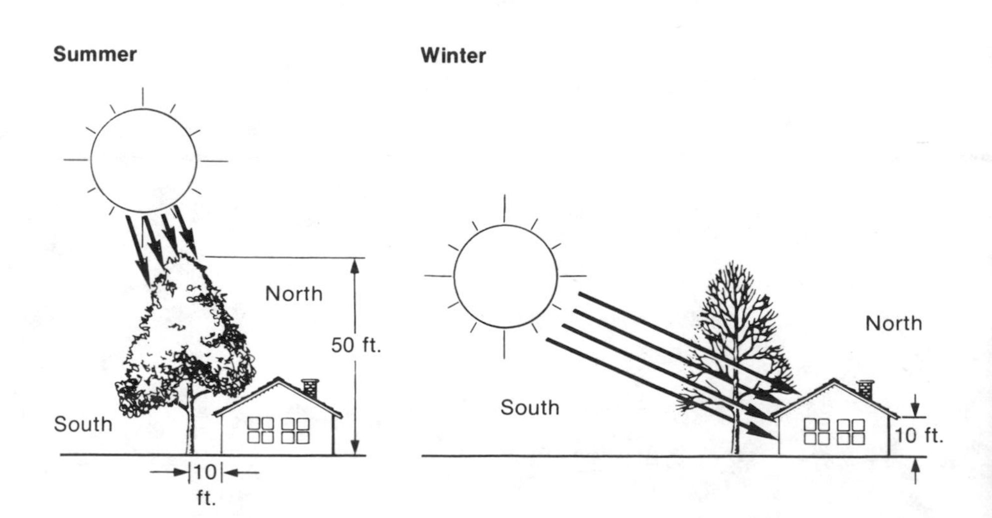

degrees above the horizon and what shading of the home does occur will be largely by the tree trunks.

For this reason only trees necessary for summer shade should be maintained along the southerly edge of the home, and the lower trunk should be pruned to allow maximum solar heating of walls in winter. Trees too far away from the home to provide summer shade may provide significant unwanted shade in winter.

Leaves in gutters in summer are undesirable consequences of large deciduous trees near a home, but most people can cope with this nuisance. Prompt removal of diseased or damaged trees is also necessary to avoid future damage to the home from falling debris. Exact placement of the trees may also depend upon maintaining a desirable view from windows, esthetic appeal in landscaping a home, and avoiding overhead wires and underground pipes.

Trees for summer shade may be present on forested home sites, provided the developer can save them during construction. If trees are to be planted, fast-growing poplars can be intermixed among the slower-growing, more desirable shade trees. As few as two or three large deciduous trees with well developed crowns may suffice, but numerous smaller shade trees with narrower crowns may be required to provide complete summer shade for the roof.

The final effect of vegetation arrangements on total energy needs for heating and cooling will vary with location, weather, and the characteristics of the home.

Up to 75 percent reduction in cooling energy needs can be achieved by providing summer shade, at least in mobile homes. Even where air-conditioning normally is not needed, summer shade would make the interior living space more comfortable.

In winter, windbreaks may save 10 or 15 percent of the heating bill, with the greatest savings occurring in loosely constructed dwellings.

Costs of developing windbreaks and summer shade must be compared to the value of the energy savings plus other advantages. Where planting is required, the investment is necessarily long-term. However, since most homeowners invest in some landscaping for their home, a little time devoted to planning the best planting arrangment and species can pay of handsomely.

Want an Energy-Saving New Home? Here's How

By Keith A. Suerdick

Efficiency is rapidly becoming the trend of today's housing design concepts, especially in the use of space, materials, and energy.

Escalating costs of construction now requires builders and designers to use the least amount of materials for the maximum amount of living space. New houses are being built with fewer interior walls, and more multi-use spaces. Home sizes are being reduced to meet today's needs, but with the capacity for future expansion.

The high cost of land and exterior building materials has caused increasing popularity in living units beging consolidated into one building envelope with little or no yards.

Advancement in cost- and space-efficient designs has been at a slow and constant rate. Design concepts for energy efficiency have developed at a much greater pace.

Only in recent years has energy efficiency been given any serious consideration in home design. Not long ago, energy costs were relatively cheap. The old theory was that any home could be heated or cooled with a mechanical system at a price almost anyone could afford. Today we are seeing a new awareness and insistence on energy efficiency.

Many design concepts for energy efficiency are not new, but rather new applications to ideas existing for decades and even centuries.

Homes using these concepts may look different, be constructed differently, and be located on a site unlike the average conventional home. Some designs are very subtle and unnoticeable, while others represent a major design feature that is easily recognized.

Concepts presented in this chapter range from ideas for selecting sites to devices for shading windows. The intent is to provide you with information on various ideas that may be appropriate for your own lifestyle, local building conditions, and weather patterns.

KEITH A. SUERDICK *is an Architect, Farmers Home Administration USDA, Denver, Colo.*

You should consider ideas compatible with the surrounding area and suitable for your construction site. Public acceptance, code compliance, and site adaptability are important when selecting a design. Some designs are better suited for regions concerned primarily with heating systems, while others deal with cooling needs. There are also designs that support both needs.

Site selection is the first and one of the key decisions to make in building an energy-efficient home. Whenever possible sites having maximum protection from cold winter winds and minimum blockage of sunlight should be selected.

Land sloping to the south will provide the best opportunities for energy conservation. Sites protected with windbreaks such as large trees, hills, fences, or other buildings will also offer good energy conserving opportunities.

Earth-covered Home Basics

The site is even important for earth-covered home. Homes covered with earth, either totally or partially, are gaining wider acceptance. When properly used, earth is a strong, durable, and weather-resistant material which can be used to create an energy-efficient home.

The site's natural contours should be kept intact as much as possible and slope gently to the south. This allows any exposed windows to face the sun, and facilitates natural and controlled drainage of the roof.

There are three basic concepts for earth-covered homes. The first is called "Elevational" and includes an exposed wall on the south side for the access and collection of sunlight. This concept is well suited for construction on sloping terrain and hillsides.

Another concept is called "Atrium" and has the earth-covered home surrounding a central open court-area or atrium. Sunlight and access are pro-

Elevational Earth-covered Home

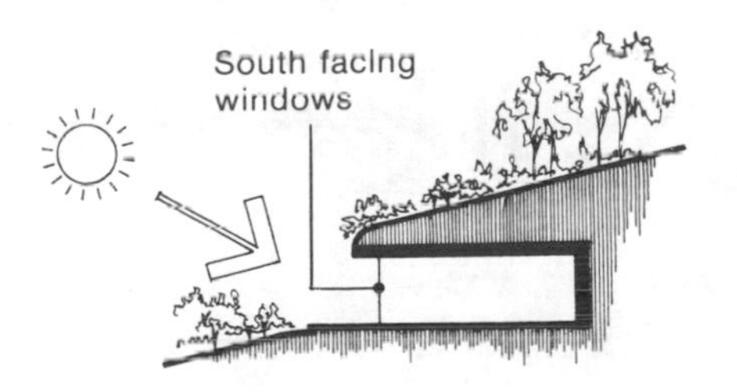

Atrium Earth-covered Home

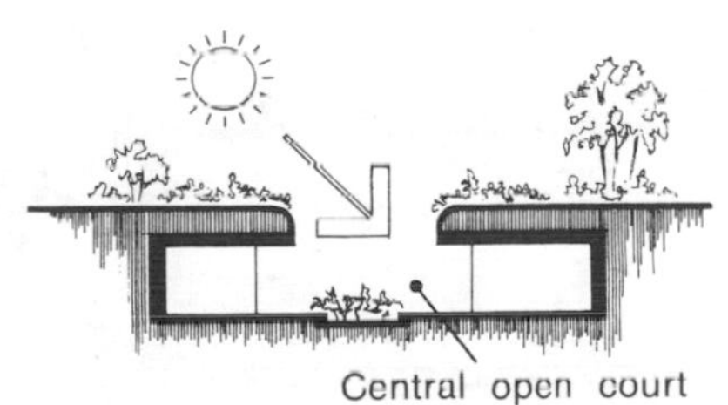

326-621 O - 80 - 17 : QL 2

vided through the central area. This idea is appropriate for a flat site or on the top of a hill or knoll.

A third idea is called "Penetrational" and totally covers the house with earth except for skylights and access doors punched through the roof.

The two most important considerations in an earth-covered home are structure and waterproofing. The structure must be very strong to hold the weight and pressure of the earth on the top and sides. It may be constructed with concrete, steel, and even wood. Definitely consult an engineer or architect in the design of the structure.

The earth-covered home must be properly waterproofed. Waterproofing and internal air circulation should be carefully determined by a professional designer.

Earth-covered homes can provide a comfortable living environment with little energy consumption. This is possible by utilizing the heat of the surrounding soil and minimizing exposure to winds. Soil temperature below the frost line fluctuates very little during the year. Thus, the home requires a little additional heat in winter and little or no cooling in summer.

Additional heat needed in winter can easily and inexpensively be provided by the sun. The combination underground-solar design concept is an excellent approach to energy efficiency.

Heavy materials used for the structure of the home can also be used to store solar energy. Heat is absorbed in massive materials during the daytime and slowly released at night. This is one of the principles used in passive solar heating which will be re-emphasized later in this chapter.

Earth-covered homes may not be appropriate for

Penetrational Earth-covered Home

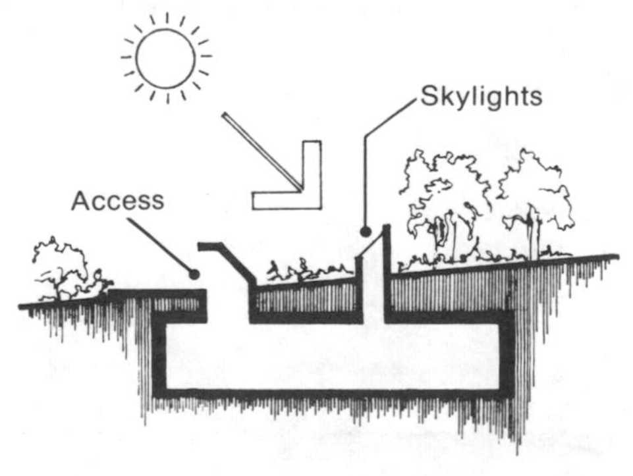

everyone, but they are indeed possible from both a technical and economic standpoint.

If you prefer living on top of the ground, many more energy-efficient ideas are available. One involves orientation of the house on the site.

Whenever possible, the home should be oriented with the long dimension placed in an east-west direction. This allows a maximum amount of wall and roof areas to be exposed to the sun for collecting natural energy as well as providing control of the sun during summer's hot season. The morning sun is usually desirable for heating a home in the early hours, but a late afternoon sun may be excessively warm and will require screening to control room temperatures.

The basic form of a house contributes to its energy efficiency. The amount of heat loss from a house is directly related to the amount of exterior surface area. Therefore, forms with the maximum amount of interior space within the least exterior surface area should be selected.

Dome Shapes

The form with the best volume/area ratio is the dome. Homes shaped like this have existed for centuries. The igloo is an excellent example of how the form contributes toward retaining sufficient heat to keep the interior temperature above the freezing point.

Domes can be circular or geodesic, which is a form with many flat polygon sides, usually triangles or hexagons. The dome home is slowly gaining public acceptance in today's society. The structures can be built very quickly with wood, metal, concrete, or plastic.

They are very strong structurally, and have an

Typical Geodesic Home

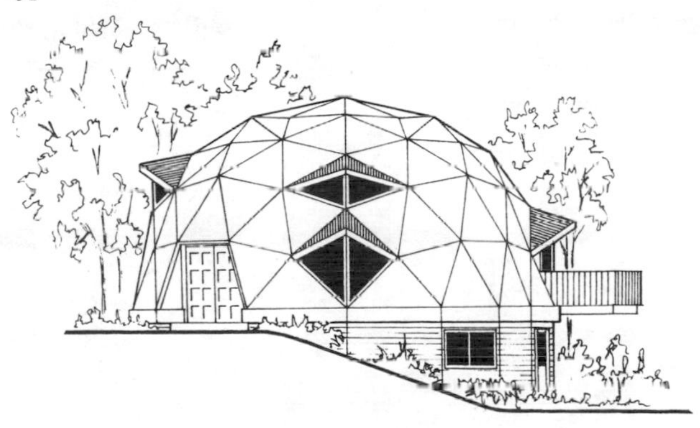

exterior shell much thinner than the shell of a flat-surfaced structure.

Geodesic domes are available in "Do it Yourself" kits that provide almost everything necessary for a complete home. These homes usually include a ground floor level with an upper loft area. Since the weight of the roof is carried down the exterior sides of the home, the interior walls can be located in almost any location.

Windows, skylights, and doors can be put just about anywhere in the structure. Orienting these openings for maximum energy efficiency can be easily accomplished. The exterior appearance of domes can be given variety with the addition of canopies, extensions, and dormers.

The contemporary dome concept can offer a surprising savings in both building and energy costs, and offer an interesting alternative to the conventional home. However, financing may be difficult.

A cube is another form that has a good volume/area ratio. Many new homes are returning to this basic form to conserve energy. A home shaped exactly like a cube may not be very attractive. So several design features can be added to improve the appearance while still retaining the basic cubical form. Good use of exterior materials, location of windows and doors, and interesting roof shapes will enliven the design.

Passive Solar Structure

The total house structure can be designed as a large solar collector. Using the forces of nature rather than mechanical devices, a house can almost be energy self-sufficient. This concept is known as passive solar. Principles used in this concept have been known for years, but the importance of energy efficiency in today's society is causing a new recognition.

Direct Gain System

Heat radiated into the rooms
Vent
Cool air
South facing windows
Storage

Indirect Gain System

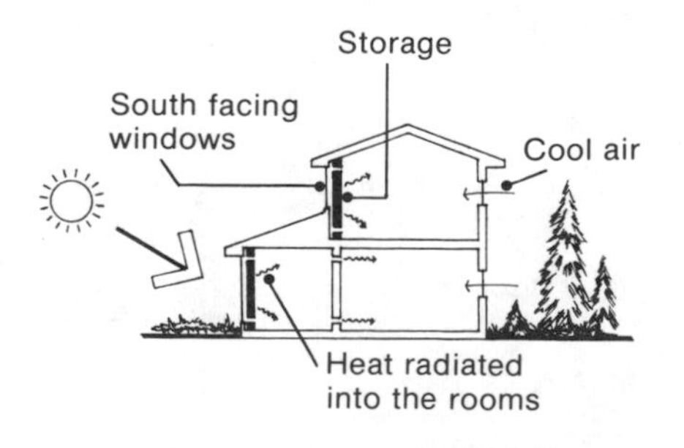

The basic idea is for the house as a total unit to collect, store, distribute, and control solar energy. Several different methods can do this.

One is known as the "Direct Gain System." Sunlight enters the home through large south-facing windows and is absorbed in the floors and interior walls of the home.

To do this, the floors and walls must be constructed of a heavy dense material, such as concrete, stone, or masonry. The heat is then slowly released back into the rooms and circulated throughout the home by natural flow. Control is provided by vents to release excessive heat, and by shades on the south-facing windows to restrict heat gain in the daytime and heat loss at night.

Another method is the "Indirect Gain System." Sunlight again enters the south-facing windows but is then absorbed by a massive wall located only inches away. The heat is slowly radiated into the rooms.

Heat circulation and control are similar to the "Direct Gain System."

Another approach to the indirect gain method is to collect solar energy in water containers located on the roof. The heat is released slowly into the rooms through the ceiling. Insulated panels are moved over the top of these water containers at night to reduce heat loss.

This system can also provide cooling in summer by exposing the water containers to the cool night air, allowing heat from the home to be radiated back into the atmosphere.

The "Isolated Gain System" collects solar heat in one specific space. The heat is then distributed into surrounding rooms of the house by simply opening windows and doors between these areas.

The isolated space for solar collection is often a

Isolated Gain System

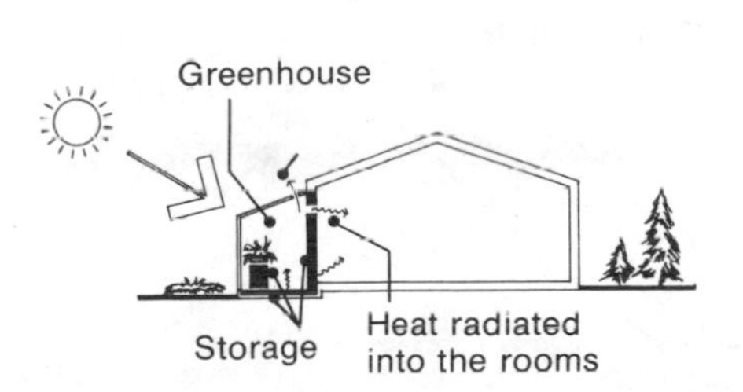

Methods of Controlling Heat in a "Greenhouse"

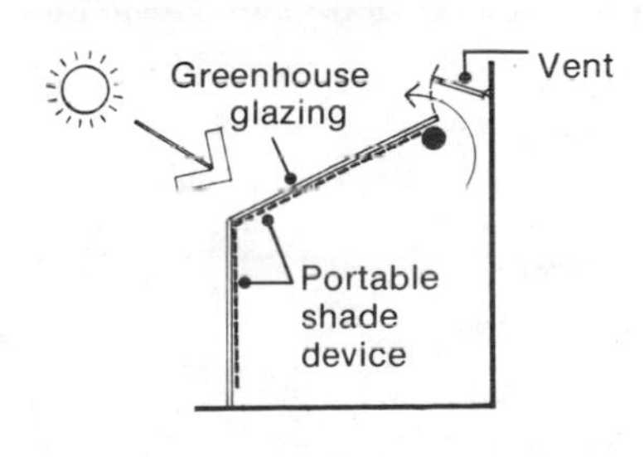

"Greenhouse," which can provide oxygen, decorative foliage, food, and heat to the home.

Energy efficiency of the space can be increased by providing concrete or masonry floors and black barrels filled with water. Kits are available for constructing your own greenhouse. Control is accomplished with vents and portable shades under the greenhouse glazing.

Another method is the "Envelope System." The house is enclosed with double walls, double roof, and open space beneath the floor. Solar energy is first collected through south-facing windows and then distributed throughout the house in the wall and roof cavities by the natural flow of heat. Heat can be temporarily stored in rocks in the space beneath the floor. The system produces a continual flow of air in the cavities and creates comfortable room temperatures.

Various combinations of these basic types of systems are possible. Each combination will create a unique home design. Designs can be as numerous and unique as the people who will live in them.

Active Solar Designs

An active solar heating system — in contrast to a passive system — involves using mechanical devices to move solar energy from an externally mounted collecting device into the house for either temporary storage or circulation to the rooms. Housing design concepts are being developed to include these collectors as an integral part of the design.

The collectors are mounted on south-facing walls or roofs. Large south-facing roofs are designed at special slope angles to accommodate the collectors. These slopes are usually much steeper than on the conventional home. Since sunlight must strike the confined area of the collector, obstructions such as trees or structures should be avoided or eliminated.

Active solar systems usually include a storage "battery," composed of rocks or a liquid solution,

Envelope System

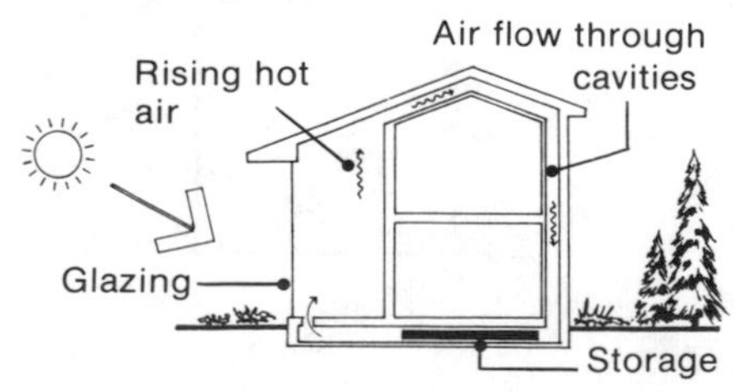

Earth Berming

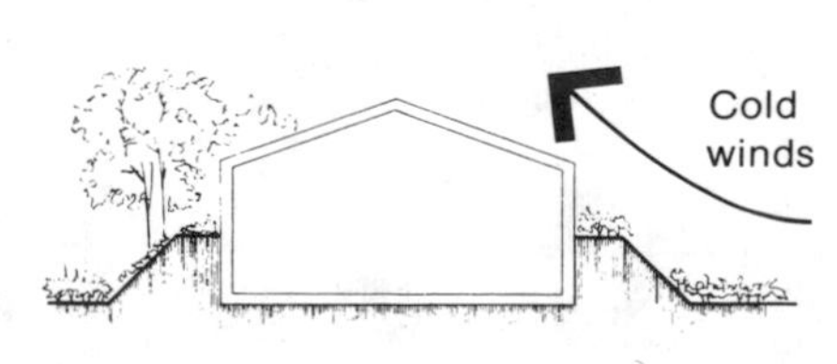

that must be included in overall design of the house. Distribution of heat is quite similar to a conventional home and usually does not have a significant effect on the basic design.

Today's concepts include special attention to landscaping. Trees, shrubs and ground cover are — among other reasons — selected for their individual beauty and for blending with the design of the home. These plants can also contribute towards energy efficiency.

Evergreen trees and shrubs planted on the north and windward sides of a home will perform as windbreaks and reduce heat loss. Deciduous trees and shrubs on the south side of the home will provide shading in the summer while in the winter, when the leaves are gone, they permit sunlight to pass through and into the home. Large trees surrounding a home can help moderate the extremes of both hot and cold temperatures.

Mounded earth, or berms, can be used to reduce the amount of exposed surface areas of a house, and thus, reduce heat loss. They can also direct winds in such a way as to cause snowdrifts to form away from the house and entrances.

Surface colors of walls and roofs can affect energy efficiency. Dark colors absorb more heat than light colors do. Materials for storing heat should have a dark-colored surface. Very light-colored surfaces and mirrors will reflect energy and should be used where heat is not wanted. The total design concept should include a color scheme that complements energy needs of the house.

Entrances and Doors

Entrances are a major concern for energy efficiency. Doors should be tightly sealed at the edges, and — whenever possible — located only on the south or east sides of the house.

One idea is to provide an airlock, two doors and an airspace in between. One door is usually closed before the other is opened. This greatly reduces the amount of interior heat loss to the outside. Other ideas include wing walls and plants at the entrance to divert cold winds away from the entrance.

Individual doors are available today in all sizes, colors, patterns, and new materials with very high insulation qualities.

Steel doors with insulation between the steel covers are becoming economical to use provided they have a thermal-break between the steel skins. Magnetic weatherstripping is also possible with the steel doors.

Sliding glass patio doors can waste a lot of

energy. Concepts for improving their efficiency are similar to those for windows.

Rooms of a house can be arranged to take advantage of the sun and the natural flow of heat. Spaces not often used — such as corridors, closets, and mechanical rooms — can be kept at lower temperatures and located between occupied rooms and the north exterior wall.

Areas such as laundry rooms, kitchens, and mechanical rooms will generate heat and should be located on the north or east sides so the heat can be easily vented to the exterior in summer, and used to heat the rooms in winter.

Living, family, and dining rooms should be located on the south side where heat gains and natural light would be available. Exterior entrances to these rooms on the south side would be functional and energy-efficient.

Windows can lose a great deal of energy. Windows are available with multiple layers of glass; between each glass layer is a dead air space which acts as an insulator.

One unique system that reduces heat loss includes particles of insulation beads blown into the air space between the layers of glass. The beads can be automatically removed during the daytime when natural light and solar gain are needed.

Heat loss can also be reduced with shutters, movable insulated panels and heavy insulated drapery.

Location of windows is very important. They should be placed to provide cross ventilation within the home and a pleasing arrangement of openings on the outside. Window sizes should be kept to a minimum on the north and east sides.

The skylight is another device to collect solar energy and create an interesting visual effect in the interior. Skylights should be constructed with multiple layers of glass and insulating panels to reduce heat loss.

Heat gained through a window can be just as important to control as heat loss. Windows with reflective glass can be located on the west or south sides to reduce the intense summer heat.

Shading Devices

External shading devices to control heat gain include large roof overhangs, sidewalls, awnings, recesses, and movable louvers, or screens. Internal devices such as insulated blinds, panels, and opaque drapery are also quite effective. Some of the devices can be automatically controlled.

Design and positioning of these devices require consideration of the sun's position in both summer and winter. The shading device should allow the low winter sunshine through the window, while rays of the high summer sun would be blocked.

These and other design concepts are in the process of continuing development for improved efficiency.

The range of house designs available today is almost endless. You must decide what is best for your specific location and requirements. As new materials, construction methods, and technologies are developed selection of a house design should be a very exciting and rewarding experience.

A solar greenhouse and residence.

R. LLEWELLYN

Further Reading:

A Treasury of Contemporary Houses, Architectural Record Book, McGraw-Hill Book Co., Princeton Road, Hightstown, NJ 08520. $18.95.

Design With Climate, Victory Olgyay, Princeton University Press, Book Order Department, Princeton, NJ 08540. $32.50.

Earth Sheltered Housing Design — Guidelines, Examples, and References, American Underground Space Assn., c/o TLH Associates, Suite 900, Minnesota Building, 4th & Cedar, St. Paul, MN 55101. $12.

Natural Solar Architecture — A Passive Primer, David Wright, Litton Educational Publications, 7625 Empire Drive, Florence, KY 41042. $8.95.

Planning and Building the Minimum Energy Dwelling, Burt, Hill, Kosar, Rittelman, Craftsman Book Co., 542 Stevens Avenue, Solana Beach, CA 92075. $10.

Sun/Earth, Richard L. Crowther, Charles Scribner's Sons Publishers, Attention: Customer Service, Vreeland Avenue, Totowa, NJ 07512. $8.95.

The Energy Issue, Progressive Architecture, April 1979.

The First Passive Solar Home Awards, #023-000-00571-4, U.S. Department of Housing and Urban Development, for sale from Superintendent of Documents, U.S. Government Printing Office, Washington, DC 20402. $5.50.

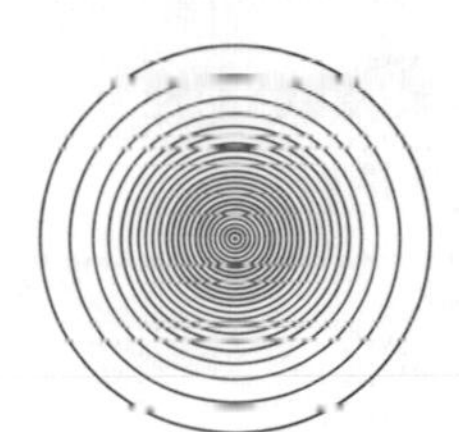

Section III

Communities

WM. CARNAHAN

Communities and Energy Saving — an Overview

By J. B. Williams and J. L. Leinhardt

Descending Round Mountain on a clear, crisp, spring morning, the scene is idyllic. Greers Ferry Lake sprawls to the north. Deep blue lake water reflects what appears to be multi-colored banks.

The springtime color spectacular is underway. Dogwood, redbud, other flowering trees, and wildflowers distinctly appear on the horizon.

State Highway 25 meanders down Round Mountain toward Heber Springs in the valley below. This quaint town is the county seat of Cleburne County and lies at the foothills of Arkansas' Ozark culture.

The beauty of the Ozarks, close proximity to Little Rock, and local culture are among the reasons people move into Cleburne County. In 1970, slightly more than 10,300 persons lived there. The estimated 1980 population is more than 16,500.

In less than decade, Cleburne County's population increased 62 percent. This, along with an expanding economy and people's higher expectations, is placing increased pressure on local government. People want more and better public facilities and services.

County Judge Dan Verser discussed the demographics of recent Cleburne County history.

"The ironic thing," Verser said, "is that many of our lifelong county residents have just in the last ten years been able to afford modern conveniences. With today's energy situation they can't afford to operate the conveniences."

"Complicating our situation, we're a growth area of the State with many people retiring here on fixed incomes. Further, many of our small business people depend on tourism — which is directly related to the fuel supplies and the economy."

Verser's comments reflect a concern that many municipal and county officials have expressed. In today's economy, with energy costs steadily increasing, what can local government do to help people cope with the energy situation?

J. B. WILLIAMS *is State Leader — Community Development, University of Arkansas Cooperative Extension Service. John L. Leinhardt is Extension Specialist — Community Development.*

Shirt-sleeve Meeting

The judge tackled this problem by asking Harold Williams, county Extension agent for Cleburne County, to arrange a shirt-sleeve meeting to air the local energy situation and plan energy conservation measures for local government and the local citizenry.

Williams arranged a meeting that included Roger Smith, energy conservation coordinator for First Electric Cooperative, and John Leinhardt, community development specialist for the University of Arkansas Cooperative Extension Service.

This meeting resulted in a commitment by County Judge Verser to form a Citizens' Energy Management Committee for Cleburne County.

The plan called for Harold Williams and Roger Smith to develop a list of names of people who work in energy-related occupations, local government, industry, schools, and churches. Representatives of the retired community and private citizens who have an interest in energy conservation also were involved.

Overall the effort has these people working in subcommittees to formulate an energy-conservation plan of action for schools, churches, businesses, local government, and private citizens. Each subcommittee's job is to develop a workable set of objectives with a common goal—energy conservation.

Many local governmental units and leaders lack overall energy-conservation programs or contingency plans for adoption during energy shortages. This lack may reflect the sentiments of constituents.

A *Washington Post* poll published on August 8, 1979 (see D42), reveals that respondents were most concerned about information on the availability of alternative energy sources (52 percent). Their least concern was getting informed about local government policies on energy (8 percent).

Local leaders have the responsibility of planning for the health, safety, welfare, and satisfaction of their citizens. Availability of energy and conservation of energy are directly related to fulfillment of these responsibilities.

Brunt of the responsibility for reacting to an energy crisis will fall on local government units and community leaders. Federal policymakers are realizing the critical role which local government and community leaders must perform in the Nation's effort to soften the impact of the energy problem.

Involving Citizens

Besides its role supporting federal policy, a local government should involve local citizens in planning to avoid energy shortages or alleviate their effects when they occur.

Obvious reasons for county or community energy management planning include: 1) saving tax monies, 2) reducing dependence on foreign energy, 3) reducing risks of shortages, and 4) setting an example.

As the cost of energy increases, more tax money is obligated to pay for energy to operate county and community facilities and services. Officials are faced with reducing facilities and services to pay for energy. With increased taxation to cover rising energy costs highly unlikely, a wise option for local governments is to develop and implement an energy-management plan.

Directly or indirectly, every person in this country is affected by our importation of energy. The role of local governments in energy conservation will lessen dependence on foreign sources for a significant portion of the energy we use.

Energy shortages have occurred in recent years, including brownouts due to demand on electrical energy and reduction of winter heating fuel in many communities. Most situations were slight inconveniences, but some reached crisis proportions. Energy management could lessen the impact of future energy shortages.

Credibility by Action and Deeds

Local government officials achieve credibility through their actions and deeds. By setting good examples with energy-conservation practices, officials provide a model for good citizenship and encourage citizens and other institutional areas to conserve energy.

Government involvement in energy conservation is in its infancy in Cleburne County, Arkansas. However, three factors are present which suggest success: commitment of local government officials, involvement of local citizens in decision-making, and development of an attainable set of objectives.

Judge Verser realizes that people can make a difference. For example, when the Cleburne County people participate in developing an energy plan and action program, certain values are expected to result:

- Decisions and actions will be enriched by the knowledge, insight, and imagination of many different people. The old adage "Two heads are better than one" certainly remains true.
- Plans that the committee makes and actions it takes are more likely to meet all the varied needs of people involved and to fit the unique features of their particular county situation.
- Because those on the committee have a part in the decision-making process, they will be more

concerned and more interested. People who are actively involved do not need to be "sold."

- Participation provides opportunities for people to learn from the involvement in decision-making and activities planned.

A county or community energy plan should be designed by the local people to reach goals they want. Some of the concerns and alternatives that might be included in a plan follow.

Conservation. This is the cheapest "energy." Based on the Nation's energy consumption habits, about one-half the energy used is wasted.

Technically, conservation is not a source of energy. It can, however, save millions of dollars, extend our energy supplies, buy time to develop other energy alternatives, lessen our dependence on foreign oil, and have a stabilizing effect on the whole economy.

Decisions. Cleburne County is a rural county in north central Arkansas, about 1¼ hours from Little Rock. Besides small manufacturing plants, the economy depends on tourism.

Government officials are concerned about conservation at the local level but also on effects the energy crisis will have upon the recreation and tourism industry in the county.

The dollar outflow now required to pay for energy would be equivalent to a several million dollar industry for Cleburne County.

In 1979, local businesses began feeling the pinch from the energy problems. Both 1981 and 1982 will bring more problems. Tourist industry representatives are striving to survive, and recognize the need to cater to folks closer to home.

The greater a county's dependence on outside energy suppliers, the more vulnerable are its individual consumers and small businesses to energy price increases and supply shortages.

Using Resources. One option available to counties is heat recovery from solid waste to produce steam or electricity.

When solid waste serves as a fuel to produce energy, it is used as a substitute for fossil fuel. Therefore, the gross value of the solid waste is equivalent to the value of the fossil fuel it replaces.

Local units of government must consider many factors in undertaking an energy recovery project. Most important is the fact that the cooperative efforts of several counties and municipalities are required in order to have the quantity of solid waste required.

The intrinsic energy in solid waste is a valuable

resource that should not be lost. Studies show that waste-to-energy systems are both technically and economically viable.

Although solid waste is not as efficient as fossil fuel in Btu output, the important point is that some of the expense that counties and municipalities incur in attempting to manage solid waste is recovered.

Other resources — coal, lignite, sun, water — should be considered. We must not only think about new or different energy sources, but find ways to live with less energy.

Community Plans. Leaders can consider several items from the planning angle to ensure an energy future. For example, cities and counties may enact programs, regulations and incentives to encourage cooperation from residents.

These may include zoning ordinances to concentrate housing for efficient use of services and facilities, orienting housing to maximize environmental effects, prohibiting the sale of property unless it has been weatherized, energy audits for all homes and businesses, and tax and financing incentives for renewable resource applications.

The field seems unlimited if people are willing to accept the challenge.

Rural Transport. Here things become more difficult for some rural counties. Urban cities and counties can study transit system improvement or traffic flow modifications. Rural communities and counties can consider ride sharing or van pooling, and encourage use of bicycles or more walking on the part of residents.

Among the highest energy consumers are our Nation's youth. They, like many adults, are looking for action. The powerful automobile, poor driving habits, excessive use of water and electricity are typical of many of today's youth. They must be a part of any community endeavor to overcome the energy problem. They want to help and can help if invited.

In summary, the future is not what it used to be, especially our energy future. We all share the national challenge to the widening gap between energy supply and demand. Adjusting to the new realities of energy scarcity and high prices after an era of abundant and cheap energy has and will continue to prove trying for all Americans.

Like Cleburne County, Arkansas, local units of government must get local people (including youth) involved with energy management if we are to have enough energy in the future.

Set Up an Energy Plan For Your Community

By Martha Drake

As we charge into the 1980's, it is apparent that the community that deals effectively with its energy needs will be the community that survives economically. This means making sure there will be the energy needed and, even more importantly, at a price the community can afford.

Starting your community on the path to effective energy planning could well be the most important service you could do at this time of drastic change in energy availability and energy cost.

The Federal Government has studied communities where energy planning is going forward. The decisive factor in success seems to be an individual who is really committed to energy conservation. Just passing resolutions and giving lip service to the concept doesn't do much good. The important thing is an individual who in turn can educate the community to the importance of this issue and instill energy conservation as a top priority with the citizens and with the local government.

We approached it in our small, northern community in Michigan with a $3,000 Rural Development Grant. This paid for a part-time Energy Coordinator attached to the county Cooperative Extension Office. However, it is not necessary to wait for a grant. The same service might be financed through CETA (Comprehensive Employment Training Act) or carried out by a volunteer. And the work might stem from the mayor's office, the Community Action Program, or the county offices. It could be a League of Women Voters project.

As the Energy Coordinator sets up an office to be a clearinghouse for energy information, the coordinator will find there is a wealth of free leaflets from government agencies, utilities, State energy offices, and universities.

Ask the mayor or chairman of the county commission to appoint an *ad hoc* energy advisory committee representing all levels of the community to give input on how energy planning should be

---

MARTHA DRAKE *is Energy Coordinator with the Michigan State University Cooperative Extension Service in Emmet County.*

326-621 O - 80 - 18 : QL 2

tackled in your community, and in turn to spread the word of what you are trying to do. Here it is essential that a member of your governing body be on the committee. Spend all the time necessary to plan these meetings well and see to it that the members attend. I found personal phone calls important.

Assessment

Now that you have your energy committee ready to go, just what do they do? What is the problem for your community? How much energy does it have? How much is it going to need? Will this be available? How much will it cost? How much of the community income will it take? What effect will it have on spending for other things?

The *County Energy Plan Guidebook* put out by the Institute of Ecological Policies is the simplest way I know of to get that information together.

This one workbook guides you to a straightforward assessment of what is going on energy-wise in your community, where you are going, and what the consequences may be.

The *Guidebook* is based on the experience of Franklin County, Massachusetts. A study was done comparing the energy used in 1950, in 1975 and projected for 2000, as a percent of the county's gross income. As most of the fuels used had to be imported, this represented money going out of the county much as our national oil money goes to OPEC countries. Some way had to be found to increase the money coming into the county to compensate.

Franklin County citizens were shocked to find that if they continued using energy as they had been, virtually all their income would be going for fuel in the year 2000. While $8 million went out of the county in 1950 for energy, $160 million would be going out in the year 2000. Furthermore, the county would have to create 450 extra jobs each year to make up for the added cost of energy. That many jobs for a county of 60,000 people is quite a challenge.

They then examined how they could harness local sources of energy such as water power, wind power, and wood supply. This had real possibilities but still left a financial burden for the county.

The next step was to take a look at where they could cut back on needs for energy. By weatherization and more efficient appliances, they found they could save 46 percent. This was a cheaper "source" of energy than producing or buying more. It also had the possibility of creating local jobs.

Plans went forward to combine efficiency with local energy production to ensure a future for the county that was affordable.

All this is incorporated into the *County Energy Plan Guidebook*, making it a practical tool to use and a good place to start.

Two-Prong Approach

An Energy Coordinator's hardest job is to get the community excited about saving energy. Anyone working closely with the economics of energy can see how fast the costs are going up and how much of a drain this will be on personal budgets. As more and more is spent for energy, all other expenditures will have to be cut. The problem is to convey this concern to the general public and to community planners.

We used a two-prong approach. The first part was to do the county study to show how much money would be going out of the county for energy, and what that would do to the county economy. Armed with this hard data displayed on slides and posters, we were ready to talk to the Emmet County Commissioners and City Councils, to Rotary and Kiwanis Clubs, Women's Groups, Church Groups, and TV programs. Our newspaper did a story. We were literally scaring people with the possibilities for severe economic problems if changes weren't made.

The second part was to install the energy conservation ethic in the county children. For this we had a carpenter build a doll house with a transparent back. We furnished it very nicely, gluing down the furniture, and putting in electric lights and a doll family.

We hired a bright, personable girl with CETA funds to put on a 45-minute presentation in each class. She talked about the need to save energy and what each of us should be doing about turning down thermostats, keeping doors closed, using showers instead of baths, turning off lights and TV sets — in other words, establishing that saving energy was "good" and wasting it was "bad."

We received good publicity from the project and used the doll house many times for State Energy Expositions, County Fairs, Builders' Shows, etc. This is an easy, effective way to educate your school population, and the children in turn will carry the message back into their homes to their parents.

Energy Audit of Each Home

As people become concerned with their rising energy costs, they seek help and the energy coordinator should be ready with concrete suggestions. Basic to this help is an energy audit of each home.

Start with *In The Bank or Up The Chimney*, the excellent booklet put out by the U.S. Department of Housing and Urban Development. This booklet takes homeowners through their house step-by-step and helps them estimate how much insulation and other improvements they need. The booklet should be made available to every homeowner.

In Michigan, information in this booklet has been put on a computer. Residents can dial the "Project Conserve" toll-free number and a form will be sent to them. They fill in data about their home which is fed into the computer telling them what various weatherization steps will cost, what they will save and what the payback will be. It shows where to start beefing up insulation in your house and how to do it. Information about funding should go along with this.

Some communities have programmed their own computers to do free audits. These can include information on local resources such as insulation installers, low interest loans, and furnace inspections.

We used the banks to relay information about this free computer audit to area residents. The banks were happy to send a letter over their signature and ours explaining the program and suggesting their customers call for an audit form.

Supplementing the computer audit are personal audits. We used CETA employees to do these audits. Many utilities are now starting audits. You may want to encourage your municipal utility or rural electric utility to start such a program. We found placing people to work in the communities where they lived was effective. Often they could get into homes with energy information where strangers couldn't.

We used CETA employees to do actual insulation, also. They caulked and put on weatherstripping, put layers of newspaper under rugs, and tacked on temporary storm windows. A program is going forward this summer (1980) under CETA to cut firewood to have on hand to give out this winter.

Programs

Many programs exist for funding weatherization. Low income people may qualify for grant monies. The Farmers Home Administration, State housing authorities, and — in some cases — utilities are granting loans. The Energy Coordinator should have a list of where funds are available.

Tax credit information is very important, too. We find this is an area with which many people are not familiar, and they need to have it explained again and again.

Ride-sharing bulletin boards are an easy way to help your community save money. Mount a State highway map with pins and slips of paper to indicate destinations. We put one at our Women's Resource Center and at a local natural food store. We find people with similar lifestyles are more apt to feel comfortable sharing rides.

Our local newspaper was happy to run free ads for carpooling. We also worked with the bigger employers to establish carpools among their employees.

Workshops were held on such subjects as Heating with Wood, Gasohol, Window Treatments for Energy Saving, Solar Hot Water Heating, Earth-Sheltered Building, Wind Power, Small Hydro, Car Tuneups, Efficient Appliances, and Solar Greenhouses. We found plenty of local experts willing to share their knowledge if we would just organize the workshop. The key to success was plenty of publicity.

Tours were held of solar-heated homes, earth-sheltered homes, and homes built with super insulation. (Invite someone from your newspaper to go along on tours you plan.)

Classes can be given through your high school adult evening school program on how to build efficient homes and how to use solar heating.

Dropout Building Aides

In our community, the CETA program working with the Community Action Program has trained school dropouts to assist in building projects. We are making good use of them for four projects, each located in a different small community throughout the county.

1) A Solar Greenhouse, built in connection with a senior citizen center.
2) An Alcohol Still, built at the county airport.
3) A Solar Heated Community Center, a one-room school converted into a well-insulated, solar-heated community center.
4) A Commercial size Greenhouse for winter vegetables, converted from an abandoned city reservoir.

Once your Energy Commission is functioning and you have assessed needs and set your goals, you can recommend many practical programs to the county or city government.

Flow restrictors can cut the use of water from a shower by 40 percent, and can also be used on faucets. These can be bought from a supplier for a small amount. It may take direct personal contact to get people to realize what they are and to put them in. Scouts, CETA, or a high school environment club could take it on as a project.

Each county needs to establish recycling programs. Plan for newspaper, crankcase oil, bottle and metal separation and recycle in connection with the waste disposal programs. We found people are willing to separate and package the various recyclables if we set up collection points. And there is money to be made. Someone picks up our used crankcase oil to reuse. We work with the trash collectors to make their pickups more efficient.

Rate structures are important. Investigate your local utility rate structures to see if they encourage conservation.

Work with your vocational building trades instructors to make sure they incorporate new building techniques. The Small House Building Council at the University of Illinois has good material.

States have programs for auditing and improving schools, hospitals, and local government buildings. Be sure your community plugs into these.

Keep records on public buildings to convince government boards of the savings potential.

Each county should have an emergency plan in case funds are cut off. Most States are starting to work with city and county officials on this. The Energy Coordinator can make sure such a plan is going forward for his or her area.

Pamphlets and Library Very Useful

Backing up all this is the Energy Coordinator's office. It should be filled with how-to-do pamphlets on all types of energy-saving actions. A small lending library on insulating and solar homes, windpower, and energy-efficient building is useful. Make it the local clearinghouse for energy information.

A weekly energy column in the local newspaper helps establish your office as a center for energy information. There is a wealth of material to use and plenty of new developments to discuss each week. Feature what local people are doing that's new.

As your plans progress, watch for barriers that prevent conservation. Some communities need to review their zoning ordinances. Do they encourage living close to the things people need or encourage urban sprawl? One community found there were ordinances against clotheslines.

Does your municipal utility need authority to insist on efficient appliances? What kind of insulation is required before electric heat is used? Is your building code strict enough?

Building and zoning codes need a complete going over to enable each building to get maximum solar access. We seek to encourage small neighborhood groceries and other small stores.

Zoning should consider possibilities of mass transit: Parking areas on the edge of town where people can leave their cars and use public transportation. Rezoning areas close to work for multiple dwelling. Bicycle paths.

In effect, take a whole new look at rearranging your community to make it possible to save energy.

The Federal government study of the communities which have been successful with their programs showed four things are important: 1) a dedicated individual to start with, 2) good data, 3) definite goals, and 4) an energy-educated local government and citizenry. Good luck!

Further Reading:

County Energy Plan Guidebook, Alan Okagaki and Jim Benson, Institute for Ecological Policies, 9208 Christopher Street, Fairfax, VA 22031. $7.50.

In the Bank... Or Up the Chimney?, #023-000-00411-9, U.S. Department of Housing and Urban Development, for sale from Superintendent of Documents, U.S. Government Printing Office, Washington, DC 20402. $1.70.

Local Government Energy Activities: Volume 1: Summary Analysis of Twelve Cities and Counties, DOE-PE-0015-1, U.S. Department of Energy, for sale from National Technical Information Service, U.S. Department of Commerce, 5285 Port Royal Road, Springfield, VA 22161. $5.25. Microfiche, $3.

Local Government Energy Activities: Volume 2: Detailed Analysis of Twelve Cities and Counties, DOE-PE-0015-2, U.S. Department of Energy, for sale from National Technical Information Service, U.S. Department of Commerce, 5285 Port Royal Road, Springfield, VA 22161. $9. Microfiche, $3.

Local Government Energy Activities: Volume 3: Case Studies of Twelve Cities and Counties, DOE-PE-0015-3, U.S. Department of Energy, for sale from National Technical Information Service, U.S. Department of Commerce, 5285 Port Royal Road, Springfield, VA 22161. $9. Microfiche, $3.

Save Energy, Save Dollars, Information Bulletin No. 125, New York State Cooperative Extension Service, Cornell University, Distribution Center, 7 Research Park, Ithaca, NY 14850. $1.50.

How Womanpower Turned Community On To Save Energy

By Chris Newman

Once most individuals have flipped the switch on leaving the room, stopped hotrodding their gas guzzlers, turned down the thermostat and done a few other things — whether they are impelled by a surge of patriotism or merely indulging in the joys of clinging to their depreciating supply of funds — they have about exhausted their ingenuity. Beyond that, if energy conservation and development of renewable energy sources are to go further, it is up to the community from the national level down to local levels.

The community at any level is a reservoir of human knowledge and skills, surprisingly sturdy and strong. It is multi-faceted and community action can take place in many forms. We as a Nation contrived to become an energy profligate society together and the only way we can get out of our fix is together.

One of the places community action in energy can take place is at the local electric utility cooperative. Electric cooperatives were founded during the late 1930's and 1940's with much community action and involvement. Small rural communities, which couldn't buy electric power from larger city-based investor owned utility companies, formed electric cooperatives. These cooperatives were founded on the principles of farm cooperatives — principles already familiar to rural communities.

In the early years of electric cooperatives, community action was needed to sign up members; borrow money from the government lending agency, the Rural Electrification Administration; set poles and meet other requirements necessary to operate an electric utility. Volunteers from the community performed many roles in order to bring electricity to rural areas. Much of their time was spent in selling the idea of electricity. Many farmers needed some strong convincing to join up with their community electric cooperative.

Today, because of rural growth, many electric

CHRIS NEWMAN *is Director of Consumer Services for the Rural Electrification Administration.*

cooperatives bring electricity to newer suburban towns on the edge of major cities as well as to rural areas. These 1980 electric cooperatives are still seen as community based organizations and member/ volunteers are encouraged to participate in *their* electric utility. Community action is needed and encouraged to help citizen/members cope with the world's energy dilemma.

Co-op Forms a Women's Task Force

One cooperative in Georgia, the Cobb Electric Membership Corporation, began a Women's Task Force in January 1976 in order to encourage citizen participation for their community's energy future. The charter membership consisted of 45 women who had expressed an interest in the business of their cooperative and the national energy situation. Even the beginning of their task force was a story within itself.

The organization was created out of a need to channel member involvement and interest into a constructive vein. Two women members of the Cobb EMC, uninformed of the world energy situation and local rate crisis problem, actually wanted to picket the co-op. But after a conversation with their Board President, General Manager and Director of Member Services, rather than working against Cobb EMC they were ready to work *for* their cooperative. The task force has since successfully undertaken numerous projects and gained both local and national recognition for these efforts.

A major accomplishment of Cobb's Task Force is its effort to involve the cooperative members in a voluntary load management project. In fact the two programs — load management and the Women's Task Force — began the same day.

Cobb EMC was one of the first power companies in the Nation to introduce and put into operation a plan to shave the summer peak caused by central air-conditioning units. This peak, which is the maximum one hour of power usage during a summer month, determines the minimum power rate for the following 12 months. If peak power use keeps rising, electric power rates keep rising.

In striving to head off possible blackouts and brownouts, and to help lower the wholesale power adjustment, concentrated efforts have been made by the co-op to find a method of curbing or shaving the high power demand period.

5,000 Signed to Start Up the Project

This "load management" project required the voluntary consent and participation of at least 5,000 members to be successful. These members agreed to have a remote control device, or switch, at no cost to them attached to their air-conditioning units, to be activated during the peak power demand period. The switch would stop the compressor for approximately 7 minutes out of every 27 minutes during the hottest days of the summer months. The fan on the unit would continue to run and circulate air.

From the very beginning the Task Force was involved in every aspect of Cobb EMC's load management project. The women talked with friends and strangers alike about participating in this endeavor. These women made over 800 phone calls to fellow members in the interest of load management for their community. Their personal contacts created a renewed belief in community-based cooperative spirit to solve a problem.

One member of the Task Force describes their first efforts: "The Women's Task Force main involvement for the first six months was with the load management switch. The EMC office provided us with lists of names and phone numbers of people who had a 2,000 kilowatt hours or higher reading on their bill in August of the year before.

"On our own time, at home, usually between the hours of 7 and 9 p.m., we called people, giving them the message about the load management switch as a followup to a letter they had received from the co-op office, asking them to send in a letter of consent to have the switch installed (at no expense to them) or to call the Cobb EMC for more expert information.

"Sure enough, by May, 5,000 signatures had been obtained for load management switches to be installed by qualified workmen on central air-conditioners in our first trial test year."

Many of the public relations and one-to-one contact functions to start this massive program were carried out by the Women's Task Force. The cooperative would not have been able to afford to hire professionals for this job or they would have had to go much slower if they could depend only on the full-time staff already on board.

The Task Force set up speaking engagements for cooperative personnel within other community groups to tell the load management story. Task Force women were also recruited to go to Cobb EMC's office on numerous occasions to assist with the actual labor involved in the many large mail-outs this project required.

'Big Brother' Fears Eased

One member said that when he first heard about the switch from a member of the Women's Task Force, he was totally against it. He said, "I couldn't imagine the power company wanting to save me money. To put something on my system sounded too much like this 'big brother' thing...and then my concern was that they would cut off my air-conditioner for an hour or so whenever they wanted to. But after reading and learning more about it, I realized that...it would be off for only a few minutes out of an hour. I work in electronics and knew it couldn't hurt my unit, nor affect other appliances like my TV."

During the first summer the remote controlled switches were in operation for a total of only 20 days. Those switches, under control, cycled off for 7 minutes, then on for 20 minutes when the kilowatt peak was occurring.

As reported in *Business Week*, Paul Weatherby, General Manager of Cobb EMC, made a survey of the 5,000 volunteers trying the switch. Of the half that replied, 96 percent were favorable, noticing little or no discomfort.

"We're talking about saving energy," said one member. "When they asked us to set our thermostats back this winter to 65, we did it. There were times when we were a little uncomfortable, but we felt we should do our part. I feel the same way about air-conditioning, even if we can tell a change. I feel that in the future much more drastic measures will have to be taken, so if a few minutes out of an hour now will help postpone this, it's no sacrifice at all."

This description of an electric cooperative carrying out a community function is only illustrative of what varied resources can be called into action. An organized community cognizant of a vital need can do many things, especially to meet the needs of a world dominated by the energy dilemma.

Membership Saved Over $4 Million

Cobb EMC's Women's Task Force rallied together for their community. Their active participation has been invaluable and cannot be entirely measured. Presently, however, four years later, as a result of the combined effort of electric cooperative personnel, task force members, and some 14,600 load management volunteers, savings to the cooperative membership has been over $4 million.

When asked if it bothered him that non-participating members benefited by his switch, a member stated, "No, but I would like to see more people participate. I am really concerned about the energy situation, and they (Cobb) are trying to do something to have this done, and consumers must know that this small inconvenience will be outweighed by the savings."

The member added that he would recommend the load management system to his friends and neighbors. He said, "I think we will profit from it in the long run. I know it's probably not going to make my power bill any lower...but if we can just do something to keep it from rising so fast, to more or less stabilize it..."

Cobb EMC and its membership has the right idea—the energy dilemma seems to be here to stay for many years. It can tear the world apart and jeopardize this Nation's strength. True, every citizen should do his part, but if the challenge is to be overcome, it will be the fruit of community planning and action—rational, vigorous and intelligent.

Electric cooperatives, unlike most utilities, have always been consumer oriented. They are owned by the members they serve but they operate and conduct business much like other electric utilities.

However, most utilities in the 1980's are becoming more consumer oriented. Even though they may be owned by stockholders who live outside the community, utilities are finding it is good business to be community and consumer oriented. Therefore, the example of Cobb Electric Membership Corporation could be used and applied in many other community settings.

Rural Transportation: How to Get Help

By Ira Kaye

Desirability of any rural region as a place to live is directly related to accessibility to jobs, basic services, and social interaction. Where a signficant part of the population has limited access to these vital activities, people perceive their situation as disadvantaged and undesirable. The region itself lies under a cloud as an unlikely candidate for development.

The face of America is changing. Population trends noted in the 70's will be confirmed when the 1980 Census is reported. The steady migration of people from rural areas to the cities that had characterized 20th Century America has halted.

Non-metropolitan counties are growing, both within and beyond commuting range of metropolitan centers. At the same time metropolitan centers are declining or exhibiting a slower rate of growth.

These trends are not universal. Rural counties that are predominantly agricultural or Black still are declining; the implications of this phenomenon are not fully understood.

The fossil fuel crisis and its impact on the availability and cost of energy will profoundly influence the overall population trends. In any case there are now rural areas experiencing rapid growth of population as well as those where decline continues.

Largely because of energy, it has become apparent to rural communities that population growth poses as many subtly complicated problems as does chronic decline. Transportation of people and products is an essential element in solving all these problems.

In rural America, transportation is the largest consumer of energy. Inefficient or uncoordinated use of transportation wastes energy and complicates development of an energy policy which could assure the non-transportation users of energy an adequate supply. While this problem is one which affects the Nation, it is especially severe in our rural areas.

IRA KAYE *was Rural Transportation Specialist, Office of Transportation, USDA. He is now retired.*

Miles to Job Are Nearly Doubled

The economy, geography and very lifestyles of rural America underscores the inseparable and interrelated nature of transportation and energy. Rural areas accounted for 40 percent of the non-farm jobs created between 1970-77. The workers, however, must commute almost twice as far as urbanites to hold these jobs. In some cases they commute over 100 miles a day. Those at the lowest fifth of the pay scale spend nearly half the family budget on such commuting.

Lack of public transportation dictates the acquisition and operation of at least one family car to enable a rural household to obtain employment. Continued rises in the price of gasoline foreshadows even bleaker prospects. Rural workers will not benefit from the new, more fuel efficient motor cars. The used car market will thrust the traded-in gas guzzlers on these workers.

Even agricultural employment is affected. In the late 1950's, 35 percent of hired farm workers lived off the farm. In 1977, the figure was 79 percent. The percentage of rural households without access to an auto is much higher than in urban areas. And in poverty areas over 20 percent of rural households have *no* access. Lack of transportation has been found to be the major barrier to obtaining and holding a job in rural areas, especially for minority and other disadvantaged households.

From the entrepreneur's side of the coin, the distressed nature of transportation endangers both agricultural and non-agricultural production as well as profitability. Under such a handicap, rational rural development is severely impeded.

Just how distressed is the present state of transportation in rural America? In the next few years thousands of miles of rails face abandonment or discontinuance. Some predominantly agricultural States face losses of 50 percent of their available rail lines.

Since 1965, a total of 114 small cities have lost their air service and 189 others have had service suspended. Since airline deregulation this trend has accelerated.

Only 40 percent of towns between 2,500 to 10,000 population and only 15 percent of towns and places under 2,500 are served by an inter-city bus line. Passenger rail serves very few rural communities. Since both rail and inter-city bus service is not geared to serve small towns and rural areas, scheduling is such that, even where available, it is often not feasible for the rural resident to use.

Poor Counties Get Little Service

A recent study of 487 predominantly agricultural and persistent low income rural counties established this profile: Four percent have a bus terminal within the county, about half have at least one bus stop. The distance travelled to reach the bus stop ranges from 8½ to 461 miles. Three percent have a passenger rail terminal or stop and the distance travelled to reach the facility ranges from 67 to 800 miles. Four percent are served by an airport with a commercial common carrier and the distance travelled to reach the airport ranges from 61 to 500 miles.

As far as local service is concerned, of the 20,000 towns under 50,000 population, only 313 have any form of public transit (about half of these are bedroom or resort communities).

Taxi service is available in less than a third of the 487 counties and such service continues to decline. Miles to the nearest taxi service range from 37 to 99 miles, making the costs involved prohibitive.

The only possible silver lining is the fact that the majority (over 60 percent) of these rural counties have some form of social-service based passenger transportation services for special groups like the elderly, handicapped, low-income and other mobility-deprived.

As the Nation, State, community and the family became aware of the extent of this problem, tentative approaches toward providing mobility and hence access to rural residents have been tried. The individual householder, family head, and the community have been involved, as well as governmental institutions at all levels.

At the time gasoline was relatively cheap and available, family decisions on how, when and for what purpose to travel were relatively easy for those fortunate enough to own two automobiles (about 45 percent of rural households). For the carless or the one-car family, decisions were and are more difficult.

Congressional hearings are studded with statements like: "So I paid someone to ride me to Prestonburg," "I gave him one-third of my Social Security check to drive me to my doctor in Charleston." Typically, by far the largest reason for missed medical appointments in rural areas is lack of transportation.

The President's Dec. 20, 1979, statement on Small Community and Rural Development Policy underscored this barrier to alternate choices. "Less than 1 percent of rural Americans who work away from home use public transportation to get to work—a statistic that dramatically reveals how dependent rural Americans are on the family car. Yet over 57 percent of the rural poor, and 45 percent of the rural elderly do not own an automobile, contributing even further to their isolation and immobility, not only from jobs, but from vital social services as well."

As far as both transportation and its relationship to energy is concerned, the essence of the announced policy is to give the rural family and the autoless a viable alternative to the private automobile for the family's mobility needs. Family and community decisions are intertwined in the suggested approaches.

It does not take expensive surveys to discover that the "preferred" mode of transportation in both rural and urban areas is an air-conditioned, chauffer-driven, comfortable limousine with door-to-door service. The cost of gasoline and other forms of energy dictate that many such expectations be scaled down.

Carpooling, Vanpooling

One highly publicized program involves ride-sharing, both carpooling and vanpooling. Many rural workers are employed at worksites either in a metropolitan area or on its fringes. Employers who draw on such a rural-based labor force are given tax and other inducements to organize and support such ride-sharing. It takes several forms.

Carpooling uses the family car in a more coordinated and fuel-efficient manner. Several owner/drivers alternate their individual driving days so that on each day the driven car is full. The individual family thus has the use of the family car many days of the week.

Vanpooling most often means purchase of the multi-passenger van by the employer. Its operation is turned over to a volunteer employee for operation

WM. CARNAHAN

These USDA employees in Washington are headed home to rural Fredericksburg, Va., about 50 miles away. They represent more than 600 commuters that use vanpools to get to work in Washington from Fredericksburg and its surrounding counties.

and maintenance. He has use of the van when it is not serving its main purpose. Passengers pay a flat periodic fee towards operating costs. It is believed the average vanpool saves 5,000 gallons of gasoline a year.

Other parties including owner operators, transit authorities, labor unions and cooperatives have begun to acquire vans for vanpooling. More than the work trip is beginning to be involved, including recreation (ski and beach trips), hospital and clinic visits, church and concert attendance.

Difficulties must be considered, especially in rural areas. A sudden call for overtime or company meetings, or diversions caused by family business, can disrupt the tight coordination.

In an urban area where there is at least some form of public transportation which, though inconvenient, can be used in an emergency, a ride-sharing arrangement can live with these variations. Not many rural families or ride-sharing arrangements will survive the 50-mile night drive to pick up a worker stranded by his vanpool.

In any event the Federal and State governments assist such programs with technical suggestions, tax incentives, and insurance coverage. Two good sources of information are: Edward F. Kearney, Executive Director, National Committee on Uniform Traffic Laws and Ordinances, 1776 Massachusetts Avenue N.W., Washington, DC 20036; and Ed Zazzarino, Vice President-Operations, Corporate Services and Buildings Department, Prudential Insurance Company of America, Newark, NJ 07101.

In areas where the typography is favorable and commuting distances are much shorter than the rural average, bicycling can be explored. But the suburbanite who pedals 15 miles to work along a safe community-maintained bike path is no model for the typical rural householder whose range is much longer and whose route might be very dangerous.

No matter how the rural family seeks to curb use of the private automobile to save energy and money, in the final analysis it will depend on the community's ability and commitment to develop some form of public transportation. It has been noted that a large percentage of rural counties have some form of social-service transportation. An October 1977 General Accounting Office (GAO) study identified 114 Federal programs which funded or assisted such transportation.

Although urban areas receive most of the funds obligated for all forms of transportation assistance, a community effort to consolidate and coordinate the

326-621 O - 80 - 19 : QL 2

existing resources in rural areas provides a nucleus for a rural public transit system.

Of the 114 Federal programs, 65 are funded by the Department of Health and Human Services (H&HS) and the new Department of Education at an estimated cost of $500 million a year. Many rural Community Action Agencies use parts of their local initiative funds to provide for transportation.

The Urban Mass Transportation Administration (UMTA) in the Department of Transportation administers a program pursuant to Section 16b(2) of its legislation. This program provides funding for acquiring vehicles by non-profit entities for transporting elderly and handicapped. Funded at about $20 million per year, it is administered on the basis of State allocations pursuant to State plans. It does not provide funds for operating expenses.

Of course, operating expenses have increased with the skyrocketing gasoline and oil prices in the past several years.

People Say They Can't Get Rides

GAO's report examined all of these programs to determine why people complained that, especially in rural areas, they could not obtain rides. One of the principal barriers was the persistent claim of recipient agencies that they were forbidden by Federal law or regulation to use their vehicles or transportation funds for any purpose other than transporting clients for program purposes. In rural areas this resulted in a proliferation of vehicles, under-utilized, costly to operate, and not providing even the fortunate client with a range of transportation services required by the average rural householder.

GAO found there were no Federal statutory or regulatory restrictions that specifically prohibited coordination of transportation resources of any of the 114 programs. Barriers were the mental attitudes that make up local agency turfdom, and costly and often unreasonable application, accounting and auditing procedures.

Since 1977, Congress and the White House have undertaken to provide the impetus and muscle to overcome these barriers. Common threads in both efforts are:

• The GAO report findings are stated in the negative, that is, no law or regulation forbids coordination. Needed was a clear statement that nothing prohibited coordination, but in fact there was a positive requirement to achieve it.

• The existing system funded largely by Federal resources was client-oriented. It jealously ran on the principle that the transportation was solely for a specific client for a specific program purpose. Any variance resulted in such accounting confusion and auditing traps that it was not worth the risks.

This resulted in visible absurdities. At times two or three vehicles had to be dispatched to a household for family members who were beneficiaries of different programs or needed different services. Often the vehicles originated or terminated within blocks of each other in the typical rural or small town setting.

Moreover, perish the thought that the client wished to vary the trip or the route to do some shopping! What was needed in rural areas was a system built to transport people rather than clients.

Early Federal efforts to achieve these ends were the Rural Bus Demonstration Program, authorized by Section 147 of the Federal Highway Act of 1973, and UMTA's Capital Assistance Program for Public Agencies, Section 3 of its basic legislation.

Under the first, 102 demonstrations were launched in small towns, rural areas, and Indian reservations. The legislation authorized expenditure of $75 million over two years, but less than $25 million was obligated over at least a three-year period.

Coordination Cuts Costs

Nevertheless, the demonstrations showed the cost per passenger mile was greatly reduced in a coordinated, people-oriented system. Many more passengers could be transported for the same number of vehicles and the equivalent amount of Federal funds. This was confirmed by studies and special projects conducted by H&HS.

Congress set aside $500 million of the $11 billion authorization for UMTA in 1972, for a capital equipment assistance program for non-urbanized areas. By the time this authorization ran out only around $30 million was obligated. One reason for the shortfall was reluctance of small towns and rural areas to acquire vehicles without having access to operating funds.

Urban transit has a huge program for both capital and operating assistance. In non-urban areas the lack of operating funds, rather than vehicle shortage, is the sticking point. Non-urbanized areas sought the same flexibility for use of their transit funds as urban areas.

This package of problems was addressed in Section 18 (Non-urbanized Public Transportation Program) of the Surface Transportation Assistance Act of 1978. The program authorizes $125 million a year for four years. A total of $75 million was appropriated for the program in fiscal year 1979, and $85 million in FY 1980. The President pledged to maintain that level for the remainder of the authorization in his

Dec. 24, 1979, statement on Small Community and Rural Development Policy. It must be noted, however, that the additional $10 million is open for subsidies to inter-city bus lines to sustain such service.

State Formula Allocations

The program envisages public transit, not client transportation. The Secretary of Transportation administers the program through State formula allocations to State agencies designated by Governors. In most cases the designated agencies have been units within the State Departments of Transportation or Highway Departments.

At the Federal level the Public Transportation Management Division of the Federal Highway Administration was established as the managing arm, even though the legislation is part of UMTA's legislation.

Key Federal official in the States is the Divisional Chief of the Federal Highway Department, most often stationed in the State capitol. UMTA officials, regional and national, have inputs on the approval process for State and local grants.

Statutory language says the funds are to be used for public transportation projects included in a State program in non-urbanized areas. The State program is to be based on equitable distribution of funds within the State (including Indian reservations), and the maximum feasible coordination of public transportation services provided by the Section 18 program with transportation services assisted by other Federal sources.

Intent of the Congress is clear. This is not to be one more program added to the previously identified programs. It is to be the vehicle to turn the GAO negative finding into the necessary affirmative charge to coordinate.

Eligible recipients include all governmental bodies, non-profit organizations, and operators of public transportation services. Purpose of the system funded is to provide local transportation service. This is to prevent competition with inter-city and charter bus lines. It should also prevent an inter-city bus line recipient from using its grant as a subsidy for inter-city service instead of providing local service.

Purchases of service contracts are included in the list of eligible activities. This encourages social service agencies to use their transportation budget to contract with a coordinated or consolidated Section 18 provider for service to its clients.

May Prove Keystone System

Carried out successfully, the new system will eliminate duplication and overlapping transportation. It will also provide the general population with an alternative to the family car for its local transportation needs. It could be the keystone in the energy-saving arch for small towns and rural areas.

Federal share of the capital costs is not to exceed 80 percent of total costs, nor 50 percent of net operating expense. Fifty percent of the local share must be in cash; the remaining half may be in the form of revenue from operation of the system or unrestricted Federal funds. The latter provision strengthens the local effort to coordinate or consolidate since local governments usually find it difficult to raise cash necessary for local match.

Typically, a recent study on use of revenue-sharing funds for public transportation in rural areas showed that while a significant percentage of the counties used the funds for street and road maintenance, and for other non-transit purposes, just a trace used the funds to support transit. This was true even in those places which received Section 147 grants.

Other sections deal with labor protection, and the emergency regulations promulgated in December 1978 (not yet replaced by permanent regulations), have provisions which may give many local providers problems in compliance. Still, the program represents the best opportunity for small towns and rural areas beset with transportation problems to begin solving them.

The White House has accepted this reality. In both its June 1979 and Dec. 20, 1979 initiatives, it has mounted a program to expedite the creation of people-oriented transit systems in small towns and rural areas. Major thrusts of the initiatives is to isolate and remove the non-legislative and non-regulatory barriers which inhibit creation of such systems.

Insurance Task Force

A task force that includes the National Governors Association and the insurance industry is to establish a classification on which reasonable insurance rates could be based. There is a group working on simplifying and unifying accounting and auditing procedures. Another group is establishing technical assistance programs for operators, governing all the difficult phases of operation. A Federal group has been set up to promulgate a definitive list of Federal program funds which may be used for local match. Application of the labor protection clause is being reviewed and monitored.

These efforts are yet to bear fruit, which accounts for the painfully slow start of the program. The danger is that the client-oriented programs are cutting back their transportation funds with the excuse that the Section 18 program is to provide the transportation.

These activities, however, are an attempt to answer a common complaint from rural America: "Local folk trying to operate often unrealistic programs imposed from above are constantly harassed to coordinate with everybody in sight. It is patently obvious to all of us in the middle that the bureaucrats pushing this are not doing it. A little more example and a little less rhetoric would be most welcome."

Prevalent rationale for neglect of rural development issues is no longer valid. Energy conservation in rural America cannot be effective without a coordinated transportation policy. A growing number of people out there must be served if we are not to be overwhelmed by problems in the closing decades of this century.

Some Good Contacts

Sheldon G. Strickland, Public Transportation Management Division, Federal Highway Administration, Department of Transportation, Washington, DC.

Frank Sherkow, Public Transit Division, Department of Public Transportation, 5268 Northwest 2nd Avenue, Des Moines, IA 50313.

Mike Peterson, Bus Transportation Division, Department of Transportation, P.O. Box 30500, Lansing, MI 48909.

Alice Garland, Division of Mass Transportation, Department of Transportation, P.O. Box 25201, Raleigh, NC 27611.

Jim Grier, Bureau of Mass Transit, Rural and Inter-city Public Transportation, Department of Transportation, 1215 T and S Building, Harrisburg, PA 17120.

Dave Cyra, Office of Statewide Transportation Programs, University of Wisconsin-Extension, P.O. Box 413, Milwaukee, WI 53201.

Further Reading:

Improving Rural Transportation — The Section 18 Program of the Surface Transportation Assistance Act of 1978, Technology Sharing Program, I-40, U.S. Department of Transportation, 400 7th Street, S.W., Washington, DC 20590. Free.

Rural Rides, Farmers Home Administration, U.S. Department of Agriculture, Washington, DC 20250. Free.

More Recreation, Less Energy Cost

By Karl Munson

Consumers need to select recreation activities that are satisfying, without heavy use of scarce non-renewable resources. Governments and private suppliers of recreation must provide activities that require less energy.

Park planners should be aware of new energy sources that can be used in present and future building plans. The parks provide an opportunity for teaching awareness of the energy problems, and techniques for conserving energy in all phases of our lives. People retain knowledge they gain while enjoying leisure time.

Activities such as pleasure walking, tennis, bicycling, fishing, canoeing, picnicking, backpacking, golf (without cart) and low organized team sports not only consume less renewable energy, but also provide physical activities leading to more healthful bodies. They are good substitutes for some of the other popular activities such as pleasure driving, power boating, waterskiing, or resort vacations.

This means local communities need to provide two things. One is more opportunities for the low energy consuming activities that will allow their citizens to enjoy recreation close to home. The second is to provide skill training in the desirable kinds of activities and encourage all age groups to participate.

Some data collected for the Nationwide Outdoor Recreation Plan from 2,500 households indicates that people would stay home more and be satisfied with less energy expensive activities — if they were available.

Community leadership could conduct some local surveys of households to discover what additional facilities are needed. The change from a lot of travel to using facilities close to home could change the long range plans and needs of parks in the community.

The Department of energy has small grants available for communities for the development of energy

---

KARL MUNSON *is Graduate Coordinator, Department of Recreation, University of Maryland.*

WM. CARNAHAN

A section of Beach Drive in Washington, D.C.'s Rock Creek Park is closed to motor vehicles on Sundays during the summer. Many people in the Washington area use this close-to-home recreation area for bicycling, walking, and roller skating.

appropriate technology. Following are some examples of successful small grants that are ideas for communities to consider.

City Building 6 Windmills

The city of Bay St. Louis, Miss., is spending just under $50,000 to build six windmills to provide electricity for lighting a large fishing pier and tennis courts.

A large private development has built a special solar heated and cooled recreation center. The $538,000 unit supplies energy for an ice rink, gymnasium, game rooms, and exhibition theater. The solar unit, serving 54,000 square feet, saves $70,000 a year in energy bills. The unit will pay for itself in less than eight years.

Much is going on in combining solutions for producing cheap energy and at the same time process large amounts of manure sewage produced at zoos and children's animal farms.

The Baltimore Zoo is developing a system integrating such technologies as anaerobic digestion, solar energy, and windpower to produce methane gas for supplementing the zoo's energy needs. This system will educate zoo visitors on use of an often untapped source of energy.

One of the problems for isolated outdoor recreation areas is sewage treatment. The Long Branch Environmental Education Center at Asheville, N.C., has installed a solar assisted composting toilet. This relatively maintenance free restroom produces much less odor, and the compost emptied every six months is used for fertilizer.

If you are a private recreation enterprise owner or manager, there are things you can do that will be cost effective and save scarce energy resources.

The Recreation Resources Center at the University of Wisconsin has developed management books on energy for resorts, restaurants, taverns, and motels.

Program goal in Wisconsin is to reduce energy consumption by 15 percent in the recreation, tavern, and motel-hotel-resort businesses. Forty percent of the energy used for heating in these businesses is estimated to be wasted. Thirty percent of the energy for cooling is wasted and 15 percent of energy used for lighting can be conserved.

Your first step is to conduct a survey of your operation. This may be a simple walkthrough of the entire operation, making notes as you go, or a detailed survey of all systems. Involving department heads or maintenance people in the survey is suggested.

Realistic Goals Urged

Next step is to set goals that are realistic for the individual operation. Make very specific goals as percentage reductions of your total electric usage, total natural gas usage, etc. A 15 to 20 percent reduction is a realistic starting goal for each of these areas. One example might be to reduce your hot water usage by 100 gallons a day.

After goals are established, specific tasks are determined and a timetable developed for implementing them. If the goal is saving 100 gallons of hot water a day, the tasks might include adjusting water temperature settings, installing flow restrictors, and installing self-closing faucets. Set a completion date for each task.

The next step is to train employees in results of the survey and to explain the role of each employee in the energy program.

Involve clientele of your program with announcements in the rooms and recreation facilities.

Develop a reporting system for your conservation efforts. Provide a continuous flow of information to employees. Reinforce employee habits that help the conservation effort. Finally, let people in the community and guests know the efforts and achievements in this area.

Turn down radiators in vestibules, lobbies, stairways. Much heat (or cooling) is wasted in these areas. Add thermostats to units without temperature controls. Corridors, vestibules and stairways are basically unoccupied areas, and need not be heated or cooled to the same comfort level as other areas.

Turn off gas pilots on heating equipment completely during non-heating months. This alone could save 4 million or more Btu's per year per unit.

Consolidate Use of Areas in Buildings

Try consolidating use of areas for meetings, conferences, and socializing to common heated or cooled areas. Reduce (or raise) the temperatures in other areas of the building that are not occupied.

Timeclocks on exhaust fans can save a lot of energy during off-hours.

In cooling, consider circulating cool night air through the building to help the cooling system the next day.

Maintenance time spent on cleaning of heating and cooling coils, and checking blower fan wheels and blades at least once a year, will save a great deal of energy.

The above are just a few details to illustrate what can be done to save energy.

To measure effectiveness of your program, establish a base such as the energy consumption for the past 12 months. This will provide an opportunity to monitor the energy conservation plan.

This kind of program is more than conservation of scarce energy. It is good enterprise management. It also is managing for profit or efficient use of the tax dollar.

You can do a monthly energy audit just as you do on monthly cash receipts. Then do yearly comparisons of energy consumption.

To conclude, don't forget that the recreation service is a good place to educate the public on energy conservation. If people could think about their energy use through a personal audit form or through a mini-computer game, it may get the point across and change consumer behavior.

For more information, contact the Cooperative Extension Service in your county, the parks service, or the Department of Energy.

Further Reading:

Appropriate Energy Technologies in Recreation and Parks — Ideas to Build Your Future On, Attention: Fred Boyles, Heritage Conservation and Recreation Service, S.E. Regional Office, Richard B. Russell Federal Building, 75 Spring Street, Atlanta, GA 30303. Free.

How Your Community Can Cut Energy Bills

By Marian S. Feeney

The explosion of information, knowledge, and technology has opened new opportunities and alternatives for communities, families, and individual citizens. Information, materials, and events surrounding the complex energy situation will influence perceptions, choices, and decisions.

As community energy decisions are made, consideration should be given as to how they affect families and individual taxpayers. Will these decisions bring higher energy bills, more taxes, continuing water problems, and more traffic congestion? Will citizens become involved in the decisionmaking process to influence these decisions? Will communities respond to the energy needs of families, citizens, voters? Will energy policy decisions encompass the social and economic consequences?

Local government and public institutions within the community can achieve significant energy savings by integrating energy conservation practices into ongoing policy, planning, and management processes.

This may call for some new strategies in management and operation procedures, but such efforts can result in immediate benefits and significant savings.

If local government and public institutions within the community reduce energy use, they provide examples that other energy consumers can use as ideas for action.

Energy conservation options for action might include: improving management; operation and repair of public vehicles; increasing carpooling and vanpooling opportunities; reducing energy used to pump and process water and sewage; adjusting lighting requirements to meet the specific needs inside and outside; and making energy efficient capital improvements to existing buildings.

As local communities make decisions about when, where, and how much public money is spent

---

MARIAN S. FEENEY *is Program Leader, Community Energy Conservation, Policy and Housing, Science and Education Administration Extension.*

on capital improvements and services for its citizens, energy concerns need to be included.

Local Citizen Involvement

Local citizens can become involved and can contribute significantly to helping make these decisions.

With local citizens and local government officials working together to plan future actions, greater benefits can be achieved. Such cooperative efforts can help protect the community environment, individual choice, and lifestyle.

Planning reduces many uncertainties and the necessity for emergency action that can accompany conditions of energy supply shortages and rapidly escalating prices. This planning process will help strengthen the community and its ability to handle economic and social conditions.

Some communities will consider a full range of opportunities from construction of more and safer bicycle paths to the generation of energy from solid waste.

Energy options with impacts on the community and its residents may include citizen involvement in zoning, codes, and ordinances.

New zoning regulations could encourage cluster, multi-family, townhouse and apartment housing developments; neighborhood grocery stores and parks; and apartments or small offices in existing single family homes. This would provide a greater variety of uses in single family zones, which will reduce travel between homes, jobs, shopping, and recreation.

Development should be encouraged in areas having low energy costs for services and transportation. Land use and zoning ordinances could regulate the location and amount of land for different uses and the siting of buildings.

Municipal codes and ordinances might specify limits of energy use for decorative, commercial, essential and non-essential lighting. Ordinances could ban all non-essential energy use. Identifying non-essential energy use could be an interesting challenge for local citizens and local government officials.

Building Code Revision May Be Needed

The primary concern of building code representatives, homebuilders, financiers, and owners has not been the conservation of energy, the conservation of materials, or the conservation of energy required to provide materials.

Building codes should be reviewed and possibly revised for all new construction, remodeling, renovation, or restoration to comply with energy efficient standards. Building codes should apply to all State and local government buildings, schools, and other public buildings. These codes should include the residential, commercial, and industrial sectors.

Design and construction affect conservation of energy and materials in a variety of ways. Conventional residential construction has evolved with little or no regard for the extravagant use of materials.

On the basis of several research studies, homes could be built with one-third to one-half as much framing lumber. Such construction techniques are well within the requirements of model building codes and minimum property standards. When the lumber requirements for home building are reduced, the energy requirements for harvesting, drying, manufacturing, and transporting are also reduced.

As zoning, building codes and ordinance issues are being discussed in relation to energy and natural resource concerns, and environmental conditions, communities need to examine carefully the siting and location of structures on the lot, lot size, space requirements, type of plumbing, and the capacity of space heating and cooling equipment.

The Potential for Recycling Solid Waste

People and communities are learning that waste does not simply go away. Since the problems of solid waste disposal affect all and has become increasingly difficult to deal with, citizens must recognize the interrelationship of the natural, regulatory, industrial, agricultural, and human sectors. When decisions are made, do they enhance or constrain recycling potentials?

As the population increases, it will become increasingly difficult to find landfill sites. Restrictions and air quality standards for incineration and sanitation maintenance of solid waste management will continue to increase costs to taxpayers.

Are families and communities willing to sort their trash? The head of a solid waste removal company states, "recycling is important because it makes the public conscious of its waste." Through awareness, people will waste less.

Recently, States have moved forward with solid waste management plans focused on energy and resource recovery. Many municipalities and utilities are pursuing the possibilities of solid waste management and energy supply.

A recent Florida survey indicates a majority of Florida residents rejected the idea of gas rationing. The majority would prefer enforcement of the 55 miles per hour speed limit, a tax break for buying a small car, and a tax on cars not getting a specific number of miles per gallon. Forty-eight percent favored a tax supported public transportation system.

Municipal traffic patterns can be reviewed and revised to regulate traffic flow in congested areas. Since about 85 percent of all travel in the United States is by auto, graduated auto registration fees could encourage use of energy efficient cars.

Besides the competition between the American market and the global market, there are the consumer issues. What kind of cars do people want? When should they appear on the market? Can the auto industry make money on them? And, can families get the money to pay for them?

The many conflicts of the transportation sector involve the political, technical, environmental and social arenas. The price pressures have given way to some adjustments in lifestyles and travel habits. It is predicted that new forms of communication, such as comparative shopping by cable television, will substitute for some travel.

There are many opportunities for residents to participate in the decisionmaking process at the local, State, and national level. When citizens exercise their voice and vote, they influence public policy.

Besides setting the energy conservation image and involving citizens in energy decisions, the community offers many opportunities to its families.

It is predicted that the costs of existing houses will nearly keep pace with new housing costs. Inflation, high interest rates, soaring land and energy costs, zoning and building regulations are some of the factors forcing many people out of the housing market today.

There are some other pressures on the housing market too. The 1957 "baby boom", the healthier and longer living elderly, and the high divorce rate —which demands two living spaces for what had been one family—are pressuring the housing supply.

The Farmers Home Administration (FmHA) programs continue to emphasize energy conservation with changes in housing regulations to encourage greater energy efficiency and the use of solar systems where possible. San Diego has changed its building regulations so that all homes built after January 1980 will have solar hot water heaters.

Energy Aid Available to Residents

Homeowners can find assistance within their communities to ease the energy/housing cost burdens. FmHA programs provide loans for weatherization under the Section 502 home ownership loan program through participating utility companies, the Section 504 home repair loan grant programs for low-income owner occupants, and other loans made to individuals to buy, build, or repair a home.

The Department of Energy (DOE) weatherization program provides grants-in-aid for low income homeowners, especially the elderly and handicapped, through the State Energy Office or the State Economic Opportunity Office.

The Department of Housing and Urban Development (HUD) assists weatherization efforts through the Federal Housing Administration (FHA) insurance home improvement loans, direct loans for rehabilitation, the basic FHA mortgage insurance program, and the Community Development Block Grant program. New legislation authorizes establishment of a Solar Bank within HUD.

Through the Department of Health and Human Services (HHS), financial assistance may be available for weatherization. Under the Administration on Aging, weatherization service may be provided.

The Tennessee Valley Authority (TVA) offers a home insulation program and the Rural Electric Administration (REA) offers a low interest weatherization program for consumers serviced by participating Rural Electric Systems. Banks, savings and loans, credit unions, and other credit agencies in many States have special loan programs for building and making homes energy efficient or for using renewable energy resources.

Many States have passed legislation for special solar and renewable energy resource grant and loan programs. Check with the State energy office or a local State government representative for information.

Many municipalities have established home weatherization resale standards and offer weatherization loans or tax credits. In some areas, tax rebates or credits are given to purchasers of new homes meeting energy efficient standards.

Tax credits are available for some energy saving techniques. The Internal Revenue Service (IRS) allows tax credits for energy conservation investments. Qualifying conservation items are limited to: insulation, storm and thermal windows and doors, caulking, weatherstripping, clock thermostats, certain furnace modifications, and meters that display the cost of energy use. The tax credits for renewable energy resources include solar, geothermal, or wind-powered equipment.

All but eight States have tax breaks for installing alternative energy systems and for conservation and weatherization projects.

Rural housing often shows a contrast of quality to homes of nearby towns and suburbs. The quality of housing in many rural areas includes older housing with relatively older residents. The family income is lower, and the general economics of the rural area often shows little growth.

Through State and local community programs, the elderly and handicapped are often eligible to receive home weatherization and fuel emergency assistance. The State Energy Office, Department of Elderly Affairs or Aging, or the local Cooperative Extension Office can assist with referring families to the appropriate agency.

Utilities Offer Residential Energy Audit

Many utility companies have initiated energy audit programs or will be implementing the Residential Conservation Service program. This service will provide on-site energy audits to residential customers, identify appropriate energy conservation and renewable energy measures, and estimate the costs and savings of such measures.

With the influx of numerous heat conserving products and devices showing up in "energy supermarkets", purchase decisions become difficult, but help is available.

Your community offers many opportunities for learning about the selection, purchase, installation, and use of energy saving techniques and technologies. Workshops, seminars, demonstrations and short courses are offered through agencies, organizations, educational institutions, and the Cooperative Extension Service. Information is available through many community organizations and agencies, the Cooperative Extension Service, and State Energy Offices.

With cooperation and coordination at the local level, it is possible to safeguard the environment, protect individual choice, reduce the cost of government expenditures on energy, and cut energy outlays for citizens too.

Some of the most important steps toward energy security will be taken by consumers and communities. A new community energy ethic hopefully will occur and become a source of civic pride. The transition will be slow, but it will create a better balance with our resources, and a community in command of its future.

Further Reading:

A Guide to Reducing Energy Use Budget Costs, #061-000-00003-8, U.S. Department of Energy, for sale from Superintendent of Documents, U.S. Government Printing Office, Washington, DC 20402. $3.

'Super' Energy Ideas For Young People

By William Whyte

Adults take a dim view of energy shortages. The words suggest gas lines and runaway inflation. Everyone would like a master plan to help replace all that imported oil or at least eliminate the need for it.

Kids, though, find some pluses in every situation. And it's good they are upbeat about it. Within their lifetimes they will have to find more ways to save and to stretch energy supplies than their parents did.

So what can a kid see that's good about the energy crunch?

- People are taking to roller skates for transportation, and great new colorful skates are now in stores to meet this demand.
- Travelers are rediscovering the romance of train travel and soon may be on sailing vessels again, just as their great-grandparents were.
- An unexpected day off from school because of a fuel shortage is bad, but not without its compensations to a student who is just not ready for school that day.
- Walking is back in fashion, as is biking, as are wood fires on chilly evenings.
- Those who turn down their thermostats at night are discovering how invigorating life can be when they get out of bed in the morning.

Yes, people are adjusting to saving energy, but it sometimes takes a kid to see that the changes can improve the quality of life, at least once in a while.

Youth groups, 4-H Clubs, power companies and schools across the Nation are sponsoring opportunities for kids to explore the positive as well as the more challenging aspects of the energy question.

They are studying energy, not in terms, of "Gee, we are not going to have enough to meet all our anticipated needs," but rather, "OK, we are going to have to change our ways and use less energy and different forms of energy, but our lives may become more interesting in the process."

WILLIAM WHYTE *is a staff member of the Special Programs Center in the Office of Governmental and Public Affairs.*

326-621 O - 80 - 20 : QL 2

These learning experiences are not all classroom oriented. The home is the natural laboratory for studying, improvising and conserving when it comes to energy. The backyard, workshop, hobbyshop, community project, daycare center, science fair, library and summer camp are all places well suited for an energy experience, too.

Teaching mechanisms are just as varied. They include the use of person-powered generators, family projects, clowns, teacher guides, computers, student packets, gamebooks, do it yourself projects and more.

Instructors are sometimes regular science teachers. More often, they are individuals who have developed special energy awareness segments for presentation before many groups. These people may be professional teachers or counselors or volunteers.

Four-H staffers frequently instruct on energy with course work prepackaged for the region and the age group. Power companies sometimes provide speakers on special topics such as home energy audits, weatherization or power generation facilities. or they may sponsor or cosponsor science fairs, field trips and other special events.

Powering One's Own Generator

In St. Paul, Minn., husky high schoolers pedal a two-seater bicycle furiously, but go nowhere. Their bicycle chain turns a small generator. While friends urge them on, a radio, connected to this uncertain power supply, plays music. A television, which needs much more electricity, is also connected but it blinks on and off. A fan and desk lamp draw enough current to keep going.

"You'll have to pedal faster," yells Mike Kirkwood their teacher-demonstrator. "The picture is fading."

After the exercise, Kirkwood commends the sweating cyclists. While they are fascinated to see their physical power converted to electrical energy, they are also more aware of how much work that electricity represents.

"What would you have done if we needed a washing machine powered by you and the bicycle?" asks Kirkwood of one boy.

"I woulda died," he gasps.

The demonstration is part of an Energy Today and Tomorrow presentation that so far has reached more than 250,000 junior and senior high school students in Minnesota. Using dramatic props and demonstrations, Kirkwood spreads an awareness of the potentials and limitations of different energy sources.

At Clinton Junior High School in Clinton, Ill., students are not part of the demonstration, they are creating it. They are building energy projects for display and competition.

Julie King constructed a windmill-generator. She had to fill shopping lists from hardware and hobby stores and improvise in constructing some of the components from scratch. It was expensive to build and it took a surprising amount of wind to operate. Satisfaction came from finishing a model that worked and from finding out that when the wind was strong and constant, the power supply was steady and reliable.

Build Tidal Plant Model, Solar Oven

Mitchell Conn built his own tidal plant model to generate electricity from simulated sea currents. He found that he could illustrate the process well in a large basin in which he could quickly raise and lower the water level.

Greg Chapman built a working solar oven that could dry fruit. His brother Donnie and Welby Mitchell built a solar box reflector for cooking food. Perhaps unwittingly, they were demonstrating the range of application of solar energy in food preparation.

Rodney Price, on the other hand, is into geothermal power. He diagrammed a system by which water flows into the earth's heated core to return as steam with which to run an electricity generating turbine on the surface.

These and other projects were prepared for a 3-day energy exposition and represented about a 5-week class effort for each entry.

The exposition or science fair influence not only the students who put it together but parents who may become substantially involved in an energy project and the public who may make up the audience for the finished products.

Expo or science fair projects help kids to understand the relationship of energy to their daily living experiences. The heat in their bathwater may serve to remind them that it takes the equivalent of several ounces of fuel oil to heat a gallon of water to 100° F. They learn what consumer goods take a lot of energy to produce and what models among home appliances take the most and the least power to operate.

Teachers' guide on energy are used to help organize course work. One 4-H energy project in North Dakota uses a guide specifically written for that area of the country.

It contains an agricultural segment on tractor selection, weight, and fuel recordkeeping. Separate from such equipment is a chapter on gasoline conservation.

A solar chapter suggests interesting individual projects.

One of the more practical chapters is on energy-conserving meals. The guide shows how complete meals can be made by using only one heating appliance. Besides saving fuel the approach saves time and cleanup.

A chapter on home appliances indicates power consumption by make and model and another shows how one can weatherize a home in a variety of ways on a modest budget.

When budgets permit and the material is available, energy kits for the students are good supplements to the teacher guides. Such an energy exploration packet was provided to each 4-H'er studying energy in North Carolina. They contained an assortment of publications that the students could add to their individual libraries. Topics included: Home Energy Use; Reading Your Meter; Energy in the Kitchen; Alternative Energy Sources; Changing Habits That Waste Fuel; Transportation; Home Energy Audit as a Community Service; Careers in Energy; and An Energy Quiz.

The packet was the basis of a statewide educational effort, culminating in an energy fair with prizes for the 4-Her's with the best demonstration projects.

First prizes were expense paid trips to the North Carolina Energy Congress as guests of the State's four power companies.

Camps Study Coal, Wood and Solar

Summer energy camps are a choice way for kids to get into energy projects. The Montana Cooperative Extension Service sponsors one a year. In 1979, 49 participants were selected from among the many who wanted to attend. The campsite enabled them to study coal, wood and solar energy resources in relationship to the environment. They had room to build and experiment with solar and wind energy devices.

Movies, debates, energy-use games and traditional camp activities were all part of the four-day encampment. Experts in energy contributed time and teaching talent. Costs were $6,000 and paid by a grant made through the Montana Cooperative Extension Service.

The United States Department of Energy selected the encampment as one of the five most outstanding educational projects in the western region in 1979.

As is frequently the case, participants' attitudes were tested before and after the encampment to record what changes may have resulted. Results showed an increased awareness, but the real indicators of success were in the enthusiasm and originality of the campers evident during the four day experience.

Energy is a subject that not only captures the interest of the student of club member but of the parents and other members of the family.

A Michigan 4-H project examined attitudes concerning energy conservation of kids and adults over a period of time. At the onset of the project the kids were more energy conservation minded than the adults. However, after sharp rises in fuel prices, adult interest increased sharply.

Use Computer in Project for Weatherizing

Potential savings was not the only incentive for families to participate in the Michigan project. For many it was the first time they were able to use a computer on a home project. The computer helped them in several major areas, such as on how much to weatherize their homes by calculating costs and savings involved in various approaches to weatherization.

The computer showed them how they could save money merely by changing their living habits and schedules slightly. An April-May savings for 906 Michigan families averaged $313 in 1979. One year later the two month savings for making the same adjustments gave an average savings of $600 per family.

Some of the Michigan families took part in an energy conservation contest among family members. Individuals filled out a preprinted record of all they did that involved energy use. After a week, they added up the credits and the winner was rewarded with some special treat. The contest helped to re-

JANE MARSH

Michigan 4-H'ers test their energy knowledge on this quiz board developed for use in county Extension offices, shopping malls, libraries and other places frequented by public.

duce energy costs. More importantly, it reminded people to correct careless habits.

Game books can make energy conservation more interesting by making it fun, especially for younger kids.

Mizer Bingo Blends Fun, Knowledge

The Mizer Series, developed by Bonnie Braun, her family and associates combines games with strong educational objectives. Bonnie, a family resource management specialist with the Family Study Center at Oklahoma State University, designed the game guide for teachers of 3 to 6 year olds. It integrates imaginative games such as one called Mizer Bingo into classroom instruction on energy. Mizer Bingo helps the player to understand different sources and forms of energy.

The Energy Mizer is depicted as a benevolent, if stingy, sunburst, an image the kids like to recreate with their own variations. The series has now spread to Louisiana schools as its popularity expands.

Kentucky finds games and contests useful in the elementary school curriculum where energy is studied at every grade level starting with the 9-year-olds.

Recently they participated in a poster contest involving all Kentucky elementary schools, and sponsored by the State Department of Energy. Winning entries went to illustrate a large 1980 wall calendar. The decorative calendar gave the kids recognition throughout the State.

Enerjean the Clown

Another successful way to involve kids in energy conservation is to introduce them to a new friend who plays games with them. This was the approach taken by the Louisiana Cooperative Extension Service when they designed a costume identified as Enerjean the Clown.

Five hundred volunteers then were recruited and trained and shown how to make the Enerjean costume. During 1980 they reached their objective of entertaining and teaching every second grader in the State, 86,000 in all. The clown's energy messages were simple: Close doors, put on more clothes when chilly, turn off TV sets, and walk or ride a bike whenever possible.

The project was a great experience for the kids and for the army of people who played Enerjean. The clown figure became an independent advertising medium that was used to extend the energy conservation message well beyond classrooms.

A similar fantasy figure used at Cornell University, New York, during Earth Day '80 observances was Mr. K. U. Conserve, the 4-H Energy Robot. The robot entertained hundreds of visitors with his energy saving messages and is now considered an "educational resource" in his own right. He is designed for use at fairs and other special events where he moves slowly around, bumping into people. That gets their attention for the energy conservation awareness messages of the exhibit.

Kids are discovering many simple inexpensive projects that they can do themselves that save substantial amounts of energy in their homes. One popular device they can make easily is the draft meter, which is a sheet of plastic wrap or similar substance, taped to a wire coat hanger. When hung near windows and doors it quickly shows the location of drafts and how strong they are.

A second device then comes into play. It is a draft chaser. These were in common use years ago. They can be made from old ties filled with sand and sewn up tight. The materials used in making them and the designs are almost unlimited. When placed at the bottom of drafty doors and windows, they stop the draft effectively.

This chapter only touches on the studies and activities of the school-aged and even preschool kids in a few States. In other schools, clubs and camps across the country, kids are developing a real appreciation of the value of energy and enlightened philosophy about how it should be used.

As we approach the next century, they will be the ones making the critical energy decisions for the Nation.

Home and Town Audits Track Down Waste

By G. McMurtry and K. C. Bittenbender

"Can you show us how to save 38 percent of the energy bills for our schools, too?" asked Mrs. Barbara Czepukaitis, a Wilbraham (Mass.) resident and also a member of the local school committee. Mrs. Czepukaitis and her husband had just received the results of a residential energy audit conducted in their home by the Massachusetts Cooperative Extension Service, a partner with USDA. Her question was prompted by long budgeting sessions with local officials centered on rising energy costs in the schools.

The transition from potential savings of hundreds of dollars for residential conservation to savings of thousands of dollars for public building conservation was right on target.

From this encounter and several similar ones, the Municipal Building Energy Auditing Program developed. The Energy Education Center (EEC) of the Massachusetts Cooperative Extension Service began to study and develop the expertise to train auditors in large building analysis. In September 1978 the first teams of auditors were trained, and eight towns were targeted in western Massachusetts — including Mrs. Czepukaitis' town of Wilbraham — for EEC's first Municipal Building Energy Audit Program.

EEC first began training residential energy auditors in June 1977. These residential teams were named the Energy Conservation Analysis Project (ECAP). By June 1978 the Massachusetts Cooperative Extension Service, through its county offices, was administering ECAP programs throughout Massachusetts.

Approximately 140 auditors were working with homeowners providing what was in effect a free short course in home energy management. This included a detailed energy audit of the physical structure and an in-depth description of how the particular lifestyle of the homeowners contributed to increased or re-

---

GENE McMURTRY *is Associate Director of the Cooperative Extension Service, College of Food and Natural Resources, University of Massachusetts. Karl C. Bittenbender is Energy Management Specialist and Director of the Energy Education Center at the college.*

duced energy consumption. Advice was given on how the homeowner could reduce their energy consumption through adding insulation, weatherstripping, improved heating plant efficiency, temperature reduction in winter and increase in summer, and numerous seemingly minor home operation suggestions with a cumulative effect that would result in substantial energy savings. Comprehensive written reports provided to each homeowner included simple payback figures for all recommended capital expenditures.

Some 3,500 homeowners were served that first year. An evaluation of the first year's work by the State Energy Office reported an average potential savings of 42 percent from the ECAP audit. Followup showed that in 95 percent of all homes audited some of the recommendations were carried out, with 65 percent of the homes audited making energy savings capital expenditures.

The initial Municipal Building Energy Audit Program was barely operational when it became apparent that a large number of school administrators were seriously interested in reducing energy costs. EEC responded by retraining 30 residential auditors and recruiting 40 new municipal auditors to work with municipalities in energy conservation techniques and energy management.

EEC provided training in data collection, calculations of energy use, development of presentation and reports, followup, lighting/electrical systems, heating, ventilation, air-conditioning, hot water systems, calculating heat loss, building use patterns, alternative energy assessment, energy management monitoring, operational and maintenance procedures, and suggestions for implementation.

The auditors provided the following assistance:

- Assembled and collated a five-year historical use profile that would also be used to determine the Annual Efficiency Index (per square foot cost of energy).
- Performed a lighting audit.
- Performed a "walk through" audit to identify opportunities for no cost/low cost conservation measures in each building.
- Assisted the municipal officials in filling out the required forms for consideration for conservation monies under the schools and hospitals sections of the National Energy Act.
- Assisted a professional engineer or architect in conducting a detailed energy audit.

The most important factor considered in training auditors was to prepare them to be energy educators.

Feedback from residential and municipal audits indicates that personal contact is the key element in motivating the carrying out of energy conserving measures.

One of the critical "teachable moments" comes as the auditors prepare an energy management plan for each building and a comprehensive plan for the entire school system or town.

The auditor must be prepared at every instance to reinforce the discovery by town officials that in energy management it often matters more who uses the building and how they use it than the physical condition of the building. If the building is in poor condition, operational patterns are often the least costly improvement. If the building is in good condition, operational patterns are the major options that need to be discovered and analyzed.

School Kids' Body Heat Seen Usable

"I had no idea that the human body produced so much heat. Those kids are little furnaces themselves. Why we could actually save fuel by estimating the Btu's generated from the student body plus the heat given off by lighting and other electrical equipment," a town official said.

And from another town official: "Both our library and Town Hall are open the same nights and there is unused meeting space at the library which we could easily use. Then we could reduce the heating load in the Town Hall." Statements like these become the rule and not the exception as energy education spreads through town governments and the potential for savings through energy conservation is realized.

The Massachusetts Cooperative Extension Service needed more auditors to carry out the programs. Local Comprehensive Employment Training Act (CETA) administrators were approached, the scope and goals of the auditing programs presented, contracts signed.

After success of the initial residential program, CETA officials became some of the strongest advocates of the programs. They saw the economic benefits to the community as well as the quality of training and the competent supervision of the auditors. This combination greatly enhanced the employability of CETA participants, and resulted in a high placement rate after completion of the program.

CETA contracts through county Extension Offices operated for a maximum of 18 months after which a new program with new auditors was encouraged. To date, approximately 78 percent of the trained auditors have secured employment or gone on to further their education. Fifty percent of the auditors now hold other energy-related positions. EEC has assimilated 17 former CETA participants into its ever-expanding training staff.

90 Cities and Towns Assisted

To date, the Massachusetts Cooperative Extension Service has conducted approximately 8,500 residential energy conservation audits, and supplied 90 cities and towns with municipal building teams that provided them with energy management plans.

The full impact of this program on improving the quality of life in the cities and towns of Massachusetts through energy education can never be accurately assessed. The economic impact is considerable: several million dollars will be saved through conservation.

P.S. Mrs. Czepukaitis got her wish. In less than a year after completion of EEC's municipal auditing, the town of Wilbraham realized a 132,013 gallon savings, which represents a 35 percent reduction in municipal fuel consumption. Wilbraham was also awarded a community energy planning grant through the Energy Extension Service monies from the Massachusetts Executive Office of Energy Resources.

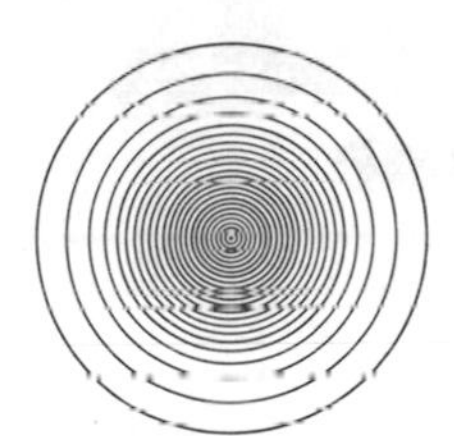

Section IV

Alternative Energy Sources

D. JACKSON

How Much Extra Energy Can Farms Produce?

By O. C. Doering III and R. M. Peart

We do not have an across-the-board energy problem. There are ample supplies of solid fuels in the United States if we can adjust our usage or change the form of the fuel to allow us to use it more widely.

Our energy problem is *liquid fuels*—the fuels required for mobile power. We will be short of liquid fuels and trying to replace them in coming years. This is not only true nationally, but also in our use of energy on the farm where liquid fuels are critical and not easily replaced by other forms of fuel.

The most pressing need will be for replacing liquid fuels, both on and off the farm. There is incentive for on-farm replacement of gaseous fuels, but gas supplies may not be as critically short and expensive as liquids.

There will be much less incentive to produce energy on the farm where that energy can be obtained from solid fuels, such as electricity from coal and uranium.

Every barrel of liquid fuel produced in the United States replaces a barrel of imported oil at the highest spot market prices. Therefore, alternative agricultural resources for producing liquid fuels are becoming more attractive.

Agriculture and forestry can produce significant amounts of fuel in addition to meeting food and fiber requirements. A goal of net overall energy self-sufficiency for agriculture is realizable. This concept means the energy requirements of U.S. agriculture would be equalled by energy produced on the farm plus energy raw materials (such as grain for ethanol) produced on the farm.

While U.S. agriculture uses only about 3 percent of total U.S. energy needs, meeting the self-sufficiency goal would mainly cut our petroleum needs. So the impact for liquid fuels would be proportionally greater than the 3 percent.

Still greater may be the impact of this potentially huge energy market upon crop production. The 1981

OTTO C. DOERING III *is Associate Professor of Agricultural Economics, Purdue University.* Robert M. Peart *is Professor of Agricultural Engineering.*

goal of half a billion gallons of ethanol production per year from corn will require about 3 percent of U.S. corn production. Enough alcohol for gasohol (10 percent ethanol plus 90 percent gasoline) for all current gasoline use would require the equivalent of over half the corn crop. This is not only a significant aid in reducing petroleum imports, but a very large new agricultural market.

Two Roles for Farms in Energy

There are two ways we can think of energy production on the farm. One is to consider it as something that would allow the farm to become energy-sufficient.

Modifications would be made in the farming system so a more limited amount of energy and material is cycled through the production process on a continuing basis. However, if the farm were not importing any outside energy, it would not have as much energy left over in food form to export to consumers.

The other concept is for farms to become energy exporters. They would not just grow crops for food, but also produce crops specifically to be turned into energy. This might be grain for alcohol or biomass for cellulose conversion.

However, the whole concept of energy production for export from the farm is very unlike that of an energy self-sufficient farm. An integrated mixed crop and livestock farm which is energy self-sufficient due to a methane digester, alcohol from grain, solar heat and manure fertilizer is a far cry from a farm with vast biomass fields where special tree or row crops would be harvested by machine for cellulose conversion.

If we look at the range of possible farm energy sources we see that some are most likely to be developed for sale to off-farm users while others are more likely to make their contribution to on-farm energy needs.

Production of Alcohol

Alcohol production is being promoted to help solve both farm fuel problems on an individual basis, and national liquid fuel problems on a large-scale plant basis. In addition to some economies of scale, usability of the product will be a major factor in whether it is produced for export from the farm or to help the farm meet its own liquid fuel needs.

Most on-farm alcohol production yields alcohol containing a small amount of water. This "wet" alcohol is O.K. for burning by itself in a modified internal combustion engine, or through injection into the airstream of a turbocharger in a diesel. But it is not suitable for large scale blending into gasoline to make gasohol for general public usage, which requires anhydrous ("dry") or 200 proof alcohol. Under currently available technology, that requires larger plants and a greater degree of attention to process engineering than is likely to be found on most farms.

So off-farm plants are likely to supply most of the alcohol that would wind up in the general public's gas tank when they purchase gasohol. However, the farm will still provide the corn or cellulosic material needed as a feedstock to make the alcohol.

Off-farm production of alcohol from grain, principally corn, is already commercially successful and expanding. This production of a liquid fuel from an easily-stored and widely-available year-round source, grain, is expected to continue to be the largest of the alternative energy sources exported from agriculture for some years.

Following that trend will be replacement of at least part of the grain by those crop residues, forages, or cellulosic wastes which can be prudently removed and used as a feedstock for ethanol. The development of practical means to produce fermentable sugars from residues would lower feedstock costs, allow greater use of total biomass from grain production areas, relieve possible strain on grain supplies, and allow biomass production from grasses and legumes on areas not suitable for row crop production.

Oil Crops, Solar, Wind and Hydro

Vegetable oils for use as diesel fuels are likely to be primarily an on-farm practice rather than an exportable energy crop. Oil crops such as soybeans and sunflowers currently are processed almost entirely off the farm, either into oils for human food and protein meal for livestock feed, or into human food directly. Fuel uses for these processed vegetable oils probably will not be able to compete economically with petroleum in the near future.

However, the possibility exists and research is just beginning for on-farm crushing of these oilseeds into fuel oil with the high-protein residue for livestock feed. The high proportion of diesel-powered farm machinery makes that option feasible for on-farm self-sufficiency for liquid fuel. On-farm vegetable oil processing could be simpler than ethanol production, and provide a reliable, if expensive, fuel for farm use not subject to oil embargoes.

In the next decade wind energy is most likely to contribute to on-farm needs. The scale of energy production from a windmill is relatively small, and in most cases not likely to be more than the needs of the farm on which it operates. Capital and management requirements are such that one or more large wind generators designed to feed into the power grid would have to be run by someone whose major concern was electric generation, not farming.

Solar energy, likewise, is expected to contribute only to on-farm needs (excluding solar energy used in photosynthesis for energy crop production). On-farm uses such as grain drying and livestock heating can often use solar energy more efficiently and inexpensively than can other industries, because of lower temperature requirements.

Low head hydro might work both ways, supplying some or all the power needs of a farm while selling electricity on a regular basis to a local utility. It is different from the wind systems in several ways.

Hydro generation is likely to be more constant and controllable — making the agricultural enterprise having the hydro system a more regular supplier of power for sale. Also, the system can be regulated to meet demand or even shut down. This is critical in terms of finding a willing buyer for alternative energy from any source. The flow has to be constant, or at least controllable to meet peak demand needs placed upon the regular supplier.

Low head hydro would also require less management time and tinkering than wind generation of electricity.

The hydro might have a higher initial capital cost, but would probably be a larger system with less capital invested per kilowatt hour of actual output.

Production of Methane; Pyrolysis

Methane production could be primarily for use on the farm. Large quantities might be available for off-farm sale depending on a number of factors, perhaps the most important of which is the scale of farm operation.

Most concepts of large scale methane systems plan on selling a portion of the gas produced to a local user or utility. Such systems usually center around a large animal operation where a vast amount of manure feedstock is available, and using the manure in fact relieves a waste disposal problem.

On this basis, methane production would be undertaken for export as well as for providing energy in large feedlot or dairy operations. Small-scale methane production could include the use of a farm digester in a family-run dairy or swine operation where the methane is produced to heat the farrowing house or heat water for dairy cleanup operations.

326-621 0 - 80 - 21 : QL 2

FRED WITTE

Methane has been produced continuously since 1976 in a cooperative USDA project at this University of Missouri swine farm. Manure is flushed from farm buildings into a settling basin where it is concentrated into solids and pumped daily into a 20-foot diameter digester. Effluent fom the digester and excess water from the basin flow into the lagoon, upper right.

The scale is not large enough to make the operation a reliable supplier, and the quality of the gas is different enough from natural gas to make small scale purchases by gas utilities difficult and costly. On a one-day cycle, methane can be stored to coincide with peak demands, but the methane production itself is not easily controllable.

Pyrolysis or gasification is somewhat similar. Quality of the gas is different enough from natural gas so that it cannot be blended into a pipeline stream easily. However, generation of producer gas can be readily controlled to match needs and can be started and stopped easily.

Large operations using forest or agricultural residues may well sell their gas, but this is most likely to be to a large user rather than to a utility. On a small scale, producer gas will be used where it is produced for a specific farm task, such as grain drying.

Substantial management skill is currently required for both methane and pyrolysis or gasification operations. Even on a small scale, good management is needed for a system that operates successfully.

Problems of Biomass

Biomass production for conversion or direct combustion is most likely to be done for export from the farm, rather than for farm use.

We are talking about production of a low value item that is quite bulky and difficult to handle. It is not a compact or easily storable form of energy. Improper biomass farming can degrade the land just as bad cropping practices do today.

Processing biomass for alcohol production through cellulose conversion or taking it through pyrolysis to obtain solid, liquid and/or gas fuels will require large operations which are capital intensive and managed by process engineers.

It is possible some of the pre-processing might be done on the farm. If a concentrated, easily handled product could be made on the farm from bulky biomass and then delivered to a large plant for final conversion to liquid fuel, it would be highly advantageous and improve the economic factor.

Generally, a key consideration in whether energy production is for on- or off-farm use is the disparity between the purchase price and the selling price of this energy. A farmer may pay $.04 to $.05 per kilowatt hour (kWh) for his electricity on the farm. If the farmer has a wind generator and wants to sell power to the utility, it will only want to pay $.02 at most per kWh for what the farmer produces. The utility cannot afford to pay more for several reasons.

At 4 to 5 cents a kWh, the utility has already transported the electricity to the farm. What it buys from the farmer it will then have to transport to the next customer. At 4 to 5 cents the utility is required to provide regular power service day and night. What it buys from the farmer will come when the wind blows and not necessarily coincide will peak needs of the utility.

The utility will have to keep its full generating capacity in place for those times when the wind does not blow, because it is the utility's responsibility to provide regular power, not the farmer's with a wind generator.

As we look at electricity and gas that might be produced on the farm, the purchase price the farmer pays for such energy is going to be much greater than the selling price for production on a farm scale. This will give tremendous economic incentive to use such energy on the farm to replace purchased energy, rather than to try to sell it.

Liquid Fuel Picture Is Different

Liquid fuels are a bit different. To some extent because we are facing liquid fuel shortages, the farmer will probably be able to sell liquid fuels produced on the farm at a price closer to the purchase price of such fuels, in comparison with electricity and gas. Processors may be willing to buy "wet" 180 proof alcohol from farmers at a discount, and then take it the last step to 200 proof alcohol suitable for blending with gasoline.

Tied in with the usual economic considerations of fixed and variable costs of on-farm energy production processes are unique technical, operational, and managerial factors that bear strongly on the economics.

Many biomass energy sources are highly seasonal in availability, and bulky and expensive to store.

In addition, weather controls the harvest and movement from the field. Thus equipment and labor demands are quite variable and not amenable to year-round mass-production concepts typical of large-scale industrial production.

Livestock wastes are produced on a more or less year-round basis. Methane produced from them is likewise produced continuously and is very expensive to store. Thus continuous uses will be the most economic for methane gas.

Plants that operate only part of the year from one source only, such as sugar beet refineries in the Midwest, are being forced out of business. Part of the reason is new technology that can produce sweeteners year-round more competitively from corn grain, available year-round on a well known market with a futures pricing system.

Alcohol production plants that are similarly restricted to seasonal operation because of limited feedstock materials might also not be economic relative to those that could produce throughout the year.

In the United States we now use about 100 billion gallons of gasoline annually. This does not include the distillate fuel oil for powering diesel engines or fuel oil for heating or industrial purposes. To make a 10 percent alcohol blend for just the Nation's gasoline we would have to produce 10 billion gallons of alcohol annually.

In 1979 we produced about 80 million gallons of alcohol from grain. We do not yet have the plant capacity to make the alcohol needed for any significant contribution to our fuel problem.

50 Percent of Corn Crop

Would there be enough corn? Making a 10 percent alcohol blend for the Nation, requiring 10 billion gallons of alcohol annually, woud use over 50 percent of the corn crop. It would call for a complete readjustment in our livestock industry, feedgrain exports, and our own diets.

It is probably unrealistic to think in terms of 10 billion gallons of alcohol just based on food or feedgrain as a feedstock. We are more likely to get an alcohol industry underway with grain alcohol, and then expand the industry further through cellulose conversion to alcohol. In three to five years technology advances should occur which will allow the conversion of cellulosic,materials, tree trimmings, old newspapers, crop residues, etc., to alcohol on an economic basis.

Such a process might release us from the very real food and feed requirements which probably limit our use of grain for alcohol to something less than 10 percent of the total crop in any given year.

Even with maximum alcohol production and a nationwide effort to use gasohol, we will be replacing a very small amount of our imported oil with alcohol. No one synthetic or substitute fuel will solve our problem, even with improved fuel economy.

In the next several decades we will have to develop liquid fuels from other sources such as shale or coal as well as from biomass if we want to make a significant impact on our national liquid fuel needs from the supply side.

Given the long lead time for liquids from shale or coal (the year 2000 before we are likely to see substantial production) much of our coping with liquid fuel problems for the Nation as a whole will have to be done on a demand management or energy conservation basis. While alcohol alone will not solve the nation's problem, the farm sector could conceivably run on alcohol or vegetable oil for its liquid fuel needs. This would give us assured food production despite oil embargoes.

Competition With Food, Feed Crops

Several questions are raised here. Energy crops will likely compete with food and feed crops for land, labor and other resources. Crops such as corn and sugar beets may be used either as food, feed or fuel.

Ideally, successful energy crops would use conventional farm equipment and have time and management requirements at a different time than the peak demand of other crops or farm enterprises.

The question of food versus fuel does not seem to require an answer yet. Food versus fiber is not considered an important policy question currently when applied to cotton vs. soybean production.

U.S. agricultural production has often helped temporary food shortage situations in the world, but malnutrition has existed broadly in periods of overproduction in the United States. Our own production does not guarantee a well-fed world.

The on-farm vs. energy export question has a bearing on the question of conflict or conformity with food production. When purchased farm energy supplies appear unreliable, the farmer must turn to on-farm sources almost without regard to costs to save a crop already grown or plant a new one.

Energy uses and simple conversion on-farm and close to the farm will have advantages of cheaper raw material and simpler supply systems. On-farm uses where supply conforms to demand will be adopted earliest; for example, corn cob or cornstalk gasification for corn drying.

Conversion plants capable of using a variety of sources for year-round operation will be needed. A possible future model is an ethanol plant with a front end cellulose conversion from cornstalks, hay or wood chips, and alternate facilities for handling grain and perhaps sugar beets, whole corn silage or sweet sorghum seasonally.

Energy crops will be raised by farmers and must compete with conventional crops for land and other resources. Entire "energy farms" may never develop because of the disadvantages of energy crop specialization.

The payoff potential is tremendous for a long term research and development program linking conversion and utilization technology with agricultural and forestry production technology.

Raising Yields

Yields can be raised for several conventional crops by dropping constraints imposed by food requirements and breeding for maximum energy production. For example, wheat yields reportedly can be improved by 30 percent if milling quality restrictions are dropped.

Ethanol production from grain, even though it is a practice thousands of years old, can be improved. New strains of micro-organisms may be able to convert part of the hemi-celluloses in corn grain along with the starches to increase alcohol yield significantly. Many engineering and biological innovations are possible to improve the energy efficiency of ethanol production.

Systems studies linking crop growth models to harvest and handling simulators driven by weather variables promise quick insights into a variety of operational problems. These system simulations should be carried out concurrently with field trials on yields, breeding work, and development of pilot plants.

There is much to be done if we are to take full advantage of our agricultural resources to meet some of our energy needs.

The ABC's of Making Farm Alcohol and Gas

By Dwight L. Miller

Basic to all human and animal life is fermentation. Through natural fermentation, yeasts, molds, bacteria, and other micro-organisms convert raw materials into usable, more simple products. Humans use controlled fermentation to make desired materials and to dispose of byproducts and residues.

Fermentation is a basic procedure for production of many of our foods and chemicals, and fermentation industries are vital to all world countries. Fermentation operations have always been basic for farm and home living.

Aerobic and anaerobic are the two basic types of fermentation. Aerobic requires supplies of air during the operation. Product yields, production rates, and overall efficiencies may depend on the air supply and its use. In contrast, anaerobic is carried out essentially in the absence of air. Production of yeast required for ethyl alcohol is primarily aerobic, but production of alcohol is an anaerobic operation.

The number of strains of micro-organisms available for fermentation is not known, but they total in the millions. Through manipulation, virtually an infinite number can be developed. Thus, results from scientific research on fermentation may well be the basis for future civilization advances.

The current U.S. transition from abundant, low-cost energy and chemical raw materials to limited supplies, higher prices, and more reliance upon foreign suppliers has generated increased interest in renewable agricultural farm crops and their byproducts — and their fermentative conversion into energy fuels and chemical feedstocks.

Agricultural raw materials offer opportunities for producing farm energy at stable and competitive costs. On-farm fermentative production of alcohol motor fuels and fuel gases are two methods that are receiving increased attention. These fuels will be used to illustrate methods of making agricultural operations more energy independent.

DWIGHT L. MILLER *is Assistant Director, Northern Regional Research Center, SEA-AR, USDA, Peoria, Ill.*

Ethyl alcohol, also known as ethanol, has been used as an energy fuel for decades. Its use as a motor fuel is almost as old as the internal combustion engine. More recently, the term "gasohol" has been generally accepted to identify a 10 percent anhydrous ethanol/90 percent unleaded gasoline motor fuel blend.

Alcohol blends have received attention for both on-farm and general transportation uses. Ethyl alcohol produced on the farm will probably be of some benefit during the 1980's in providing partially for farm fuel self-sufficiency.

Raw Materials That Are Used

Fermentative production of ethyl alcohol is based on such raw materials as cereal grains (corn, wheat, barley, sorghum, rye); sugar cane (molasses); sugar beets; fruit product residues; other starch crops (potatoes, rice); cheese whey; sulfite liquors (paper); wood and nonwood cellulose-containing materials. Beverage alcohol has always been limited to fermentation of cereal grains and natural materials high in starch and sugar.

It is technically possible to produce fuel alcohol from practically any agricultural material containing high ratios of carbohydrates, including such high cellulosic materials as wood, crop residues, and cultivated biomass.

Corn and sugar byproducts (molasses) have been the major commercial fermentation raw materials because of their availability, high carbohydrate content (starch and sugar), and normally lower cost. However, wheat and other grains have at times been used.

Alcohol yield from all these materials is theoretically in direct ratio to their starch and sugar contents. The theoretical yield of ethyl alcohol is 0.568 pound per pound of starch; 0.511 pound per pound of dextrose sugar; and 0.538 pound per pound of sucrose sugar. In actual operations, the chemical and physical properties of each natural raw material affects the operations. Commercially, at least 2.5 gallons of anhydrous alcohol is normally obtained from a bushel (56 pounds) of most cereal grains.

Ethyl alcohol results from the action of yeast or other micro-organisms on the starch and sugars present in the raw material. Basically, the micro-organisms used in fermentation require various nutrients for growth; in alcohol fermentation, the major nutrient is carbohydrate. Yeast, the culture commonly used, can ferment sugars but not starch or cellulose. Thus, these raw materials must be changed to sugars before fermentation.

Environmental conditions most favorable to the micro-organism must be employed to obtain maximum yield in minimum time. The optimum desired metabolic changes taking place in fermentation normally have a narrow temperature range, and the fermentation can be influenced by acidity, cell concentration, and many other controllable factors.

In the basic farm or industrial process for production of ethanol from grain for motor fuel use, grain is milled (ground) and then mixed with water to form a slurry. The grain slurry is cooked to boiling, and special enzymes and/or acids added to make the starch soluble. Additional water is then added and a different enzyme used to convert the solubilized starch to sugar.

The mixture (mash) is cooled to below 90° F and placed in large fermentation vats. Yeast is added and fermentation takes place over about three days during which the sugar is mostly converted to alcohol and carbon dioxide. Heat produced during fermentation is removed by external cooling; cooling is necessary for good yields. Most factories discharge the carbon dioxide to the atmosphere. However, in some locations it is economical to manufacture dry ice or liquid carbon dioxide from this gas.

Alcohol is removed from the fermentation mash (beer) with steam further purified, and all water removed by distillation. Anhydrous alcohol is denatured with chemicals for non-beverage fuel use. The still bottoms (slop-containing unfermented grain byproducts and water) are fed to animals wet or processed to dried distiller's grains for animal feeds.

Cereal Grains Byproducts Are Valuable

Byproducts or unfermented materials from various raw materials may be valuable or if not recovered or properly processed may cause pollution problems. andling of the byproducts is an integral part of any fermentation operation.

Cereal grains byproducts are valuable and normally have a market price per pound higher than the original grain. These byproduct grains contain practically all the original ingredients (protein, oil, etc.) except the starch or sugar (carbohydrates) that was converted to ethyl alcohol. They serve as protein ingredients for animal and poultry feed mixes. There is also potential for at least partial use in human foods. Thus, for cereal grains the starch has been upgraded into more valuable energy products, and the most-needed materials for food and feeds are still available for these uses.

For now, known technology for converting starch through fermentation to ethyl alcohol has received the most attention. In the future, however, cellulosic materials undoubtedly also will be used as alcohol fermentation raw materials.

The weight of residues (stalks, straw, stems) produced on the farm along with grain production on the farm is more than the weight of the grain harvested. Also, part of the crops used for animal feed and forage that is not digested remains as residues (manure). Currently, the bulk of agricultural residues is returned to the land during harvest, or disposed of in some manner.

Some return to the land of crop residues is essential, because residues provide organic nitrogen, phosphorus, and potassium to the soil. They may also increase soil tilth, reduce wind and water erosion, and provide humus to condition the soil and provide nutrients for soil micro-organisms.

The amount of byproduct residues that can be removed from the soil varies with the type of soil and geographic location. However, a considerable quantity can be made available for energy fuel use on the farm through fermentation.

Quantities of residues are large, annually amounting to over 650 million tons. Straw, corn stover, and manure account for about 140, 180, and 185 million tons (dry weight), respectively. About 1.5 pounds of straw and 1.3 pounds of corn residue are produced per pound of grain harvested. Cattle, swine, and poultry each produce annually about 2,000, 250, and 20 pounds of manure per animal. In many locations, confined animal production has become so large and concentrated that disposal back on the land is no longer possible or environmentally acceptable.

Anaerobic fermentation of farm byproducts, such as animal residues to biogas (methane, carbon dioxide, other gases), can assist in making the farm energy independent. The technology has been known for many years, and sewage treatment plants have used this procedure to generate biogas for their own use.

For example, anaerobic digestion of animal residues generally produces an average of about 7 cubic feet of gas per pound of input of dry matter. This gas contains about 60 percent methane and 40 percent carbon dioxide, with traces of other gases. Such a gas would have a heat content of about 500 Btu's per cubic foot, or about half that of natural gas.

Anaerobic digestions of animal residues generally leaves about 40 to 50 percent of the original materials as undigested residuals. Residues are slurried with water and placed in a fermentation digester. A suitable bacteria then converts the carbohydrates to carbon dioxide and methane gas. Since the digestion temperature must be about 200° F (93.3° C), some heating may be necessary and part of the generated gas can be burned to supply this heat. The fermentation residue is partially dewatered by settling or mechanical equipment (filters, centrifuges, etc.).

If used as a fertilizer and if land is readily available, the residue need not be dried. However, if dried, the fermentation residue can be stored indefinitely and used for an animal feed ingredient or fertilizer as needed. The water portion can be recycled to the slurry tank or digester.

No nitrogen is lost in the system if the liquid portion is recycled after recovery of the solids. Therefore, the solids contain most of the original organic nitrogen (protein). Thus, protein content of the solids (feed) has essentially doubled from that in the original raw material.

To sum up, on-farm fermentation processes that use various residues offer a significant opportunity for assisting in energy self-sufficiency. Through fermentation, agricultural products, byproducts, and residues may become significant sources of on-farm energy.

Ethyl alcohol may be produced from the starch in cereal grains; from sugar in such materials as sugar cane or sugar beets; or from the cellulose in crop byproducts and residues, through fermentation. Biogas may be produced from crop and animal residues through fermentation to replace nonrenewable natural gas.

Further Reading:

Fuel From Farms: A Guide to Small-Scale Ethanol Production, Department of Energy, #061-000-00372-0, for sale from Superintendent of Documents, U.S. Government Printing Office, Washington, DC 20402. $4.50.

Small-Scale Fuel Alcohol Production, #001-000-04124-0, U.S. Department of Agriculture, for sale from Superintendent of Documents, U.S. Government Printing Office, Washington, DC 20402. $6.

Ways to Burn Wood For Industrial Use

By Peter Koch

Direct burning is the most familiar way of producing energy from wood. Forest products industries are the main users of wood as fuel on a large scale, because they have much woody debris left over from milling and harvesting.

The basic strategy is to reduce leftover wood to walnut-size or smaller particles. This size reduction is usually done by a "hog." Large pieces enter the top of the hog and are forced down by rotating hammers. The small pieces fall through spaced bars, which control their size. This particulate fuel is then stored in piles at the mill, and from there reclaimed to fire boilers that produce steam for heat and power.

The largest wood-fired boilers commonly used in pulp and paper plants or in small utility plants produce enough steam to generate 35 to 50 megawatts of electrical power. This is enough electricity to drive machines demanding 35,000 to 50,000 horsepower—or to heat, cool, and light 10,000 to 14,000 households in the South. Such a boiler consumes about 500,000 tons of green wood fuel annually, or about three 20-ton truckloads an hour, 24 hours a day, 365 days a year.

Wood has a lower heating value than coal or oil per unit of weight. In other words, it takes more pounds of wood than of coal or oil to produce a given amount of energy. Wood has its advantages, however. For example, wood has a much lower ash content than coal and, unlike coal, contains little or no pollution-producing sulfur.

Chief drawbacks of wood are high moisture content and bulkiness. Most freshly cut wood is approximately half water by weight. Such green wood gives off only about half as much heat as dried wood. If wood is burned when green, furnace efficiency is lowered because heat energy is required to vaporize the moisture in the wood and much of this heat is lost up the stack. If fired with dry fuel instead of

PETER KOCH *is Chief Wood Scientist, Forest Products Utilization Research, Southern Forest Experiment Station, U.S. Forest Service, Pineville, La.*

green, a furnace can burn about twice as much wood per hour.

Boiler tests have shown that drying hogged fuel both increases the efficiency of steam generation and reduces waste emissions. Most furnaces designed for wet wood operate best if weight of water does not exceed that of wood, that is, if moisture content is 50 percent or less on a wet basis. At moisture contents over 60 percent, most furnaces operate poorly, if at all.

It is not yet clear whether the benefits of drying wood for boiler fuel in a separate operation offset the costs. Many combustion engineers feel that the cheapest procedure is to admit green fuel to the furnace and dry it in the firebox before combustion.

Pressing, Air-Drying, Hot Gases

If wood fuel must be dried, it can be dried in several ways. Mechanical pressing (visualize squeezing a sponge) removes water with simple equipment that requires no heat. Moisture content can be reduced to 50-55 percent of wet weight by this method.

Air-drying in thinly spread piles is laborious and takes many days, but can reduce the moisture content to about 20 percent if the climate is suitable. Today, however, fuel is most commonly dried with hot gases. The most common type of hot-gas dryer is the rotary drum.

In a typical rotary drum dryer system, wood to be dried is first screened to remove large pieces that must be "rehogged." This wood and hot gases obtained by burning gas or dry wood enter one end of the rotating drum or cylinder and are brought into contact with each other by forced flow of the gas. A fan draws the hot gases through the dryer, and these gases push the dried fuel toward the outlet end of the dryer.

Two- to four-inch pieces can be dried in 20 minutes or less. At the dryer outlet, fuel is separated into different sizes. Very small pieces that are airborne go to the cyclone separator with the gas flow.

Rotary drum dryers can handle large quantities of wet fuel. Inlet temperature can be as high as 1,600° F if there is enough moisture in the fuel to absorb the heat without scorching the wood. However, one must be careful to prevent formation of blue haze, a form of air pollution caused by distillation of some components of the wood. Douglas-fir dried above 750° F creates blue haze. The best drying conditions for hardwoods are unknown.

It is likely that large-scale industrial users of wood for fuel will continue to burn it green and in particulate form — that is, as "hogged" fuel. Some smaller-scale users, however, may need fuel not only dried but reduced in bulkiness. The problem of bulkiness of wood fuel can be solved, at some cost by compressing it and thereby densifying it.

There are several ways to densify wood for fuel. Compression baling can reduce wood residue volume to one-fifth its loose bulk while squeezing out 12 to 15 percent of its moisture.

Elasticity Breakdown

Most of the densified products can be formed by compressing the residue in a die under heat and pressure. Apparently the key to success is to break down elasticity of the wood or bark. If the elasticity is not destroyed, the densified form will not last.

Some of the compounds in wood and bark act as natural binding agents or glues when subjected to heat and pressure. Fire logs for home use may employ a wax or other binder to hold the densified dry wood particles together.

The technology for densifying particulate wood and bark has been around for over 50 years. The famous "pres-to-logs" used for hand-firing fireplaces and stoves were first made about 1933. In the 1950's, machines were developed to extrude dense wood residue rods suitable for fueling coal stoker furnaces. Generally, the rods are about 1 inch in diameter and can be cut to desired lengths.

In 1959 a company in Tennessee first pelletized bark for fuel. These oak bark pellets were used with coal to fire a steam boiler, and reportedly gave burning rates equivalent to soft coal.

Pelletization can be accomplished with standard agricultural pellet mills. The product is generally 3/16- to 1/2-inch in diameter and 1/2-inch long. The compression ratio in pelletizing is usually about 3 to 1. Because of their uniform density, fuel pellets are easier than hogged fuel to meter into a furnace and can be burned at more closely controlled rates.

Wet fuel cannot be pelletized unless it is first dried, however, and part of the fuel must be used to dry the material to be pelletized. Because of this, those industries such as furniture and cabinet manufacturers that have dry wood wastes may find pelletizing most economically attractive.

A company in Alabama pelletizes sawdust and bark after pre-drying it in a rotary dryer fired by some of the pelletized product. The pellets are sold to a power plant. Estimated total investment is about a half million dollars including land. The pelletizer sells for around $32,000.

A company in Oregon markets pelletized Douglas-fir bark. Reportedly, the product sells for about half the price of the amount of coal needed to produce the same amount of energy. Plant operations use the equivalent of 12 percent of the energy contained in the pelletized product.

Combustion is the rapid chemical combination of oxygen with the elements of a fuel that will burn. It results in release of heat energy. The major combustible elements in wood are carbon and hydrogen.

Burning of wood can be divided into three stages. In the first stage, the moisture is evaporated to dry the wood. In the second, temperature of the fuel rises to the point where some gases are driven off and burned. In the third, remaining carbon is burned as fast as oxygen from the air can be brought into contact with it. About 75 percent of the average wood will burn in the second stage, and about 25 percent in the third.

Ash and incompletely burned carbon are the solid residues from burning wood. In boiler furnaces, where high burning temperatures are achieved, slag and clinkers are formed from the melting and fusion of ash.

Wood ash generally has not been considered chemically active, but this may not be entirely true. In at least one case, wood ash has been shown to be an effective catalyst in gasification of wood.

Increased use of wood for fuel might make ash disposal a problem. Perhaps ash could be used as a soil conditioner, and the alkalinity of ash could help raise the pH of acid soil. Ash also has the potential to be used as a fertilizer. It is a good source of potash but contains no nitrogen. One mill in central Louisiana uses clinkers for roadbed surfaces around the plant.

Wood gives off both gases and small solid particles when burned. Carbon dioxide and water vapor combined with nitrogen and oxygen from the combustion air comprise 98 to 99 percent of the total material emitted from an efficient combustion process.

Air Pollution Concerns

In terms of potential air pollution, the Environmental Protection Agency (EPA) is concerned with the amounts of particulate matter, sulfur dioxide, carbon monoxide, nitrogen oxides, and other unburned gases (hydrocarbons) that enter the atmosphere. In wood combustion, sulfur dioxide emission is negligible, and carbon monoxide and hydrocarbon emissions usually present no problems. The situation with nitrogen oxides is less certain.

When combustion is poor, hydrocarbon emissions are increased. In extreme cases, these emissions may be 55 to 85 pounds per ton of fuel.

High hydrocarbon emissions could present a twofold pollution problem. First, some compounds produced through the incomplete combustion of solid fuels such as coal are suspected of being cancer-causing agents. The second problem is production of other compounds that react with sunlight to form smog. However, neither of these kinds of compounds is likely to form in wood burning if combustion is efficient.

Nitrogen oxides are instrumental in smog formation. Fortunately, the ambient concentration of nitrogen oxides is low enough in most areas that emission control for them from wood burning should not be required.

Particulate emissions can be controlled by any of four basic devices. These are cyclone separators, scrubbers, baghouse filters, and electrostatic precipitators. Most wood-fueled boilers are equipped with cyclone separators that spin the gases to centrifugally separate them from particles, or scrubbers that wash particles free of the gases.

Basically, there are two classes of wood-burning furnaces — grate burners and suspension burners. Dutch ovens and spreader stokers burn the fuel on a grate, either in a pile or spread into a thin bed.

Dutch oven furnace and boiler.

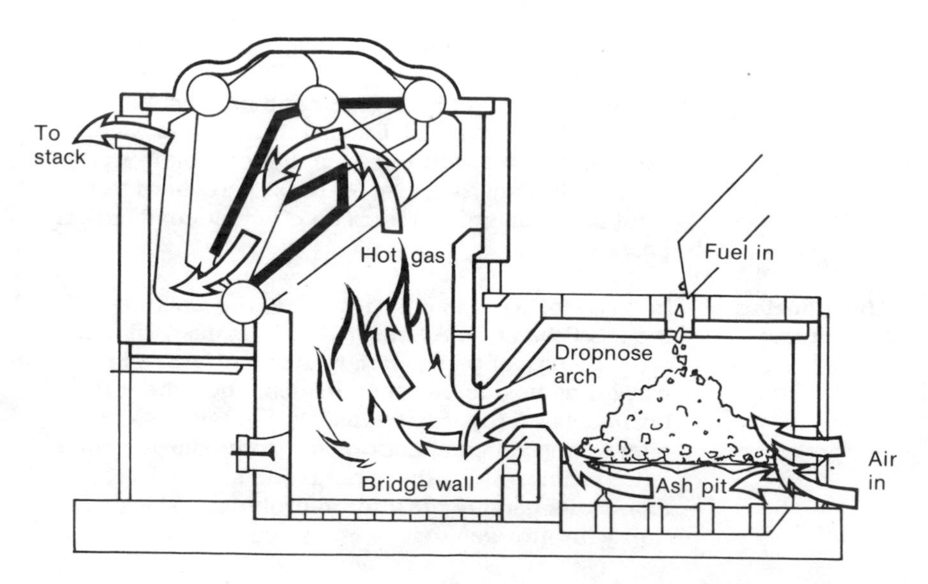

Historically, Dutch ovens provided steam for many industries in this country. While thousands are probably still in use, they are now considered obsolete for new installations because they are expensive to maintain and respond poorly to load changes.

Fuel cell burners are an adaptation of the Dutch oven design. Fuel chips are fed into the primary furnace, which is a vertical cylinder with a water-cooled grate. The cylinder is lined with firebrick which protects it from the intense heat. Fuel is partially burned in the primary furnace and gases given off pass into the upper chamber where burning is completed.

Boilers of this type are common in the western United States, where they are used to kiln-dry lumber. They generally produce 10,000 to 30,000 pounds of steam per hour. Dryers are needed when fuel moisture content is above 50 percent of green weight.

The spreader stoker is probably the most commonly used wood and bark burning furnace. With little difficulty, these furnaces can burn wood and bark alone or in combination with coal, oil, or gas.

In spreader stokers, fuel in the form of chips is spread into an even, thin bed across the grates. When the fuel is added above the grate, smaller particles and gases burn in suspension while the large pieces of fuel fall to the grate and burn in the fuel bed. Flames from the particles suspended above the grate radiate heat that aids in combustion of the fuel bed.

Furnace walls are normally lined with heat exchange tubes (water walled). Because there is no refractory to reflect heat back to the fuel, combustion air is sometimes preheated. Spreader stokers are used with boilers that generate from 25,000 to 600,000 pounds of steam per hour.

Suspension burning of wood and bark in large boiler furnaces is similar to the burning of pulverized coal. Usually bark hogged to a small size and blown into the furnace is the fuel. If injection is high enough in the furnace and the fuel particles are small enough, then the fuel will be competely burned before it falls out of the combustion zone.

In one system, turbulence is provided by preheated air injected from the sides of the furnace at various heights. The airflows create spinning air masses or fire circles that hold the fuel particles in suspension while they burn.

With suspension burners, a small dump grate at the bottom of the furnace catches and burns larger fuel particles that fall. Suspension-fired

326-621 O - 80 - 22 : QL 2

boilers are often large units, some capable of generating over 500,000 pounds of steam per hour.

Cyclonic Burners

Cyclonic furnaces also burn wood in suspension, but it must be dry (15 percent moisture content, wet basis) and sized (1/8-inch or less).

In the horizontally mounted cyclonic burner, a drumlike combustion chamber is closed at one end. Hot combustion gases are let out from the opening in the other end called the choke. Combustion air is forced by a blower through the air manifold into tuyeres, which admit the air.

The airflow pattern created is a double cyclonic action. Fuel is injected into the burner from the side with a stream of high velocity air. Fuel and air are mixed around the sides of the burner as they move toward the choke. Both the high turbulence of the cyclonic airflow and time in the burner contribute to complete combustion as long as proper temperatures are maintained.

Cyclonic burner and airflow pattern in cyclonic burner.

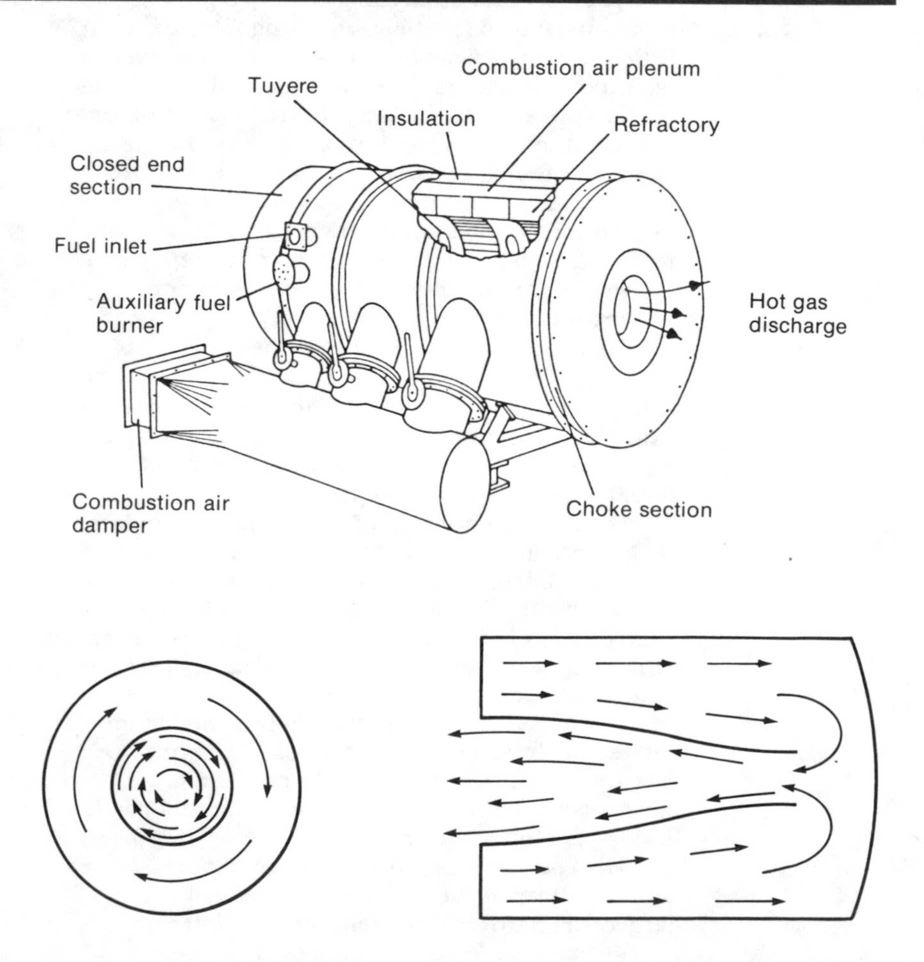

This type of burner can be used for direct firing — that is, heating with combustion gases instead of steam — lumber kilns, rotary and veneer dryers, and boilers.

Much wood available for burning is of low quality, that is, dirty, mixed with rock or metal, wet, and variable in size. Such wood can be burned effectively in a fluidized bed burner: within a bed of hot sand through which hot gases are passed.

The Jasper-Koch burner takes a new approach to suspension burning. The unit can burn wet wood or bark efficiently in a small furnace that costs less than grate-type furnaces of comparable capacity.

As already stated, bark or sawdust that is half water by weight burns very poorly and must be partially dried before it is burned. This drying can take place in a separate dryer before wood enters the burner, in a pile on the floor of the furnace combustion chamber, or in an integral dryer that passes through the burning zone. The Jasper-Koch burner works on the latter principle.

Huge Screw Forces Fuel to Bottom

In the Jasper-Koch design, the combustion chamber is a doughnut-shaped space between two concentric vertical cylinders; particulate fuel burns in suspension in this chamber. In the commercial prototype, a stainless steel inner cylinder 29 inches in diameter with walls ¼-inch thick houses a huge screw that forces fuel down into the bottom of the chamber. The outer stainless steel cylinder through which the upward-moving combustion gases travel is 49 inches in diameter and has walls ¼-inch thick. The fuel is partially dried (nearly ovendried) in its 15-minute trip from the fuel hopper to the combustion zone.

Surrounding the outer cylinder, along the entire 7-foot-high burning zone, is a heat exchanger that preheats air to about 500° F and forces it into the bottom of the burner. This air carries fuel particles upward into the combustion zone, where the temperature is about 1,600° F. A 30 horsepower blower is required for the preheated air to assure proper airflow and velocity.

The burner has neither grate nor fuel bed. Combustion occurs throughout a zone in which particles are suspended in the airstream. The outer cylinder is flared at the top of the combustion zone. Since the inner cylinder has constant diameter, the flare increases flow area for upward-moving combustion gases, slowing their velocity. This causes particulate matter (other than fine ash) to fall back into the burning zone so it continually recirculates until completely burned.

Because combustion temperatures do not exceed 1,800° F, neither the laboratory model nor the commercial prototype has formed slag. Ash formed during combustion is discharged upwards along with the hot combustion gases for later separation. The burner is equipped with a gas jet of one million Btu per hour capacity to facilitate startup.

Prospects for Future

Several driving forces will strongly influence the use of wood as industrial fuel. Currently built central utility plants that burn coal, gas, or oil generate about 800 megawatts, whereas the largest current wood-burning boilers are sized for about 50 megawatts. Even a 50 megawatt wood-fired boiler requires a substantial fuel procurement program. Thus it seems unlikely that wood will compete with coal in firing large-scale central utility plants in the future.

The forest products industry is the fourth largest consumer of purchased energy in the Nation (the petroleum, chemical, and primary metals industries are the three largest users), and purchases about 2 percent of the Nation's total energy use.

Although the forest products industry is only about 50 percent self-sufficient in energy, it is in a good position to achieve greater self-sufficiency by burning more wood and bark residues to replace or supplement purchased fossil fuels. Such action would free oil, natural gas, and coal for use elsewhere as a fuel or chemical feedstock. The forest products industry has experience in handling bulky wood materials and its mills are close to wood sources.

In past years, cull wood from the forest has not been harvested for use in mill power plants because harvest costs were high and gas, oil, and purchased electricity were cheap. Now that fuel oil costs about $1 a gallon, green fuel wood has a theoretical fuel value close to $40 per ton. The high cost of building and operating wood-fired boilers compared to gas- or oil-fired boilers prevents this theoretically equivalent price from being offered in the market place.

It seems likely, however, that a price of $20 per ton for green fuel wood delivered to a mill's fuel pile will be widely offered before the end of the 1980's. At this price, it will be profitable to harvest cull wood and logging slash from many forested sites for use as industrial fuel.

Turning Farm Wastes Into Usable Energy

By John I. Zerbe

Agricultural biomass (generally waste materials) may be converted to more concentrated forms of energy through various chemical processes. One of the most important of these processes is pyrolysis, which is a chemical change brought about by the action of heat.

Pyrolysis occurs when biomass is heated in the absence of air or with insufficient oxygen to provide for complete combustion. In the simplest form of pyrolysis, destructive distillation, biomass is heated in a retort to drive off condensible vapors and gases. The residue is charcoal.

The products of pyrolysis are variable, depending on heating rate and reaction temperatures attained. Wood structure differences also give rise to different pyrolysis products.

Biomass breaks down to form gases, liquids, and char when heated to about 500° C (932° F). Heat is generated in the process, and the outside heat required to dry the biomass and bring it up to the reaction temperature is less than 10 percent of the heat of combustion.

Biomass from wood and related materials is composed of three substances—lignin, hemicellulose, and cellulose. Each has a different chemical structure relating to their different functions in the living plant. The differences in structure also result in different compositions of liquids, gases, and char formed in pyrolysis.

The complex bond breaking and rearrangement processes that components of biomass undergo on pyrolysis lead not only to a variable product mix, but the relative proportions of liquid, gas, and char also show a high sensitivity to the rate of heating.

If wood, for example, is finely divided and rapidly heated, a higher proportion of gaseous products relative to char and liquid are produced. Conversely, slow heating of larger pieces of wood will produce a maximum of charcoal at the expense of gas and liquid.

JOHN I. ZERBE *is Program Manager, Energy Research, Development, and Application, Forest Products Laboratory, U.S. Forest Service, Madison, Wis.*

Gasification (the act of converting to gas) processes depend on modifying the pyrolysis process to produce maximum gas and minimum char and liquid. By some means, the char and liquid from pyrolysis of biomass are generally used to supply the process heat and increase gas yields.

The fuels may be used as a source of heat applied externally to the reactor. But usually the systems are autogenous (produced independent of external influence) with the char oxidation and gas generation taking place in the same reactor.

In the autogenous reactors, circulating air or oxygen may be used to provide the oxygen needed for char oxidation. Depending on the movement of air or oxygen relative to the bed of char, gasifiers (gas manufacturing apparatus) are classified as updraft, downdraft, or cross-flow.

Gasifiers may be either fixed bed or fluidized bed. In the fluidized bed, char is oxidized very rapidly in contact with inert material such as sand. The sand is kept in constant, turbulent motion by movement of gas through the bed.

Pyrolysis Systems

Pyrolysis systems in use or in the later stages of experimental development in the United States include 1) experimental vertical bed reactors, 2) industrial charcoal furnaces, 3) charcoal kilns, and 4) a flash pyrolysis system.

Charcoal retorts with heat supplied by external source were used in the United States up to July 1969.

The Tech-Air process was developed at Georgia Institute of Technology and demonstrated in a 45 metric tonne per day (50 tons per day) unit at Cordele, Ga. Fuel products generated were solid, liquid, and gaseous forms.

Basically, the system consists of steady flow, low temperature processing of biomass through a porous bed. An oil fuel product is condensed from vapors generated during pyrolysis. Similar processes are under development by others.

The Nichols-Herreshoff furnace process is widely used to manufacture barbecue charcoal in the United States. Furnace hearths are arranged with alternate vertical disk and doughnut shapes.

Material enters at the top and is reacted as it proceeds through the hearths. Gases are generated along with the charcoal. Normally the gases are burned off but they have also been used for fuel gas or burned for waste heat steam generation.

Kilns produce charcoal by using part of the charge for partial combustion to initiate carbonization of the remainder.

Earthen pit kilns were used in the United States and are still used in some developing countries. A later development is the brick beehive kiln.

A popular type of charcoal kiln in the United States today is the Missouri type. It is a reinforced concrete design, about 22 by 35 feet (6.71 by 10.7 meters) in plan, with an arched concrete roof and reinforced concrete floor cast in place.

The Occidental flash pyrolysis process was developed by the Occidental Research Company, a subsidiary of Occidental Petroleum. It provides for a short residence time flash pyrolysis that converts finely shredded wood waste into char, a combustible liquid, and a fuel gas.

Gasification Systems

Generator gas, producer gas, and low British thermal unit (Btu) gas are common terms applied to the output from simple vertical shaft gasifiers. Such gas has been produced from both coal and biomass for various applications for more than a century.

Use of generator gas, also known as gasogens, from biomass or charcoal has had widespread use as an internal combustion engine fuel in times of severe gasoline shortages.

During World War II many civilian vehicles in Europe were operated on gasogens, and studies of the possibilities for using this type fuel were conducted in many other parts of the world, including the United States. However, problems of power loss and maintenance caused these gas producers to be set aside as soon as gasoline became readily available.

In France, several manufacturers market gas generators today. Moteurs Duvant diesel-electric units can be operated on a combination of diesel and producer gas fuels. A number of such units are operating in the Ivory Coast and other parts of Africa. Others have been delivered and installed in Europe, the South Pacific, Asia, and Central America.

Imbert of Germany also has installed gasifier/ diesel power plants, and Powergas Corporation Limited, a British company, built many biomass gasifiers. Some may still be operating.

In the dual fuel installations, fuel intake is about 10 percent diesel fuel and 90 percent producer gas.

Distibois in Urchamps, France, has a large gas producer fueled with wood. It supplies gas for a 1,000-kilowatt, diesel-electric generator as well as charcoal for home heating.

Other suggested uses for producer gas are: boiler fuel, fueling gas turbines, direct heating dry or lime kilns, and as a feedstock for making methanol—sometimes called wood alcohol. Although many of these applications are promising, none have advanced beyond experimental stages.

Storage Potential

Generally, the conversion of solid biomass fuels to liquid, gaseous, and charcoal fuels provides new opportunities for storage and transportation of the final products. Deterioration of the raw materials, through fungal decay and heat generated in storage piles, is halted. Wet, bulky materials with low-heating value are usually transformed to more uniform and efficient fuels.

Charcoal has a better fuel value per unit weight than the raw material from which it is derived, but its weight per unit volume is reduced. Therefore its fuel density per unit volume may not be significantly increased. Nonetheless, deterioration during storage is avoided.

Because of its low fuel density, producer gas cannot be transported by pipeline or stored. But as a boiler fuel, it is more readily handled than solid fuels that require grates for combustion.

Pyrolysis oils have the shipping convenience of all liquid fuels. However, the oils are acidic and exhibit some corrosive properties. They must, therefore, be handled with acid-resistant equipment.

Marketing of fuels produced from pyrolysis and gasification is in competition with fossil fuels and direct burning of unmodified biomass.

For direct combustion requirements such as boiler fuel, home heating, or cooking requirements, burning biomass such as wood directly is usually more economical if the biomass does not need to be shipped more than 50 miles.

However, there are other reasons for using converted fuels. Charcoal is more convenient to use for cooking and imparts a desired flavor to barbecued meat. Liquid fuels are easier to use in boilers, especially for standby operation.

Liquid fuels from biomass pyrolysis and gasification are in more direct competition with liquid and gaseous fuels from petroleum and natural gas.

Pyrolysis Oil and Methanol Front Runners

Pyrolysis oil and methanol from synthesis gas are the front runners to substitute for fossil fuel liquids and gases, but other liquid fuels as products from pyrolysis and gasification are possible. In fact gasoline may be made from methanol, or more directly from synthesis gas.

When charcoal is produced as a coproduct with pyrolysis gas and oil, the gas and possibly the oil may be used for plant process energy and only the charcoal is marketed outside the plant.

Probably the most intriguing potential product from gasification to fill a large market is methanol. Conceivably, a large demand for methanol could occur if it were to be mixed with gasoline in the same way that ethanol is used to make gasohol.

If all the gasoline used in the United States were to be blended with a 10 percent addition of methanol, 1,242 million gallons of methanol per year (4,707 million liters) would be required. This is about 10 times the present U.S. production capacity for methanol.

Were this amount of methanol to be made from waste wood, it would require about 30,000 dry tons (27,200 metric tonnes) of wood per day, about as much as 30 moderate sized pulpmills.

A gasohol program in which methanol was used would require some components of the fuel system to be redesigned because methanol is more caustic than gasoline or ethanol.

Cost of producing methanol from wood was estimated in a study by Raphael Katzen and Associates in 1975, and the Katzen estimates were updated by Zerbe and Baker in March 1980. Costs calculated were $0.96 per gallon in 1975 and $1.16 per gallon in 1980 (see table).

Summary of fuel costs of methanol, gasohol, and gasoline

	Dollars per gallon			Dollars per million Btu		
	Methanol from wood	Gasohol	Gasoline	Methanol from wood	Gasohol	Gasoline
1975	0.96	—	0.50	14.16	—	4.17
1980 With subsidy	.68	1.25	1.20	10.03	10.78	10.00
No subsidy	1.10	1.00	1.20	17.11	11.31	10.00

In 1975 methanol from wood at $0.96 per gallon would have been competing with gasoline from petroleum at about $0.50 per gallon. Today methanol at $1.16 would compete with gasoline at about $1.20.

If methanol were to be used in 10 percent blends with gasoline to produce gasohol, the $1.16 price could be reduced further by $0.40 for the Federal gasoline tax credit and by $0.08 for investment tax credit and entitlement credit. The selling price for methanol would then be $0.68 per gallon. Selling price for the gasohol would be $1.25 per gallon.

Energy Balance

Raw materials considered for biomass pyrolysis and gasification are generally materials such as waste wood, urban wastes, rice hulls, coconut shells, and walnut shells. This is in contrast to food crops such as corn, grain, and potatoes, often used as a source of fermentation ethanol.

The waste materials do not incur fossil fuel consumption to provide energy for cultivation and fertilization that agricultural crops do. Therefore, the energy balances in displacement of fossil fuels for producing fuels through pyrolysis and gasification are generally better than for producing fuels through fermentation.

Overall efficiencies for pyrolysis and gasification processes can conceivably attain 85 to 90 percent, but this requires complete utilization of the char, oil, and gas produced. Moreover, the gas must be used without significant cooling from the temperature at which it leaves the generator.

If a ton of dry wood with a total energy content of 17 million Btus (17.9 million joules) produces 670 pounds (304 kilograms) of charcoal as the sole product, with a total energy content of 8.38 million Btus (8.84 trillion joules), overall efficiency of this process is 49.3 percent.

With present technology, if it could be successfully applied in a commercial plant, it is estimated that a ton of wood could yield 647 pounds (294 kg) of methanol for a total heat value of 6.33 million Btus (6.68 trillion joules). Overall efficiency of the methanol from wood process is 37.2 percent.

Application on Farms

Operating pyrolysis and gasification units provides an outlet for agricultural wastes such as rice hulls, walnut shells, and wheat straw. Farm woodlots might also be a major source of fuel for these plants. The wood generally would be available to keep plants operating year-round, whereas crop residues are usually generated seasonally and may need to be stored for the remainder of the year to allow plant production throughout the year.

Generally, the pyrolysis and gasification plants would be larger than required for farm use, but there are some potential applications of smaller gasification units of farms.

In the future, gasogens might be used to operate stationary engines for such purposes as irrigation pumps and, as in the past, producer gas might even be used for tractors and other vehicles. Direct-coupled gas producers may also be used to generate a substitute fuel for oil and natural gas for use in small boilers.

Additional information may be obtained from the following sources:

Agricultural Engineering Department, Purdue University, West Lafayette, IN 47907. Battelle — Northwest, P.O. Box 999, Richland, WA 99352. Department of Agricultural Engineering, University of California — Davis, Davis, CA 95616.

Also, Department of Chemical Engineering, Texas Tech University, Lubbock, TX 79409. Division of Forestry, Tennessee Valley Authority, Knoxville, TN 37902. Energy From Wood Program, Forest Products Laboratory, P.O. Box 5130, Madison, WI 53705.

Also, Georgia Institute of Technology, Engineering Experiment Station, Room 1512-A, C&S Building, 33 North Avenue, Atlanta, GA 30332. ME Department, University of Missouri-Rolla, Rolla, MO 65401. Solar Energy Rsearch Institute, 1536 Cole Boulevard, Golden, CO 80401.

Further Reading:

Chemicals From Wood Waste, Raphael Katzen, Allan E. Hokanson, et al., PB-262-489, for sale from National Technical Information Service, U.S. Department of Commerce, 5285 Port Royal Road, Springfield, VA 22161. $14.

Updated Cost Comparisons of Alcohol Fuels, John I. Zerbe and Andrew J. Baker, Forest Products Laboratory, Box 5130, Madison, WI 53705. Free.

Capturing and Storing Energy From the Sun

By Charles K. Spillman

Current interest in solar energy is not the first time people have been excited about its potential. Reportedly, the first flat-plate collector appeared in 1774. It consisted of a wooden box with three layers of glass that heated air to 140° F. By the turn of this century, development had progressed to the point that efficiencies were about as good as they are today.

Other sources of energy were more economical and convenient to use, so there was little incentive to put solar energy to work. But the finite supply of fossil fuels is now recognized, and we must prepare for the time when their cost may be much higher. An added benefit of solar energy would be reduced pollution, which will become more important as population increases.

The first consideration for any application is to reduce the energy requirement to the point where the economics of using solar collecting equipment is more favorable than investing in energy conservation measures. Most homes were constructed when fuel was plentiful and extemely cheap, so investment in solar heating and cooling should be thought about only after adequate weatherization.

The real cost of energy delivered from solar systems may range from the equivalent of $1 up to $10 per gallon of propane. At these levels, many energy conserving improvements will be economical. There is another payoff for weatherizing homes: they will be more comfortable because cold drafty conditions are reduced.

Equipment Can Prove Expensive

Energy from the sun is free, but equipment for collection, storage, and use can be expensive. A number of factors are involved in determining how much can be invested for a solar collecting system but the first cost of the equipment and the amount of energy that can be effectively used during its practical life are most important. The energy that can be used is determined by the solar energy available, ability of

CHARLES K. SPILLMAN *is Professor, Department of Agricultural Engineering, Kansas State University.*

the collector to deliver energy, and whether that energy can be put to work or stored at the time it is collected.

An application such as water heating requires energy on a regular basis throughout most of the year, so more money can be invested in reliable, efficient hardware. Grain drying requires very large amounts of low-quality energy during a short period of time, so the system must be inexpensive or used for other applications during the rest of the year.

Investing in a solar collector depends to a great extent on tax credits granted by a State. With limitations, the Federal income tax credit of 25 percent plus the State tax credit in some States will now pay for up to 55 to 75 percent of the investment in solar equipment — which makes many solar systems economical.

Grain drying usually requires large amounts of low quality energy for short periods. This experimental tube-type solar collector at Manhattan, Kans., passes air from the drying fan (foreground) to the drying bin (background).

J. VALBUENA

Solar energy collecting systems often are classified as either active or passive. In active systems a fan or pump moves the working fluid or air through the collector. The fan or pump is turned on or off depending on whether the working fluid temperature is high enough to provide heat for storage or a process.

In passive systems the working fluid moves because of difference in density (hot air or hot water moves up and cold air or cold water moves down) or where the energy is moved by radiation or conduction heat transfer. Passive systems sometimes are defined as those where only a small amount of energy from fossil origin is used for moving the collected energy, for example one unit from fossil origin to 50 units derived from solar.

A system that combines both active and passive features is sometimes called a hybrid system and some authors classify this as a third type.

Photovoltaic collectors convert sunlight into direct current electrical energy but that method of energy collection is very expensive and used only for special purposes such as providing a small amount of energy for remote communications equipment and powering space vehicles. Therefore, this discussion is limited to applications where the function is to convert solar energy into heat energy.

Active Systems

Focusing collectors and flat-plate collectors are used for heating applications. Focusing collectors have a large area for entry of solar radiation that is then reflected onto a receiver. The entry area must be positioned so it sees the sun. This requires some type of mechanism to move the collector assembly during the day, which increases the cost of the collector.

High temperatures can be attained by focusing collectors. But most applications for heat in residences and farm service buildings can make use of energy gathered with flat-plate collectors.

Many different types of flat-plate collectors are being used or under development for putting solar energy to work in homes, farm service buildings, and agricultural processes. They range from simple systems costing very little to incorporate in the design of a new building, to more expensive equipment where cost is so high that the system would be economical only if conventional energy expenses increase.

Examples of inexpensive, simple systems are transparent roofs on farm service buildings for heating air to dry grain, or south-facing windows on residences that allow solar energy to be trapped inside. Complete systems for heating water may have an installed cost of $50 or more per square foot of collecting area.

Active systems are generally regarded as more complicated than passive systems, but a process such as grain drying can use a simple collector and maybe only one thermostat. Besides, passive systems can become complicated when controls and equipment are used to restrict natural air movement or when movable insulation is incorporated into the design. The prospective user should keep in mind that it is best to use as simple a system as possible that will provide heat for the user's needs.

Flat-plate collectors may be designed for operating only a few degrees above the outside temperature for uses such as grain drying. Those required to provide heat to a residence during winter may be designed for operating at a temperature differential of 100° F or more. Generally, cost of a flat-plate collector rises as the operating temperature differential increases.

The typical active system consists of a collector assembly, an energy storage unit, a control system, and two energy transport systems — one between the collector and storage and another between the storage and the process requiring heat.

Some vendors provide complete systems while others offer components that can be used to make up a complete system. Choosing between them depends on the type of process involved and abilities of the individual or contractor installing the system. Competent assistance should be found when planning a components system, because each component must be sized correctly to work with other parts of the system.

Backup System Needed

A backup heating system is needed because there are cloudy periods when solar energy cannot provide the necessary heat. The control system is quite important because it must be able to sense when heat can be added to storage, removed from storage, or when the backup furnace is required.

All these functions must work automatically because the typical user will not be present or may not be inclined to provide the manual controls needed to make the system work effectively.

The flat-plate collector for an active system consists of one or more of the following: 1) An absorber plate 2) A transparent cover or covers 3) Insulation behind the absorber plate 4) A box to contain the parts 5) An inlet and outlet to let the working fluid pass. The working fluid can be either liquid or air.

The bare-plate collector is used where low temperature differentials are adequate. Adding a transparent cover above the absorber allows a higher temperature to be maintained because heat loss from the absorber is reduced. A second transparent cover can be added to obtain even higher temperatures.

The absorber plate is generally made of sheet metal, or a flat surface of other material, and painted black to absorb the sun's rays. Flat black paint used for absorbers in high temperature collectors should be capable of operating at temperatures to 300° F, and possibly higher, without damage.

The absorber plate must serve to transfer absorbed solar heat to the working fluid. Fins protruding into the air may be added to the absorber, giving more surface area to transfer heat. With the liquid-type collector, the distance between liquid tubes determines how well heat can be transferred.

The weight of material in an absorber plate influences the time it takes to heat up before the working fluid can be circulated. Heavy plates require more time to heat up than light plates. During intermittent cloudiness, the plate might not heat up before a cloud cuts off solar energy. Then the heated plate would cool down while waiting for another period of sunshine.

Insulation Important

An exposed hot surface quickly loses heat, so the back side of the absorber must be insulated. Insulation between the absorber and the back of the collector box should be stable at high temperatures. Some insulations have organic materials in them that break down at high temperatures.

Liquid-type flat plate collectors.

Bare plate collector

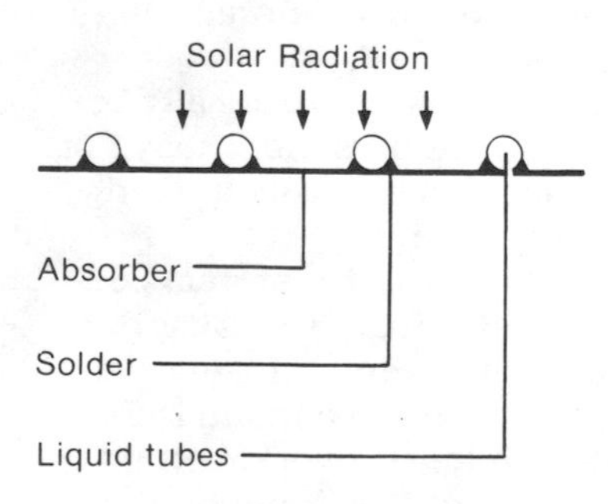

Serpentine tube pattern

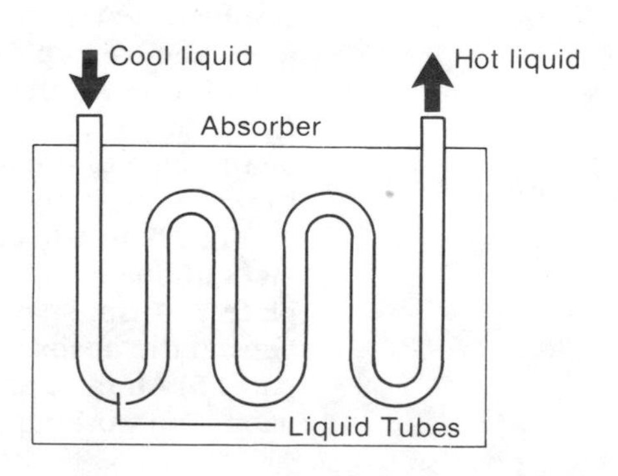

Vapor may deposit particulate matter on the inside of the transparent cover. This could make the collector useless until a new transparent cover is installed.

Features to reduce heat loss from the sides and ends of the collector should be incorporated into the box for the absorber plate. Collector boxes need to be sealed to exclude water, and strong enough to resist the loads imposed on them by wind and snow. Pipes or ducts entering or leaving the collector box should be insulated to reduce heat loss.

Glass has been commonly used as a transparent cover for collectors, but some plastics have desirable characteristics. Low-iron and plate glass are recommended because they absorb less solar energy than ordinary glass. The glass surface can be treated to reduce reflection, increasing transmitted energy.

Plastics are being used in many applications because construction of frames is not so critical and most plastics are somewhat less expensive than glass. Plastics resist impact stresses better than glass and generally transmit as much or more solar radiation. However, plastics generally allow more thermal energy loss than glass.

Care should be taken in selection to get plastic resistant to ultraviolet rays in sunlight and to the high temperatures encountered. The plastic should not retain a static charge which would attract dust.

Fans or pumps for moving the working fluid between the collector and storage need to be capable of long term, efficient operation. Ducts and pipes should be sealed and insulated; the amount of insulation recommended depends on the temperature difference between the working fluid and the surrounding air. Liquid leaks in pipes can be easy to spot, but air leaks in ducts present a problem because they aren't easily detected.

The control system needs to make decisions for operation of components and to be as simple as possible but still adequate to control all the aspects of operation. Where possible, users should understand the system so as to recognize when service is required or make their own adjustments and repairs.

Passive Systems

Passive solar systems are generally simple and low in cost for the quantity of heat added. Most are operated with a minimum of controls designed into the system, but may require manual adjustment.

Careful design may be required to obtain reasonably stable temperatures in the environmental space. Overheating or very cool conditions can result if the right combination of glazing and storage are not provided.

326-621 O - 80 - 23 : QL 2

The four main types of passive solar systems are direct gain, thermal storage wall, attached sun space, and convective loop.

The direct gain system uses south-facing transparent walls, or windows, that allow solar radiation to enter directly into the environmental space that is to be heated. A part of the solar radiation is absorbed by the floor and a part reflected onto the walls and ceiling where it is absorbed.

The absorbed radiation is converted to thermal energy (heat). Some of it goes to heat up the storage material and some is lost by convection to the air which comes in contact with the floor and walls.

Movable insulation to reduce heat loss through the transparent cover at night increases overall thermal performance of this system.

The direct gain system is effective for south-facing surfaces because of the sun's low position in the sky during winter months. In summer when the sun is at a higher position in the sky, the glazed area can be shaded by overhang on the structure, awnings, or deciduous trees.

Advantages of the direct gain system are that it is one of the least expensive, simplest solar systems and can function without constructing a storage component in cases where the floor or wall can be used.

Disadvantages are degradation of fabrics and other materials in the room by ultraviolet radiation in the sunlight, temperature swings in the room which can be quite high unless thermal storage is carefully designed, the need for movable insulation to reduce heat loss through the glazing at night, and too much glare which can occur in the room during the day.

Thermal Siphon

The convective loop system has an absorbing surface placed behind the transparent cover on the south wall. This surface converts the sun's rays to heat energy that heats up the air and causes a thermal siphon effect. Cool air from the room flows up past the absorber where it is heated, and then exhausts near the ceiling. A small collector can be effective at heating a room during daytime, but there is limited storage and the room will cool off quickly at night.

Air movement caused by the thermosiphon would not be very effective at adding heat to massive walls inside the room. Thus one must be careful not to have too large a collector. At night, reverse thermal circulation can occur since the cold glass near the absorber cools it and will cause cool air to exist in the space between them which sets up a reverse circulation process. This should be prevented by closing off the loop at night.

Advantages of the convective loop system are that glare and ultraviolet degradation of fabrics are not problems, it is relatively inexpensive, it can be readily added to existing buildings, and night heat losses can be lower for other types of passive design. Disadvantages are that careful engineering and construction are required to insure proper airflow, prevent overheating, and assure adequate thermal isolation at night.

The thermal storage wall typically is a masonry wall with the south-facing side painted black to absorb solar radiation. The wall has one or two transparent covers. During the day, the south face of the wall is heated and starts the process of conducting heat through the wall. A so-called temperature wave moves through the concrete, causing the inside surface to be the warmest a few hours after sundown.

With thermal storage walls, glare and ultraviolet degradation of fabrics is not a problem, the temperature swing in adjacent living space is much lower, and designs are becoming available for allowing the proper sizing of units for homes. Disadvantages are the increased cost of constructing the wall, the space it occupies, and the amount of heat lost to the outside at night unless movable insulation is used.

Greenhouses, or similar structures called attached sunspaces, can be attached to new or existing buildings. The greenhouse is heated during the day and this warm air can be added to adjacent living space to reduce heat requirements.

A massive thermal storage wall can be used to absorb some of the solar radiation directly and transmit it to the adjacent living space and greenhouse during nighttime hours. The wall can reduce the amount of overheating that occurs in the greenhouse during daytime.

The sunspace acts as a buffer zone to reduce heat loss at night from the building to the outdoors. Advantages of the attached sunspace are that it provides smaller temperature swings in adjacent living space, reduces heat loss from adjacent living space to the outside, and is readily adaptable to existing buildings. Disadvantages are that thermal performance varies greatly from one design to another, making performance difficult to predict, and cost can be quite high if commercial buildings are used.

Storage systems

Solar energy is received during the day and some type of storage system is required to allow that heat to be available at night. The two basic mechanisms for storing energy are to use sensible heat capacity of materials and to use the latent heat of fusion (heat given up during a change in phase from liquid to solid states).

Sensible heat capacity of a material is the amount of energy it takes to heat a unit of material. For example, it takes 1 British thermal unit (Btu) of energy to increase the temperature of 1 pound of water by 1° F. It takes about 5 pounds of rocks or concrete to store as much energy as 1 pound of water.

Even though water has the highest sensible heat storage capacity, rocks and concrete have advantages in applications such as air-type collectors and passive solar applications. Data in the table show the quantity of rocks or water required to store 500,000 Btu's of energy. This amount of energy would be equivalent to the heat produced by burning 7 to 8 gallons of propane.

Thermal energy storage properties and requirements to store 500,000 Btu's with a 30° F change in temperature.

	Rocks	Water	Phase-change material
Specific heat capacity, Btu per lb per degree F	0.2	1.0	0.5 (ave.)
Heat of fushion, Btu's per lb	—	—	100 (ave.)
Density. lbs per cu ft	90	62	100
Storage of 500,000 Btu's			
Weight, lbs	88,500	16,670	4,350
Volume, cu ft	930	270[1]	55[2]

[1] 2,000 gallons.
[2] An additional 25% for passage of air is added to volume.

Density of a material is the weight of that material that can be put in a box which is 1 foot in all three dimensions.

Multiplying the specific heat capacity by the density gives the volumetric heat capacity of a material. The volumetric heat capacity of water would be 62 while that for rocks would be 18 Btu's per cubic foot per degree Fahrenheit of temperature change. Thus water has a volumetric heat capacity over three times as great as for rocks.

Materials that change from liquid to solid at a temperature of around 90° F are being developed for the phase-change process, because large quantities of energy can be stored in a relatively small space. When water changes from liquid to solid (forms ice), 144 Btu's per pound of heat (the latent heat for fusion) are given up. Obviously, water cannot be used as a phase-change material in solar heating applications because 32° F is much too low to provide comfort.

Glauber's salt — sodium sulfate decahydrate — melts and freezes at 90° F and is one material being used for phase-change storages.

Considerable work is being done on these phase change materials because large quantities of heat can be stored in a small space.

Phase-change material properties shown in the table are characteristic of those being used or considered for applications with solar systems. It takes four times the weight and five times the volume for water to store the same quantity of heat as this typical phase-change material. That has obvious advantages for retrofit applications because much less space is required to provide heat storage.

Rocks, Water Are Common Materials

Most energy storage systems that have been installed to date use the specific heat capacity of materials for storage. Rocks and water are both common materials and storage structures can be purchased or easily built.

An insulated steel tank is commonly used for liquid storage systems. Underground concrete tanks have been used for some larger systems, and fiber glass tanks for a number of smaller ones. Materials used to construct the tanks should be compatible with any chemical treatment the water requires.

Designs of a storage tank for water should allow for temperature stratification in the tank. This means hot water can be added to or removed from the top of the tank, and cold water can be added or removed from the bottom.

The void space between rocks in a storage allows passage of air. The rocks must be small enough so there is adequate surface area to allow heat transfer from the working fluid, air, to the rocks but large enough so the passageways allow easy movement of the working fluid. Rocks with an average diameter of 1 to 2 inches are usually recommended.

Rocks and packaged, phase-change materials are commonly used for air-type collectors. Packages for phase-change materials must be designed so there is adequate surface area for transfer of energy into or out of the unit.

All heat storage units — liquid, solid, or phase-change — must be insulated whether in the building, outside, or underground.

Reflectors

Reflecting surfaces can be positioned so they increase the amount of solar energy arriving at a collector. The correct position for a reflector depends on orientation of the collector and the season of the year during which it will be used. No general rule of thumb can be used to estimate the increase in collected energy because the changing position of the sun with the seasons affects the direction where solar energy is reflected.

The increase in collected solar energy per dollar invested in a reflector should be greater than from additional investment in collectors.

A computer simulation has been used to predict the increase in energy collected by a south-wall solar collector installed on a farrowing house in Kansas. A white-painted refector in front of the collector and extending out as far as the collector is high (8 feet) increases collected solar energy by 15 to 16 percent. However, not all the reflected energy can be effectively used during spring and fall, so the net increase is only about 12 percent. Experimental testing has shown the computer simulation approximately correct for this Kansas location.

Information Sources

The prospective user should spend some time learning about solar energy technology. Another method is to enlist a good consultant, but the number of experienced technical personnel is limited and most are quite busy.

Sources for further study are textbooks and publications from State and Federal agencies, industrial associations, and companies selling components or complete systems. The National Solar Heating and Cooling Information Center, P.O. Box 1607, Rockville, MD 20850 provides a broad range of general information about solar energy.

Most State energy offices have personnel assigned to provide assistance on solar energy that is applicable to local conditions. They would be helpful in locating engineers and architects.

The Cooperative Extension Service provides publications and educational programs for agricultural applications. They will have plans available as they are developed.

Further Reading:

Direct Use of the Sun's Energy, Farrington Daniels, Random House, 400 Hahn Road, Westminster, MD 21157. $2.50, plus $1 postage and handling.

Low Temperature and Solar Grain Drying Handbook, MWPS-22, Midwest Plan Service, 122 Davidson Hall, Iowa State University, Ames, IA 50011. $3.

Passive Solar Design Handbook, Volume 1: Passive Solar Design Concepts, DOE-CS-0127 Vol. 1, for sale from National Technical Information Service, 5285 Port Royal Road, Springfield, VA 22161. $19.

Publications Catalog, National Solar Heating and Cooling Information Center, P.O. Box 1607, Rockville, MD 20850. Free.

Solar Energy Systems, Copper Development Association, Inc., 405 Lexington Avenue, New York, NY 10017. Free.

Sun Up to Sun Down, Shawn Buckley, McGraw-Hill Book Company, Princeton Road, Hightstown, NJ 08520. $6.95.

Warm Water Solar System Brings Greenhouse Saving

By W. J. Roberts and D. R. Mears

A Rutgers solar greenhouse heating system has been successfully demonstrated in a 1.3 acre greenhouse at Kube Pak in Allentown, N.J. The greenhouse is gutter connected with ten 20-foot bays, each 290 feet long.

Two layers of 4 mil polyethylene film separated by a small inflation blower are used to cover the greenhouse.

Heart of the system is the floor, which serves as warm water storage and primary heat exchanger.

The water is contained by a 20 mil biocide treated vinyl swimming pool liner, which is filled with approximately 9 inches of ¾-inch gravel or stone and capped with a 3-inch layer of porous concrete.

The floor composite is capable of holding a maximum of 4 gallons per cubic foot in the area between the vinyl liner and the lower edge of the

WILLIAM ROBERTS *is Chairman and* David Mears *is Professor in the Biological and Agricultural Engineering Department at Cook College, Rutgers University.*

porous concrete cap. Storage capacity of the greenhouse floor is about 100,000 gallons.

Porous concrete has been used by commercial growers for many years when they are producing crops directly on the floor of the greenhouse. This provides a solid weed-free surface which allows excess irrigation water to pass through it, eliminating low wet spots which would seriously damage the crop at that location.

The concrete is made by mixing 2,700 pounds of .375 aggregate, 5.5 bags of cement, and 22 gallons of water per cubic yard. It is handled the same as regular concrete except that it is only screeded and not troweled. Principal difference is the absence of sand in the mix.

Water is pumped from the storage pumping pit to the collectors through 6-inch PVC pipe which is connected to each of the five collectors through two 1.5-inch headers drilled with 7/32 holes spaced on 6-inch centers.

Water flows down over the surface of the black plastic layer and is collected in a gutter at the bottom of the collector. The gutters drain into a covered flume and the water flows by gravity back to the greenhouse floor and is distributed throughout the greenhouse.

The 7.5 horsepower pump is controlled by a sensing device located in the solar collector which measures temperature difference between water in the floor storage and the collector. When the temperature difference is greater than 10° F, the pump starts. When the temperature difference falls to 4° F, the pump stops, and water in the collectors drains back into the storage so there is no freezing problem.

The solar collectors operate in the 40 to 60 percent efficiency range at temperatures of 68° to 85° F. The high efficiency is realized because the collectors operate at low temperatures and losses from the collector are minimized. Data recorded indicates that on a good day the equivalent of 80 to 90 gallons of oil are collected (from the 10,000 square feet of solar collectors) and stored in the floor.

When insufficient solar energy is available to warm the floor, the auxiliary heating system is activated. Two 60 horsepower boilers provide hot water to the heat exchanger located in the return flume. Water is pumped through the floor system and heated as it passes over the heat exchanger in the return flume. This process is controlled by a capillary bulb thermostat located in the rock-water section of the floor.

The boilers also supply hot water to a pipe loop located under the greenhouse gutters to provide maximum snow melting potential in extreme snow situations. The gutters must be kept ice and snow free in this type of structure. The pipe loops also provide the last stage of heating for the greenhouse in extreme cold weather.

A system previously designed for greenhouses to control day length for chrysanthemum production has been modified and is being used as an energy saving system.

A horizontal blanket is drawn across the greenhouse at night to enclose the crop and the floor heating system. Temperature measurements indicate that the aluminized blanket will reduce heat loss from the greenhouse by a factor of two. In the morning, the blanket is withdrawn and stored in a narrow band parallel to the gutters to minimize shading in the greenhouse. The blanket is automated and operated by a time clock.

The blanket is supported by a series of monofilament plastic cables and powered by a steel cable system which is spaced 10 feet on centers. As the blanket is closed in the evening, the leading edge intercepts a hanging section of the curtain in an adjacent bay to form an airtight seal.

Several blanketing materials have been tested and a woven polyester fabric, which is aluminized on one side, has been the most successful to date. This woven fabric allows condensation — Which forms on the roof of the greenhouse and drips on the closed blanket — to pass through. Earlier materials, which were solid, did not allow this to happen and large pools of water formed on the blanket which was not acceptable.

Crop response to date has been very favorable. Five crops have been grown in the solar heated section — three spring bedding plant crops and two fall poinsettia crops. Effect of the warm floor has been dramatic in crop response and in reducing energy requirements.

Temperature at Night Cut by 10 Degrees

It has been possible to reduce the night ambient temperature as much as 10° F with some bedding plants with no decrease in plant response or timeliness. The warm floor maintains the proper root temperature without having to maintain the entire greenhouse at an elevated temperature. The floor heating system also maintained a higher temperature at the poinsettia plant canopy than at the 6-foot level.

It was also learned that spring bedding plants could be planted as much as three weeks later and

View of greenhouse showing energy saving blanket in partially closed position.

still be ready for sale because the crop responded so well to the warm soil temperature.

Effect of root temperature on flowering plants has not been determined, but response from most vegetative growth has been dramatic. This is not altogether unexpected since plants grown on greenhouse benches equipped with under-bench heat have shown the same response. Heretofore, growers in greenhouses with no benches, growing on the floor, have had to maintain higher night temperatures than necessary to ensure that root temperatures would be adequate.

The demonstration project has been very successful. Growers are happy with the results and have applied several of the developed and tested to the remainder of their facility.

The combination of the blanketing system, the advantage of the warm floor, and the solar collector has reduced energy consumption by 70 percent compared to a similar greenhouse without any of these features. These are average results for the overall project.

Specific data for the fall 1979 poinsettia crop indicated that 640 million British thermal units (Btu's) were required for the season. of this 640 million Btu's, 340 million Btu's were supplied by the solar system. Projected use for a similar section without the features mentioned would be 2,280 million Btu's. With the solar system, the fossil fuel requirement would be only 300 million Btu's or a savings of 87 percent.

The greatest saving is in the blanketing system and in the strategic use of the warm floor. The solar system provided about half of the energy required.

Present costs of the installation of this solar system indicate a payback of about six years. The blanketing system will pay for itself in less than two years and should be a consideration for every greenhouse producer.

The warm floor concept is valid for crops requiring very little or no hand labor. Crops which require hand operations should be grown on elevated movable benches to reduce labor requirements and increase growing space within the greenhouse.

Rock Storage Solar System Saves Greenhouse Energy

By R. Scaffidi and C. Vinten-Johanson

Several years ago labor was the most costly input to grow greenhouse crops. And, of course, the main interest became automation to replace labor. Now fuel costs have surpassed labor costs and attention has switched to reducing those fuel costs.

This chapter describes a small commercial nursery located in the Washington, D.C., area featuring a solar energy air collection system and a rock storage unit used to both heat and cool. The authors designed and supervised building of the "heat sink" greenhouse.

Objective of the project was to design a simple active heating system to supply a substantial amount of the annual heating load without economic penalties resulting from oversizing the building.

Several modes of operation were incorporated in the system to determine minimum design standards

RICKY SCAFFIDI, *who has a B.S. in ecology, is project designer, builder, and part owner of the solar greenhouse described here. Christian Vinten-Johanson has a B.S. in agricultural engineering, and is now attending graduate school at Penn State. He was involved in setting design criteria and predicting performance of the greenhouse.*

for solar greenhouses. With this information one can determine maximum fuel savings for the least amount of money.

Contents of the greenhouse act as a collector (framework, plants, cement floor, etc.) and the energy is collected and transferred from these items to the air. In addition, the air can pass through a second collector made of aluminum cans located inside the greenhouse.

The rock storage, located underground, is split in two units. Either unit can be shut off from the system. Thus a minimum storage size can be determined. Pressure drop through the rock storage in this case was large enough to provide an even air distribution in the rock storage.

Solar Gardens faces south and the entire greenhouse acts as a solar collector. In winter, heated air rises to the greenhouse peak. From there it passes through an aluminum can collector and is pulled down the north wall and into the rock storage.

Air can be drawn from outside or recirculated inside the greenhouse to provide for winter heating and summer cooling.

In winter, air inside the greenhouse is heated and rises to the peak. The air has two choices: To pass through a second collector made of aluminum cans, then continue down the north wall. Or to bypass the second collector and flow down the north wall.

The north wall is constructed of 2 X 2 joists with 6 inches of insulation and a 6-inch air space to provide a duct for the hot air. Air enters an air chamber at the end of the north wall and is pulled by two ¼ horsepower fans into another air chamber located in the center of the floor.

WM. CARNAHAN

The two fans create a positive air pressure and forces the hot air through the rock storage and back into the greenhouse. At night the collector is shut off by dampers, and a thermal blanket is drawn across the plexiglass. To maximize heat gain from the rock storage the fans are reversed. Heat is transferred from the rock storage to the greenhouse and cycled back to the rock storage in a closed loop.

Rick Scaffidi, part owner of "Solar Gardens" in Silver Spring, Md., waters plants in his "heat sink" greenhouse.

WM. CARNAHAN

In summer, the collector is shut off. During the day, hot air rises to the peak and is exhausted through the ceiling vents. Warm air at the bench level is cycled through the rock storage, cooled, and exhausted back into the greenhouse. Heat captured by the rock storage during the day is exhausted outside the greenhouse at night.

A cooperative Research Agreement with the U.S. Department of Agriculture to test performance of the solar greenhouse commenced during the summer of 1980. The test results will provide information for designing solar greenhouses that are economically competitive with conventional greenhouses.

Windpower Can Save Your Energy Dollars

By Herschel H. Klueter

Once almost every farm in the Midwest and other parts of the United States had at least one windmill. Many had several. Between 1840 and 1940, an estimated 6.5 million windmills were sold in this country. They were used primarily to pump water for livestock and the home.

The windmill provided water to cattle that grazed the Plains and eventually led to the settling of the West.

Many of these "water pumps" still operate in remote areas on large ranches.

A second major use of the windmill was for generating electricity.

The electricity generated was stored in batteries and used in the home for lights, and a few small electrical appliances and motors. Simple windmill systems proved adequate for the required tasks, until the availability of central station power distribution by public utilities to rural areas in the 1930's and 1940's.

This made possible an abundant, reliable, and inexpensive supply of electricity. One requirement for converting to a utility was that there be no other power sources to compete with them. So for the most part the windmills were abandoned and left to rust.

The current energy shortage has opened a renewed interest in wind as a source of energy. Considerable effort has been expended by the Department of Energy (DOE), the U.S. Department of Agriculture (USDA), other agencies and private companies to develop and evaluate the technical and economic feasibility of wind as a source of energy. USDA has been given the task of assessing the wind energy potential in agriculture and developing techniques for using that energy.

Thrust of the initial work was to identify areas in agriculture where wind energy could most likely have a sizable impact on energy use. Four criteria were

HERSCHEL H. KLUETER *is Research Agricultural Engineer, Agricultural Equipment Laboratory, Plant Physiology Institute, Science and Education Administration-Agricultural Research.*

used to evaluate possible uses of wind energy.

These were:

- Is it a major use of energy?
- Is it used over a considerable portion of the year?
- Does it have the capability of inherent energy storage?
- Is it located in an area of reasonably high wind?

Three areas stand out as likely for wind energy use: irrigation, heating of buildings, and product processing and storage. It is unlikely that any one of these uses will make the wind turbine economically feasible. It will take several uses in sequence throughout the year. One such sequence might be irrigation, in spring and summer, crop drying in fall, and either residential or livestock heating in winter.

Electrical Grid Tie-In

One difficulty with multiple use of a wind turbine is that all the loads will not likely be the same. Irrigation takes considerably more energy than either crop drying or heating. Typical irrigation requirements are 40 to 100 kilowatts (kW), while heating and drying run 10 to 40 kW. This problem can be overcome by having an electrical output that ties into the electric utility power system. Any excess electricity produced by the wind turbine can be fed back into the electrical grid.

An extra benefit from using windpower with the electrical grid can be achieved if storage is available. This could provide some load management of the electrical demand. An example is a dairy operation with both an ice builder (for milk cooling) and hot water storage. When wind energy is adequate, storage of energy for three days use could be provided.

With this storage capability, even if the wind did not blow, the refrigeration and heating could be turned on during nonpeak load periods between midnight and 6 a.m. to provide enough ice and hot water for that day. The refrigeration-heating system could then be locked out for the peak demand period for the utility. The wind turbine could also supply electricity back to the grid at peak demand. Numerous other possibilities exist if the right wind turbine can be found.

There are two basic classifications of wind turbines. These are horizontal axis and vertical axis. The difference is in the position of the rotating axis. There are various configurations within both of these.

1) **Horizontal Axis.** Among the horizontal axis wind turbines frequently seen are the American multiblade, the multibladed bicycle, the 4-bladed Dutch and the high speed 2 and 3 blade propeller type.

Of these the 2 to 3 blade high speed is the most appropriate for modern use as a wind turbine. It has high efficiency in high wind regions where the high energy is available. Sizes of rated output from less than a kilowatt to 2.5 megawatts are being made and tested. This type turbine will probably provide the major portion of the windpower produced.

The other types of horizontal axis turbines may have some applications, but they will be limited to small size and relatively low wind areas.

2) **Vertical Axis.** The two types of vertical axis wind turbines are the Darrieus and Savonius, both named after their inventors.

The Darrieus is a 2 or 3 bladed low-solidity, high-speed turbine that looks like an egg beater. It has characteristics similar to the high-speed horizontal axis turbine with two major exceptions. The Darrieus is not self starting; it requires some type of motor to start it. However, it is somewhat less complicated, since the turbine itself is a major part of the tower. Turbines up to 500 kW are under development and test.

A variation of the Darrieus is the Giromill, which has extra gearing to keep the turbine blade at maximum angle of attack (power) during the power part of the rotation. The blade is then turned to provide least resistance for the return.

Both the Darrieus and the Giromill offer good possibilities for considerable use in generating wind power. On the other hand, the Savonius has severe limitations in both size and the windspeed in which it will operate.

Energy output from these major types of wind turbines is rotary, which can be converted to mechanical, or either AC or DC Electric. A number of companies are currently developing and producing a variety of wind machines. Check your local public library for a classified directory listing wind generator manufacturers.

Availability of Wind

One of the major criteria for having a feasible wind energy system is the amount and distribution of the wind. The wind varies extremely from day to day and even from moment to moment. This is true for both direction and speed.

An attempt has been made to measure available wind over the United States. Most of the information was obtained from weather data recorded at various airports, and is quite general.

An open rounded hill usually provides a good location for a wind turbine, while buildings or trees tend to reduce windspeed as well as make the wind more turbulent. When considering an extensive wind

326-621 O - 80 - 24 : QL 2

Rising 57 feet above a 30-foot steel tower, this vertical axis "Darrieus" wind turbine can harness at least 30 percent of the enormous energy carried by the wind. This one is at Bushland, Tex.

R.A. BARCLAY

energy program, you should find out if your specific location has sufficient winds to make a wind turbine feasible.

Things to consider in evaluating the feasibility of wind energy on an individual basis can be grouped into four general areas: Do I have enough wind energy? Is my application reasonable? Are the necessary items available to put the system together? Are the financial considerations such that it will be economical? Each will be discussed in some detail.

Wind Availability. This topic has already been considered, but on an individual basis it might be checked more closely to answer such questions as: Do I have enough wind? How does it vary annually, seasonally, daily? How gusty is it?

These questions can best be answered by checking records of nearby weather stations and by measuring the wind in your own location. Wind measuring instruments can sometimes be borrowed from State energy offices or rented from dealers of wind energy systems.

Other questions to consider are: Can I locate the wind turbine so it will be reasonably close to the energy use? Will it interfere with other operations on the farm? Will it be too noisy or unsightly? Will it create a safety hazard? When these and other pertinent questions have been answered favorably the next area can be considered, that of application.

Application. The major consideration here is, can I use the major portion of the wind turbine energy output directly in some application? If not, can I provide storage for the energy, or can it be fed back into the utility grid? Before it can be connected to the utility it will require clearance from the power company.

An example of a good application is on a dairy farm for cooling milk and heating water. This operation is done every day of the year with a fairly constant daily demand. Energy supplied to the compressor can provide both ice and "warm" water, at a very efficient level. That is, for a watt of power put into the compressor motor and taking into account the coefficient of performance of the compressor, you can obtain two or more watts of cooling for ice and three or more watts for heating water.

In contrast, the energy required for milking is not a good use of wind energy. Very little energy can be stored in a vacuum system, and the energy need is essential at the time of milking. If the wind is not available at that time the wind system would be useless. On the other hand, if the energy could be delivered to the electric grid and drawn when needed, this arrangement would be quite satisfactory.

Each specific application on the farm should be evaluated in a similar way. Once all applications are considered, the total wind energy system can be developed.

System Availability. A main deterrent to using wind energy on farms is the lack of large, reliable systems that can be purchased and installed. And like any other farm operation it is important to think in terms of a complete system.

While great strides have been made in the last few years to develop wind systems, the more reliable ones at this time are limited to a rated output of 2 kilowatts or less. Larger ones are being developed but are mostly in the prototype stage. No long term durability studies have been conducted.

This doesn't mean wind systems should not be considered. On the contrary, there is a great opportunity and need for innovative farmers to become involved.

Individual companies, the American Wind Energy Association, and government agencies are anxious to cooperate any way they can in the development of wind energy systems. Companies involved in wind systems need the input of the farm user to purchase, test, and provide feedback to the wind industry.

Individuals should investigate a number of possibilities before making any major decision. The power company representative should also be contacted in the early planning stage, for helpful suggestions.

Financial Aspects. The final area to consider in evaluating the feasibility of a wind energy system for your application is financial. Such questions as: Is the money available at a reasonable interest? Can I apply this to a Federal or State tax credit? Do other tax considerations apply? How much maintenance will be required and how long will the system last? What will alternate energy cost 10 or 20 years from now?

It is difficult to predict how long the systems will last, or how much fuel or electricity may cost 10 or 20 years from now. These questions however, must be addressed with the best knowledge available. Risks are sizable but at the same time the financial gain may also be large.

The Future

Fifty years ago nearly all farms had at least one windmill. Fifty years from now it is likely that many farmers will again have one or more windmills. The size and type of windmill will be greatly different.

The modern windmill of the present and future will be much larger — some may be as large as several hundred kilowatts, but more likely 20 to 100 kW. They will also be used for a wider variety of uses. Certainly a greater portion of the available energy will be used.

It is conceivable that some electric cooperatives and smaller power companies may generate a majority of their power through windmills located on individual farms or on wind energy farms developed for that purpose.

Even so, it will take more than one energy source to satisfy all the energy needs. The windmill will fit in with other energy sources. Solar has more potential for summer, while wind is usually greater and more consistent in winter. Also, biomass — either from crop residue or animal waste — can be used as a backup fuel. Where energy storage is available, a number of energy systems will likely provide the necessary energy supplies.

The future for wind energy looks bright. It will be used to power irrigation systems, heat and cool buildings, animals and crops, and to process and preserve products, for the farm and the consumer. Wind will contribute greatly to maintaining the quality of farm products at a reasonable cost.

Further Reading:

Wind Energy Information Directory, Solar Energy Research Institute, #061-000-00350-9, for sale from Superintendent of Documents, U.S. Government Printing Office, Washington, DC 20402. $1.75.

D. JACKSON

Fifty years ago nearly all farms had at least one windmill, like one in foreground. It was primarily used to pump water. Fifty years from now farmers may again have windmills, but more like one in background. It is a wind turbine generator that supplies part of electric power for people of Clayton, N. Mex.

Tapping Geothermal Energy, Heat From Within the Earth

By F. Abel and B. Walker

Does it surprise you to know that in 1890 a heating system using geothermal energy was installed in Boise, Idaho — the same year the State was admitted to the Union? If so, you may be interested to learn about geothermal energy. In Boise, the geothermal resource is a large natural reservoir of hot water (170° F) about 400 feet under the city.

The 170 homes in Boise's Warm Springs Water District have derived benefit for almost a century from this geothermal heat at a cost far below that of conventional fuels. Boise is now increasing its supply of this economical energy by expanding the original geothermal system to include additional residential and commercial buildings, and eventually a major industrial park.

Geothermal energy is also used to produce electric power in California, dry onions in Nevada, grow fish in Idaho, supply energy to a ranch in South Dakota, heat a hospital and public building in Texas, and is the basis of an economic development project underway in California.

Geothermal resources are available in many parts of the country and can be tapped to meet a number of energy needs. Hot water reservoirs are exploited by drilling wells and pumping the hot water to the surface. The cost of energy depends on how it is used, although in many cases it is available at prices competitive with fuel oil, and in some instances with natural gas.

Present production of geothermal electric power and direct hot water use in the United States is sufficient to satisfy the needs of a city larger than San Francisco. Many western homeowners are currently developing hot water resources on their own property to heat their homes.

Geothermal resources, dispersed over much of the United States, can be used to provide heat at a

FRED ABEL *is Senior Economist for the Division of Geothermal Energy, Resource Applications, U.S. Department of Energy. Beth Walker is a research associate for The MITRE Corporation, McLean, Va.*

cost that is below and in some cases far below current electric rates. Further, geothermal energy has the advantage of being one of the most environmentally acceptable energy sources. While monitoring of geothermal development is necessary to ensure minimal environmental impacts, in most cases environmental effects are not serious.

Temperature Increases With Depth

Geothermal energy is the heat naturally contained within the earth. Under the earth's surface, temperature increases with depth. The rate of increase varies and depends on the heat flow in a region and conductivity of the rock. At some spots below the earth's surface, high temperature water may be trapped, usually in a porous rock formation.

This underground water may be hot simply because it is very deep, or because low level radioactive decay in hard rock creates heat that warms the water. Occasionally, where there is a combination of intense underground heat and small amounts of water, superheated steam is produced.

Another way geothermal energy is produced is by rainwater at the surface draining down cracks in rocks until it reaches hot rock where it is heated. Some of the hot water or steam may return to the surface as hot springs or fumaroles (steam vents).

Energy is obtained by drilling into the rock and pumping the hot water or steam to the surface where it can be used.

Low temperature geothermal water can be used as the direct source of heat for warming homes or

Liquid-Dominated Geothermal System

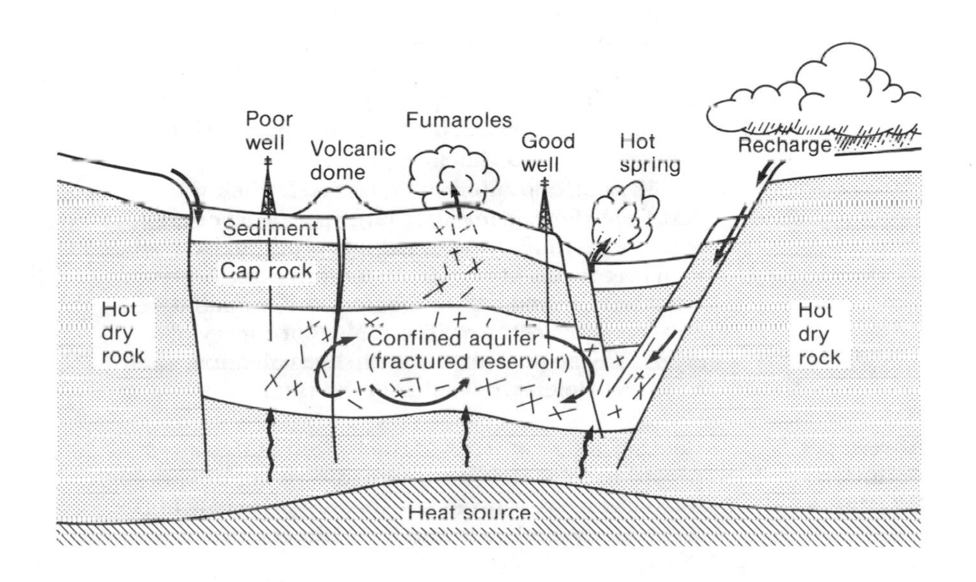

for agricultural or industrial uses, especially when the user is near the geothermal resource.

Higher temperature hot water can be used directly to supply heat for generating electric power. Superheated steam can be used simply and easily to produce electric power. In high temperature hot water systems, steam must be separated from water before the steam can be used.

In addition to energy from hot water and steam, geothermal energy exists as geopressured, hot dry rock, and magma resources. Geopressured reservoirs are located in deep sedimentary basins beneath the Texas and Louisiana Gulf Coasts. These reservoirs consists of deeply buried fluids under high pressure at moderate temperature. Natural gas (methane) is dissolved in these fluids.

Thus three forms of energy can be recovered from geopressured resources: methane, thermal energy, and mechanical energy from the pressure. The recoverable methane is likely to be the most significant and valuable type of energy. Although the geopressured resource is extensive, the amount of methane which can be recovered at a reasonable cost is uncertain at present. Experimental wells are being drilled and tested to determine how much geopressured energy is available, and how much it will cost to recover the energy.

The hot dry rock resource consists of hot rocks located beneath the earth's surface that have not come in contact with water, because they or the rocks above them are not porous enough to allow fluid to filter through. Usable energy is extracted by circulating water through deep wells that are connected by manmade cracks in the rock.

Hot dry rock might in the future be used to generate electric power or be a direct source of heat. Difficulties in tapping this resource arise from complexities in extracting the energy. Development is in an early experimental phase.

Magma, or molten rock, buried far below the earth's surface, is another large potential energy source. Technical and materials problems associated with recovering energy from molten rock, however, must be resolved before magma can be considered an accessible resource base. Magma energy may eventually be recoverable from live volcanos, such as Mt. St. Helens in Washington State.

Resources Found in 37 States

Geothermal resources of the United States are dispersed in 37 States, although known significant high temperature resources are located primarily in the West. Many moderate and low temperature resources, suitable for direct use, may be found on both the East and West coasts.

Many high temperature geothermal resources are located on Federal lands. Special procedures have been established by the U.S. Bureau of Land Management to lease these lands for commercial development.

Existence of geothermal resources is often revealed by a hole in the ground which emits steam or gaseous vapor, termed a fumarole or geyser, or hot springs. Some regions with geothermal resources potential do not have such obvious characteristics, and scientific measurements and drilling are required to locate the resources.

A superheated steam resource exists at The Geysers steam field in northern California and at Old Faithful geyser in Yellowstone National Park. Old Faithful will not be developed because geothermal energy development is not permitted in or near national parks. Development at The Geysers reached 792 megawatts of electric power capacity in 1980.

Geothermal hot water can be used in many ways, depending on the water's temperature. Two major use factors must be considered. First, the minimum temperature range of the geothermal fluid that can satisfy the potential use needs to be determined. Second, energy costs of the application must be assessed. If the process and resource temperatures are compatible, it is likely the use of geothermal energy for that process will be cost effective.

The geothermometer illustration shows temperature ranges and associated potential uses. These applications represent the scope of geothermal energy utilization as the direct source of heat.

Use of geothermal hot water has provided a reliable energy source for the cities of Klamath Falls, Oreg., and Boise, Idaho, for decades. Development of geothermal aquacultural, agricultural, residential, and industrial applications has begun anew since the 1973 oil embargo, with an accelerated pace in the last two years.

Low temperature geothermal energy applications use equipment that is presently available. After a geothermal reservoir has been drilled into, the hot water is piped directly to the application. It may be economical in the case of large district heating systems or industrial parks to pipe the fluids up to 50 miles.

In many cases, direct use of geothermal resources is substantially cheaper than that of conventional fuels.

Hot springs have been used for therapeutic

Temperature °F	°C	Use
356	180	Evaporation of Highly Conc. Solutions. Refrigeration by Ammonia Absorption.
338	170	Drying of Diatomaceous Earth.
320	160	Drying of Fish Meal. Drying of Timber.
284	140	Drying Farm Products at High Rates. Canning of Food.
266	130	Evaporation in Sugar Refining. Extraction of Salts by Evaporation and Crystalization.
248	120	Fresh Water by Distillation. Most Multiple Effect Evaporations.
230	110	Refrigeration by Medium Temperatures. Drying and Curing of Light Aggreg. Cement Slabs.
212	100	Drying of Organic Materials, Seaweed, Grass, Vegetables, etc. Washing and Drying of Wool.
194	90	Drying of Stock Fish.
176	80	Space Heating. Greenhouses by Space Heating.
158	70	Refrigeration by Low Temperature.
140	60	Animal Husbandry. Greenhouses by Combined Space and Hotbed Heating.
122	50	Mushroom Growing.
104	40	Soil Warming.
86	30	Swimming Pools, Biodegradation, Fermentation. Warm Water for Year-round Mining in Cold Climates. De-Icing.
68	20	Hatching of Fish, Fish Farming.

Temp. Range of Conventional Electric Power Production. (180–140 °C)

Saturated Steam (180–100 °C)

Water (20–120 °C)

A Geothermometer

purposes for many years. The Greeks treated the sick by soaking them in natural warm springs. The Romans bathed in hot springs. Native New Zealanders used geothermal springs for cooking.

In the United States, the following hot springs have been used extensively for bathing over the last hundred years: Steamboat Hot Springs, Nev.; Hot Springs, Va.; Lava Hot Springs, Idaho; Glenwood Springs, Colo.; and Calistoga, Calif. This simple use of geothermal energy continues to be evident today, especially in the Western States.

About 47 thermal springs exist at Hot Springs National Park in Arkansas, covering an area about 1,000 feet long and a few hundred feet wide. A decline in outdoor bathing has resulted in plans to exploit this energy to heat park buildings and then use the cooled water for therapeutic baths.

This shift toward using the geothermal energy for heating bathhouses and other recreational facilities is also occurring at other natural hot springs.

Radiators for Space Heating

Geothermal energy space heating can be accomplished in several ways. After direct extraction from the ground, geothermal water can be circulated in radiators throughout a building. Alternatively, hot water can flow through a central radiator, over which air is blown for hot air heating.

In both cases, the used water can be injected into the ground, or discharged into rivers or ponds. Disposal on the surface will require a permit and is allowed only if salt content is low and the discharge will not cause excessive thermal pollution.

When the geothermal water is too corrosive to run through ordinary radiators, it can be directed first through a heat exchanger and then injected into the ground. Fresh water pumped into the heat exchanger emerges as hot water which is then circulated through radiators. When geothermal fluids are corrosive, special materials will be required for the wells and heat exchanger.

The oldest geothermal application in this country, the space heating of city buildings in Boise, Idaho, began in 1890. By the 1930's, water from two wells was used to heat about 400 residential and commercial buildings. In the 1950's, however, when low cost natural gas and oil became available, services were discontinued. Property owners wanting to maintain service organized to form a water district that now provides geothermal heat to 170 homes.

As a result of recent energy costs and shortages, Boise is renovating and expanding the geothermal system. Expansion is beginning with a major downtown redevelopment project.

This large-scale space heating system will directly tap hot water at depths to 400 feet. Heat exchangers will be used to transfer heat from geothermal hot water to air or water. Heat will then be provided from water flowing through pipes in the buildings or from hot air blown to the buildings.

The project encompasses more than 2.5 million square feet of building space, including an 800,000 square foot mall in downtown Boise.

Present geothermal wells serving the city's district heating system will be enlarged, new wells drilled, and new pumps installed. Boise's large population and its location atop a significant geothermal resource make it an ideal prospect for geothermal development.

Cascading to Several Users

One advantage of geothermal heating systems is that the hot water can be "cascaded" to several users. This means the hot water will first serve a high temperature use, and then the cooler water resulting from that use will supply energy to lower temperature applications.

In Boise, water from a production well will be used to heat buildings and then applied to heat animal cages, to warm streets and sidewalks, to irrigate farmland, and to warm fish ponds.

A geothermally-heated industrial park is planned for the city over the next three years. The expanded system will save over 300,000 barrels of oil per year and reduce fuel costs by 30 percent.

In Texas, geothermal energy is being used to heat a college building and hospital. The project was initiated to decrease the dependence of Navarro College and Navarro County Memorial Hospital on conventional fuels by maximizing use of low temperature geothermal water for space heating. This system includes a fossil-fuel boiler for extra heat needed on very cold days.

The system will supply heat to the domestic water, forced air heating, and outside air preheating systems of the college and hospital. This project is partially funded by the U.S. Department of Energy and provides additional evidence of the feasibility of using geothermal energy to heat public use facilities. The Department of Energy is currently supporting 10 projects demonstrating geothermal direct heat use in public buildings.

Three Major Agricultural Applications

The three major agricultural uses for geothermal energy are in greenhouses, animal husbandry, and aquaculture. Though greenhouse heating is now the most prevalent agricultural use of geothermal energy, hot water is being applied to meet a variety of energy requirements.

Near Rapid City, S. Dak., the Diamond Ring Ranch extracts energy from a low temperature geothermal resource. The geothermal energy heats farm buildings, dries grain, and warms drinking water for the ranch's livestock. The system pulls together several small heating applications into a unified network.

A further agricultural use of geothermal energy is underway at Kelley Hot Springs, Calif. Wells are being drilled to supply geothermal hot water for specially designed livestock feed production, swine feed lots, and a slaughterhouse operation The project is still in the preliminary drilling and exploration phase.

Use of geothermal energy for commercial fish farming has proven very successful. There are geothermal fish hatcheries in California, Colorado, Idaho, Oregon, Utah, and Wyoming. Warm and germ-free geothermal water year-round enhances the growth rate and taste qualities of the fish.

Fish Breeders of Idaho has grown catfish in geothermal water for more than six years. Without the geothermal water, which is used directly in the raceways, the climate would be too cold and the growing season too short to operate a fish farm.

Production facilities consist of four series of concrete raceways with four sections to a series. Each section is 24 feet long, 10 feet wide, and 4 feet deep. The raceways are located on a hill. This facilitates reuse of water from raceway to raceway because oxygen is replaced as water cascades over a series of waterfalls.

Six artesian wells 700 feet deep with a combined flow rate of 6,000 gallons per minute supply 90° F geothermal water. Area springs and streams supply cooler water which is mixed with the hot water to bring the temperature to approximately 80° to 85° F, the best temperature for the fish.

Industrial processes presently consume 40 percent of the U.S. energy supply. Studies on temperatures needed for industrial applications reveal that a significant amount could potentially be supplied by geothermal energy.

Vegetable Dehydration Plant Fueled

At Brady Hot Springs, about 50 miles east of Reno, Nev., a vegetable dehydration plant is fueled by geothermal energy. Geothermal Food Processors, Inc., is producing 10,000 pounds of raw onions per hour with geothermal energy as the sole source of heat. Ordinarily the process would consume 10 million cubic feet of natural gas per month.

Not only is geothermal hot water used to dry the onions, but it is also used to wash them before drying. The plant, in constant operation, uses geothermal water from several hundred feet below the ground. Water temperature is about 230° F.

Geothermal Food Processors plans to expand this operation. Financing was aided by a Federally-guaranteed loan and partial funding from the Department of Energy.

Use of geothermal energy for intensive industrial applications is increasing. A planned development at Susanville, Calif., includes construction of an industrial park. This community development, centered around a geothermal resource, will provide jobs and a central location for efficient industrial development.

The city of Susanville has given high priority to this project to hold down the escalating cost of heating and to create employment opportunities. In the project, public buildings will be heated and the discharged water cascaded to the industrial park.

The city intends that the industrial park have a feed mill, greenhouses, and confined animal raising units. Temperature of the water reaching the park will have to be increased by use of fossil fuels for some applications.

Recognizing that the local geothermal resource is limited, a city ordinance has been introduced to ensure efficient use of the resource for maximum benefits to city residents. The City Council intends to make geothermal energy available to private enterprise at the lowest possible cost. The city's ownership of the total supply and distribution system will enhance this position. The system is expected to become operational in 1981.

Groundwater Heat Pumps

Most groundwater reservoirs are not unusually hot, especially those found near the surface. Nevertheless, energy for space heating and air-conditioning can be efficiently extracted from or rejected to these reservoirs by using groundwater heat pumps.

A groundwater heat pump is similar in design to a year-round air-conditioning system. It uses refrigeration equipment to provide heat during winter and to remove unwanted heat in summer. Not only does a groundwater heat pump extract heat energy from the ground for space heating but it also rejects heat to the groundwater when cooling is required.

Groundwater is a more efficient energy source than air for heat pump operation. The temperature of shallow groundwater in the United States ranges from 40° to 75° F, which is well matched to the efficient operating limits of a groundwater heat pump. Use of groundwater heat pumps in residences can result in a 25 percent reduction of energy consumption for cooling and 50 percent for heating.

Many States currently use energy obtainable from shallow groundwater. At Cape Canaveral, Fla., groundwater has provided energy to heat and cool homes for many years.

In Westport, Conn., a 4,100 square foot home is partially heated by use of groundwater heat pumps at an annual cost of less than $500. The groundwater is piped into a heat pump where it passes through tubes filled with cold freon gas. After heating, the gaseous freon is compressed, causing its temperature to rise. Air is blown over the pipes containing hot freon gas, and the resulting warm air is circulated throughout the house. In summer, the process is reversed. Hot air warms the freon, which transfers unwanted heat to water. The water is then returned to the well.

In Salt Lake City, Utah, the headquarters for the Church of the Latter Day Saints is heated and cooled solely by use of groundwater heat pumps. Water at 63° F is supplied to the heating system from four wells. Two wells are 300 feet deep and two are 700 feet deep.

Energy supplied to the 676,000 square foot church office building is equivalent to about 1,000 barrels of oil a year. The system, which includes an automatic switchover from heating to cooling, has been in operation since 1973.

Groundwater heat pumps offer many advantages. Heat energy may be extracted from groundwater when heating is required, and heat may be expelled to the water when cooling is desired. Groundwater source heat pumps allow for simultaneous heating and cooling of different rooms in the same building. Further, they are adaptable for use in solar energy applications.

To sum up, farmers may be able to use geothermal energy to heat greenhouses or dry grain. Communities may be able to institute a geothermal heating system that provides energy to a network of houses. Homeowners may be able to tap both geothermal energy and the energy obtainable from shallow groundwater to heat residences. Whether applied to heat homes in Idaho, dry onions in

Nevada, or provide energy to a ranch in South Dakota, geothermal hot water can be used to satisfy critical heating and energy requirements.

If you think you may have a geothermal resource, you can contact a State or university geologist to confirm its existence and assess its potential. Detailed resource maps illustrating known and potential geothermal resource areas are available from the U.S. Geological Survey and many State energy offices. Your community may be able to institute a geothermal district heating system and thereby supply heat to a series of adjacent homes at relatively low cost.

How We Can Double Hydroelectric Power

By Walter E. Matson

Most new hydroelectric energy is likely to come from fully using existing dams and from small-scale hydroelectric potentials in small river and stream and irrigation systems. These site developments could more than double the present hydroelectric generation capacity.

The problem arises that much of the small-scale hydroelectric potential is in areas designated as Federal Wild and Scenic Rivers or waterways or are situated on coastal streams where there is substantial potential for impact on fisheries or special problems with debris. Accordingly, State water laws and environmental concerns must be considered.

Development of future hydroelectric projects, large or small, will be expensive. Many new sites are in remote regions and would require large expenditures for reservoirs and transmission lines. Besides, the cost of equipment (turbines, controls, etc.) used for hydroelectric development has increased at a rate greater than the general price level.

Seeming to hold the greatest promise are sites near where energy is needed. Switching a small community, forest industry, newly developing area, or remote farm to locally produced electricity has major economic advantages. In addition to creating self-sufficiency and independence of the power grid system, energy normally lost in long distance transmission can be saved. Discussions in this chapter will be primarily aimed at small-scale hydroelectric plants of less than 50 kilowatt (kW) capacity.

Harnessing a stream for hydroelectric power is a major undertaking. Careful planning is vital if a successful and economically justified power plant is to result. Data must be carefully obtained on the site to compare the amount of power that can be expected at various times of year from the hydroelectric installation to meet electrical demands of the small community, home, or farm. After carefully sizing up available power, detailed plans that cover both construction and maintenance must be completed.

WALTER E. MATSON *is Extension Agricultural Engineer, Oregon State University.*

326-621 O - 80 - 25 : QL 2

Perhaps the greatest error made when considering small hydroelectric installations is overestimating the proposed plant's capability.

Measuring Streamflow

One of the first steps in planning a small hydroelectric plant is to measure the stream's power potential. The power potential at any one period of time depends on the waterflow rate; the height which the water falls (head); and overall plant efficiency.

Streamflow rate can vary greatly from season to season, generally according to rainfall intensities during a season. In some areas, mountain snow depth and rate of snowmelt could determine streamflow fluctuation.

Take as an example the discharge rate from 20 to 30 square miles of hilly to mountainous drainage area during one year's precipitation. For this example, the maximum discharge rate could be 500 cubic feet per second (cfs), with an average daily discharge rate of 25 cfs, and a minimum discharge rate of under 1 cfs.

Unless careful considerations are made for ample water storage capacity, generator design capacity in the example could be limited to a 1 cfs streamflow rate even though the average flow is 25 times that amount and peak flow is 500 times greater.

Generally, the manufacturer of small-scale hydroelectric plants will have literature available to provide instruction on how to estimate waterflow.

To generate power from a stream, a given amount of water must flow through a given amount of fall. The fall can be achieved or increased by constructing a dam or using natural change in stream elevation over a given distance. The dam thus could provide increased head or fall, and in many cases additional water storage capacity to regulate streamflow and increase the base power generation capacity above the stream's minimum waterflow rate.

Check Points for a Dam

Before pursuing dam construction, consider the following points:

- Constructing an approved dam is highly technical. A professional engineer can best advise you on necessary State and Federal approved construction and design for a safe dam.
- Permits may be required. Laws vary from State to State. Your State environmental conservation office should be able to supply the necessary information.
- In event of dam failure, you will be responsible for all downstream damage. Determine your insurance coverage.

• Respect the rights of others — you may face resistance from adjacent landowners and conservation-minded groups or individuals.

• Develop accurate cost estimates to determine long term economic feasibility.

Legal requirements and high costs of dam construction may dictate other ways of waterpower development. These might include systems to divert part of the streamflow through pipes to a downstream turbine.

The best site for diversion on a given stream is usually a natural waterfall, an area of swift current, or a steep slope. The slope should be 10 percent or more so a long diversion pipe is not needed for necessary head efficiency. A table indicates head loss for plastic pipes per 100 feet of length per waterflow rate.

Head loss for plastic pipe

Nominal pipe diameter	Flow Rate, cubic feet per second[a]						
	0.2	0.4	0.6	0.8	2.0	6.0	10.0
	Head Loss, feet per 100 feet of pipe						
160# PVC Plastic Pipe							
2″	8.22						
3″	1.34	4.83	10.2				
4″	0.39	1.42	3.01	5.12			
80 psi Plastic Irrigation Pipe							
6″	0.07	0.26	0.54	0.93	5.06		
8″		0.06	0.14	0.23	1.27	9.70	
10″				0.08	0.43	3.27	8.42
12″					0.18	1.35	3.47

[a] 1 cubic foot per second = 449 gallons per minute

Because a diversion system may not necessarily have backup water storage for periods of low flow, potential power is sometimes based on the runoff in a year of normal rainfall which is exceeded on half of the days of the year.

In the example given earlier, the watershed had an average daily waterflow of 25 cfs. The same stream had a flow of 8.4 cfs or higher for half the year. With a 12-foot fall, this stream can sustain a 5 kW generator at full capacity for half the year and nearly 50 percent capacity for the remainder.

For periods of very low flow, batteries would be needed to provide electrical storage from one to three weeks to supply minimum electrical power needs. It is more suitable to use batteries under the low flow conditions and have a larger capacity generator based on rated capacity for flow rates available for at least one half of the year.

If commercial power is available, the electrical power could be purchased from the power utility during periods of low streamflow with any excess power sold during periods of high streamflow. This option would normally be cheaper than using storage batteries and gives more flexibility in sizing of the turbine and generator. Contact the nearby utility for more details on local code requirements and rate schedules available.

Although the average efficiency of small plants will vary, plants of 1 to 50 kW may have an overall average efficiency of about 50 percent.

The second table lists waterflow and head needed to run various small hydroelectric plants operating at 50 percent efficiency. Manufacturers of hydroelectric plants also list power outputs of their units at various flows and heads.

Required waterflow and head for small hydroelectric plants

Generator output kilowatts[1]	Head, feet				
	10	20	50	100	200
	Waterflow, Cubic Feet per Second				
0.5	1.2	0.6	0.24	0.12	0.06
1	2.4	1.2	0.5	0.24	0.12
2	4.7	2.4	0.9	0.5	0.24
5	11.8	5.9	2.4	1.2	0.6
10	23.6	11.8	4.7	2.4	1.2
20	47.2	23.6	9.4	4.8	2.4
40	94.4	47.2	18.8	9.6	4.8
100	236	118	47	24	12

[1] Overall hydroelectric plant efficiency is 50%

Most present day hydroelectric power is produced at large commercial multi-purpose dams with generation capacity of 40,000 kW to over 6,000,000 kW (6,000 megawatts).

There are also many smaller dams built during the same period when the Columbia River and Tennessee Valley Authority (TVA) areas were developed. Some of these reservoirs provided domestic water supplies, irrigation, and aided timber industries. Today many of the sites are being reassessed for environmental acceptability as economically feasible power sites.

In the past, water wheels were traditional for converting the energy in flowing and falling water into useful mechanical energy. Usually large diameter wheels turning slowly, they were mostly used to supply power for grinding, processing, and pumping operations. Such wheels are not efficient. However, a water wheel can be used to generate electricity when the rotational shaft has been geared up to a higher speed.

Water wheels provide some advantages over higher speed turbines. First, a layman can build one. Water wheels develop high torque and can drive slow turning mechanical equipment.

Some types of water wheels will accommodate large variations in flow rate and require minimal maintenance and repair. Trash racks and screens are usually not required since most wheels can operate with small stones and leaves entrained with the water.

Disadvantages of water wheels include 1) they are bulky, slower, and significantly less efficient than higher speed turbines, and 2) it is often necessary to house them in large protective structures to avoid freezeup if year-round operation is required.

There are basically two traditional types of water wheels.

The *undershot wheel* is sometimes called the current wheel because water passes under the wheel and strikes the blades or paddles, causing the wheel to rotate. The undershot can turn on a minimum of one-foot head but would, under that condition, produce very little power.

This wheel is very inefficient. Its optimum head range is 6 to 15 feet with a minimum wheel diameter of approximately 15 feet. Its maximum efficiency is about 20 percent. But even to attain this efficiency level requires that the wheel be built with sides or shrouds to minimize the effects of turbulence or problems associated with water entry from wider channels.

In the *overshot wheel* water is supplied from a nearly horizontal chute to the top of the wheel. Weight of the water in the rim brackets causes the wheel to turn.

Overshot wheels are generally the most efficient of the water wheels. Although these wheels have attained efficiencies of 80 percent, their speed is slow, they generate little power for their size, and they can't operate if the water level in the discharge point tailwater rises.

They can generally operate on heads of 10 to 30 feet. The upper limit of head is around 30 feet because of the cost of constructing a wheel of greater diameter.

In general, the towering water wheels were used for slow speed grinders in old mills grinding cereal grains. These wheels create a romantic image but they are too slow and ponderous to efficiently convert waterpower to electrical power. As an example, a 5-foot diameter wheel that has a 16 inch wide bracket or paddle will generate only 300 watts or less of electricity.

A compact turbine and associated generator make a better choice, as they are much more suited for generating electrical power and far more efficient in electrical power production.

Hydroelectric plants using small turbine generators are available normally in capacities of one-half kW to 100 kW. Some units can be purchased in much larger sizes.

The water turbine differs from the water wheel in that there is a smooth, steady flow of water through passages created by the turbine blades or brackets. These blades or brackets are so designed that water enters and leaves with minimum energy losses,

Undershot wheel

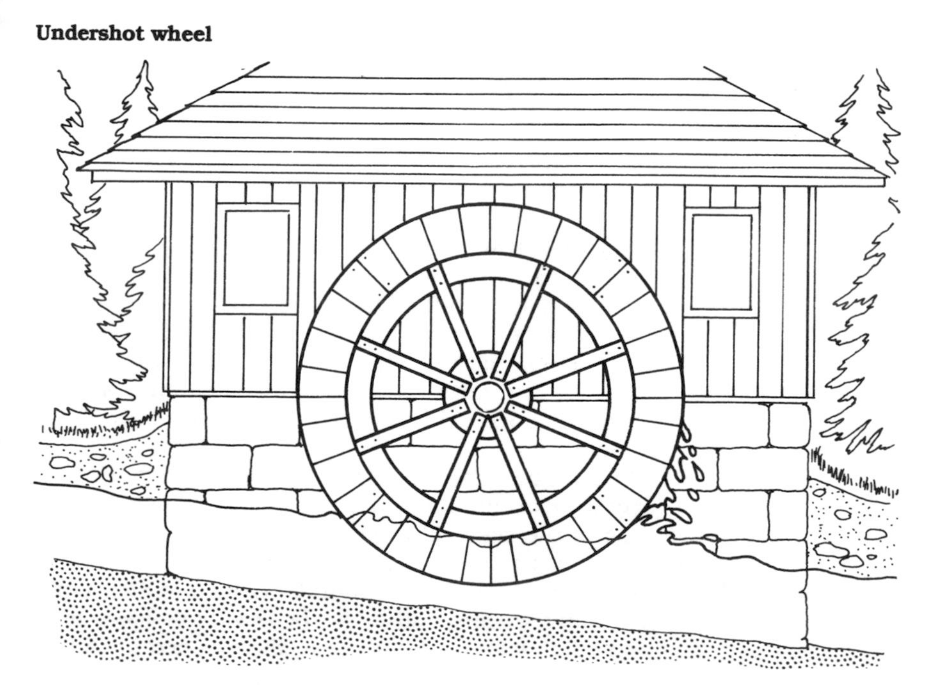

having transmitted most of its available kinetic energy to the rotor.

There are three well established classes of turbines normally classified according to the names of their developers and promoters. These are: a) the Francis, b) the Pelton, and c) the propeller of which two, the Nagler and Kaplan, are examples of classifications according to names. Each class dominates a range of heads and speeds and has a unique form of runner or rotor.

In the Francis turbine, water enters the rotor around its complete circumference. Despite the complex runner, its rotor structure development was a direct response to needs in rural areas in the early 1900's. In the United States a need was found for higher speeds, greater power, and greater economy than could be provided by the old water wheels.

This traditional type of turbine suitable for small-scale farm use typically had a runner diameter of about 17 inches and developed about 15 kW at approximately 294 revolutions per minute (rpm) when operating at a head of 10 feet. Generally, its low speed would require a belt or gear connecting to an electrical generator.

Propeller-type turbines with fixed blades such as the Nagler are normally available for small plants and are connected directly to the electric generator. This does away with the inconvenience, expense, and

Overshot wheel

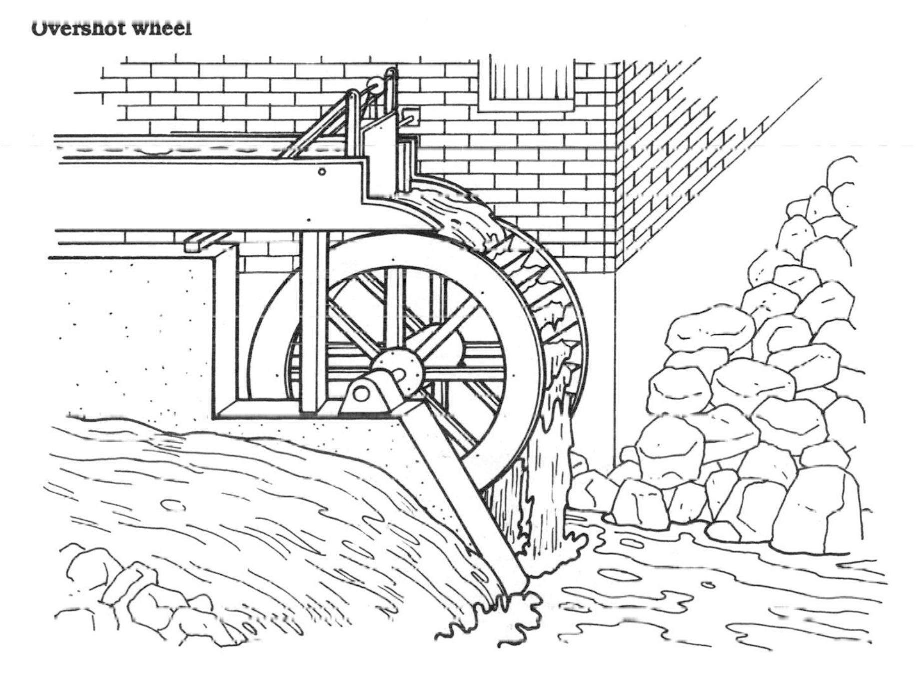

reduced efficiency of using belts and gears.

The fixed blade propeller turbine resembles a ship's propeller and is of a simpler design than a Francis turbine. These small propeller turbines are normally used with low heads (up to 30 feet) and operate at high speeds, thus making them suitable for direct connection to an electrical generator.

Fixed bladed turbines for small-scale hydroelectric plants are being built in the Soviet Union, Finland, Sweden, Canada, West Germany, and other foreign nations for uses up to 100 kW or more. The United States now has several manufacturers of fixed blades as well as variable pitched propeller-type turbines. Most of the U.S. firms can also offer other units such as the Francis-type turbines should the hydroelectric site be more suitable for this type of turbine.

A Kaplan turbine with adjustable guide vanes has a greater range of efficient operation when the streamflow has a wide flow variation such as 15 to 110 percent of average flow, but its cost limits its use at present to larger than 100 kW capacity power generation units.

Turbines described above can be classified in general as reactor turbines since the wheel or propeller is turned by a mass of water falling through a duct encasing a wheel.

The Pelton turbine is often called an impulse turbine. Generally a high velocity stream of water is directed onto its hemispherical buckets to overcome resistance of the load and to transfer energy to the rotating turbine. The Pelton turbine normally is used

Impulse Turbine

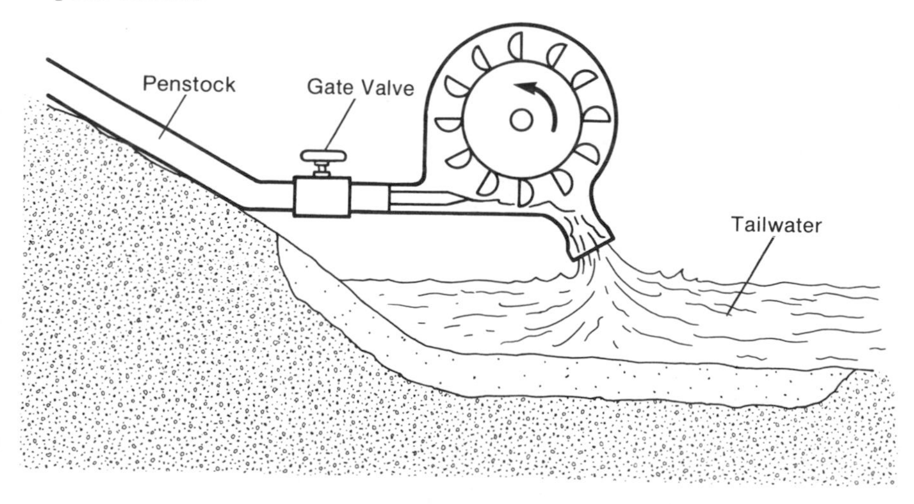

in mountainous areas where heads of 50 to over 500 feet are available with water volumes as little as 1.5 cubic feet per minute.

Trash Racks Head Gates

Besides purchase of a turbine and associated electric generator with the necessary controls, most installations need trash racks and head gates for proper operation and protection of the turbine. Even small streams can become roaring torrents of floodwater carrying trees and other debris.

The plan should provide for protecting the turbine and its associate water passages from debris by installing a trash rack at the head of the turbine penstock. A good trash rack may be steel bars set on edge to the flow of water and spaced about 1 inch apart.

Normally the racks are set on an incline to increase the area of trash collections and also decrease water velocity to a value less than 1.5 feet per second through the racks. An inclined rack is also easier to clean with a rake. This feature is important in autumn because leaves may blanket a rack in a short time.

A headgate or valve is recommended below the trash racks to control waterflow and allow for turbine repair and inspection.

After figuring available power from the stream at various streamflow rates by using the power equation, an estimate of the electrical loads that need to be served by the hydroelectric plant must be made. If the generator is sized to the waterflow rate available at least 180 days in a year, then this sets the maximum demand load that can be attached to the generator.

Another concern is that as the waterflow rate decreases below the flow rate considered available at least 180 days during the year, the load on the generator must also be removed. Under very low streamflow rates, as noted previously, batteries may be needed to provide power for the electrical loads to avoid a system breakdown or a "brownout" — unless your system is tied into the local electric power utility system.

Decide in advance which electrical equipment is to be kept running under minimum streamflow rates. If the decision is to include the entire load as estimated for sizing the generator, then the backup power system must be designed to meet this power demand.

Make a list of the essential equipment and lights that will be operated by the plant. It is important to understand that the generator must provide extra capacity for starting motors. Motors require from 3 to 5 times and occasionally 9 times as much electrical current to start as compared with the current needed to run under full load.

To determine the estimated kilowatt hours of energy used per month by various electrical devices, use the chart which lists some typical monthly energy requirements. Another way of estimating your energy needs if you are presently connected to a commerical electrical system is to make some spot surveys of your present energy use at several different times of day over a week or more. Include power demand and energy consumption data for various periods of the year, especially if the location is a farm operation. Seasonable variations of electrical demand and electrical energy consumption may be important to consider.

You can quickly discover how your energy needs vary over time and what your peak energy demands are. As a check, you could project your energy use over a full month and compare the total kilowatt hours of energy consumption with your utility bill.

Contact your local commercial supplier for more information on how to measure your peak electrical demands and how to accurately estimate your monthly electrical energy consumption.

Causes of Failure

- Not realizing the importance of accurate field data for proper design of the system.
- Overestimating the amount of streamflow in determining available power output to meet electrical power needs.
- Overestimating the proposed plant capacity. The average home has a demand peak variation from 5 to 15 kilowatts. The average farm power demand may vary from 10 to 40 kilowatts. When drying, heating, and irrigation systems are included, the needs may be much higher.
- Not obtaining approval from various Federal and State agencies for construction of turbine generator installation on a stream.
- Underestimating installation costs to justify long term benefits.
- Homemade equipment put together with junked parts.
- Trash racks, penstocks, valves, pipes, and flumes too small to allow the plant to operate at full capacity.
- Not designing the system for winter ice buildup.

Manufacturers of small turbines and hydroelectric generation sets of 100 kW or less listed in the 1980 Thomas Register are: James Leffel & Co., 436-T East Street, Springfield, OH 45501; Gilkes Pumps Inc., P.O. Box 628-TR, Seabrook, TX 77586; Allis Chalmers Corp., Hydro Power Division, P.O. Box T12, York, PA 17405.

Approximate Electrical Energy Used by Typical Home Appliances and Farmstead Equipment

Home Appliance	Common Size Electrical Load	Average Kilowatt Hours Used
Room Air-Conditioner	1,330-2,760 watts	2-3 per hour
Frypan	1,200 watts	20/month
Freezer, Home	300-800 watts	90/month
Furnace, Blower	1/6 - 1/2 Hp	20/month
Furnace, Burner	1/8 - 1/2 Hp	20-40/month
Iron, Hand Automatic	1,350 watts	10/month
Radio, Table	40-150 watts	6/month
Range, Electric	8,000-12,000 watts	100/month
Refrigerator	200-600 watts	60/month
Television	200-350 watts	40/month
Toaster	600-1,200 watts	4/month
Washing Machine, Automatic	300-800 watts	6/month
Water Heater, Standard	1,550-4,500 watts	300/month
Water Heater, Quick Recovery	8,000-9,000 watts	300/month

Farm Equipment	Common size Electrical Load	Average Kilowatt Hours Used
Silo Unloader	3-7.5 Hp	1-4/ton
Electric Welder	7,000-9,000 watts	60/year
Water System Deep Well	600-1,200 watts	3/1,000 gallon
Water System Shallow Well	400-800 watts	2/1,000 gallon
Elevator, Bucket	1-3 Hp	3/1,000 bushels
Feed Mixer, General	1-7.5 Hp	1/ton
Auger, Horizontal (20′ run-grain)	1-2 Hp	1.5/1,000 bushels
Small Mill, grind, mix, automatic	2-5 Hp	4/ton
Barn Cleaner	1-3 Hp	1/cow/month
Milk Cooler, Bulk	3-10 Hp	11/100 gallon cooled
Milking Machine (with Pipeline)	1-5 Hp	4/cow/month
Egg Cooler	1/2 Hp	2/case

Credits

Photography

Photo editor for this Yearbook was William E. Carnahan, Communications Program Leader in the *Science and Education Administration-Extension.*

He took many photos for the book, but also relied on others. Photos came from authors, industry, State universities, the Cooperative Extension Services, *USDA* and other Federal agencies, State agencies and others.

Where the source of the photo is known, credit is given with the photo caption. On the facing page, photographers are further identified with their organizations.

Special thanks go to Bobbe Baker of the *Texas Agricultural Extension Service* for her help. Ms. Baker spent several weeks photographing energy activities in Texas, primarily for use in this Yearbook.

Design

Deborah Shelton, Office of Governmental and Public Affairs

Cover

Sara Tweedie, Office of Governmental and Public Affairs

Colophon

Typography
Text: ITC Bookman Medium 9 point with 2 points leaded, flush left, irregular right. Titles: ITC Bookman Demi. Type was composed on an Addressograph-Multigraph Compset 500 with automated program.

Printing
This book was printed on a 25" x 38" Hantscho Web press by the U.S. Government Printing Office

Paper
Text: 120 lb. White Offset Book. Cover: Coated Kivar 3-17 Linen Weave finish by James River Graphics.

Photos

Bobbe Baker, *Texas Agricultural Extension Service*
Earl R. Baker, *Soil Conservation Service*, Spokane, Wash.
Robert A. Barclay, formerly *USDA*
Charles L. Benn, Extension Service, *Iowa State University*
Glenn Berkey, *Ohio Agricultural Research and Development Center*, Wooster
Robert C. Bjork, *USDA*
Herb Brevard, *Texas Agricultural Extension Service*
D.R. DeWalle, *The Pennsylvania State University*
Dick Dodds, *University of Nebraska-Lincoln*
Carroll R. Douglas, Extension Poultryman, *University of Florida*
Lowell Georgia, freelance
Stan Griffin, *D.C. Cooperative Extension Service*
Grumman Energy Systems Inc.
Dave Jackson, *U.S. Department of Energy*
Paul Hixson, *University of Illinois*
Con Keyes, freelance
Edward Kim, freelance
James Larison, *Oregon State University*, Sea Grant College Program
George Lavris, *Cornell University*
Murray Lemmon, *USDA*
Robert Llewellyn, freelance
Lockheed Corporation
Jayne Marsh, Extension Service, *Michigan State University*
George A. Robinson, formerly *USDA*
Jack Schneider, *U.S. Department of Energy*
M. Bart Stewart, Extension Service, *University of Nebraska-Lincoln*
Tri-Valley Growers, Modesto, Calif.
Joseph Valbuena, formerly *USDA*
Valmont Industries, Lincoln, Nebr.
Fred Ward, *Black Star*
Fred Witte, *USDA*
Yuen-Gi-Yee, *USDA*

Index

Glossary

Active solar design: An assemblage of collectors, storage devices and distribution equipment along with mechanical devices to transfer solar energy (heat from the sun) in a controlled manner.

Ambient temperature: Prevailing air temperature of a surrounding area.

Anhydrous: Free from water.

Aquifer: A water-bearing geological formation. Underground natural reservoir.

Biomass: Any organic matter which is available on a renewable basis, including food, feed, and fiber crops and agricultural wastes and residues, wood and wood wastes and residues, animal wastes, municipal wastes and aquatic plants. It is useful as an energy feedstock.

Broadcast seeding: To sow seed in all directions by scattering.

Btu or British thermal unit: A standard unit for measuring heat energy. The quantity of heat needed to raise the temperature of one pound of water one degree Fahrenheit.

Cellulose: A sugar compound found in the woody parts of plants (for example, corn stalks). It makes up the chief part of plant cell walls and is the raw material for many manufactured or processed products, including alcohol production.

Cogeneration: To provide a contribution of power to another power supply system. To operate in parallel with another power generation unit.

Denitrification: Process by which nitrates or nitrites in the soil or organic deposits are reduced to ammonia or free nitrogen and escape into the air.

Direct burning: Combustion of solids, liquids and/ or gases to produce heat energy without any other energy separation process. Normally refers to the burning of dry solids of biomass such as wood, wood residues or other plant materials.

Distillation: A process that consists of deriving gas or vapor from liquids or solids by heating and then condensing to liquid products such as ethanol.

Drawbar: That part of a coupling device which is fastened to a power unit such as a tractor and which transmits the pull of the power unit to the object to be drawn.

Dryeration: Use of a separate bin to cool dried grain to increase drying capacity of a dryer system. This is an energy conservation measure.

Economy of scale: A point reached in the production process in which the cost per unit is approaching the optimum or most favorable condition.

EER or energy efficiency ratio: Listing of efficiency on selected major home appliances. The rates of useful energy output of the appliance to the energy consumed by the device.

Energy intensive: Using large amounts of energy per unit of production.

Ethanol (ethyl alcohol): The alcohol product of grain fermentation used in alcoholic beverages and for industrial purposes. At present industrial ethanol is produced primarily from natural gas. Alcohols including methanol and ethanol can be produced from biomass.

Feedstock: A raw material that can be converted to one or more end products (methanol or synthetic natural gas, for example). Biomass is an energy feedstock.

Fermentation: An enzymatically controlled anaerobic breakdown of an energy rich compound. For example, a carbohydrate such as in corn to produce carbon dioxide and alcohol. (Anaerobic is without the presence of free oxygen.)

Foot candle: Unit of illumination when a foot is the unit of length. The illumination on a surface one square foot in area on which a flux of one lumen is uniformly distributed. It equals one lumen per square foot.

Fossil fuel: Fuel derived from remnants of animals and plants of past geological ages that have been preserved in the earth's crust, such as coal, oil, and natural gas.

Gasohol: A blend of gasoline and ethanol alcohol composed of 90 percent gasoline and 10 percent ethanol by volume. Gasohol is a registered trademark in Nebraska.

Geothermal: Natural heat of the earth.

Grain alcohol: Commonly a reference to ethanol which is ethyl alcohol. Normally it has been converted from grain feedstock through a fermentation and distillation process.

Head: A measure of water pressure in feet of water or pounds per square inch (psi). One psi equals 2.31 feet of water.

Kilowatt hour: Unit of power that measures the rate at which energy is produced or used. One kilowatt hour (kWh) of energy equals 1,000 watt-hours. A rate of one kilowatt (kW) maintained for one hour produces or uses one kilowatt-hour of energy.

Leaching: Dissolved out by action of a percolating liquid such as water.

Legume: A plant with a fruit called a legume or pod that opens along two sutures when ripe. It makes use of the free nitrogen of the air. Examples: alfalfa, clovers, peas, vetches, soybeans, cowpeas, and beans.

Methanol: Methyl alcohol, or wood alcohol. Methanol can be made from coal, petroleum byproducts, or from biomass and can be used as a fuel in internal combustion engines.

Minimum-till culture: The minimum soil manipulation necessary for crop production or for meeting tillage requirements under the existing soil conditions.

No-till culture: A planting made directly into an essentially unprepared seedbed.

Passive solar design: A design that incorporates the use of solar energy (heat from the sun) in a building for purposes of heating and cooling without relying on moving parts.

Photosynthesis: The process by which plants use sunlight to convert carbon dioxide and water into higher energy products such as carbohydrates and oxygen. The end result is the storage of solar energy in the form of biomass.

PTO or power takeoff: An external shaft on the rear of a tractor to provide rotational power to implements.

Pyrolysis: Chemical changes brought about by the action of heat, as applied to waste. The waste is chemically decomposed in a closed system by means of heat. The waste is converted to fuel gas, oil, char, and water containing some dissolved organic compounds.

Quad: One quadrillion Btu's (British thermal units).

Retrofit: Upgrading of a structure. For example, making changes to a home or other facility which will result in energy saving benefits, adding or making changes to an existing building, adaptation of a technical innovation to an existing building.

"R" value: Measure of resistance to heat flow, used comparatively in rating insulation materials. The higher the "R" value the greater the insulating ability of the material.

Solid waste: The waste residue remaining after all or most of the liquids have been removed from the materials. A byproduct or discarded fraction which is handled as a solid material.

Trickle system: A trickle or drip irrigation method of slowly applying small amounts of water to the plant root zone.

LC 80-600168

U.S. GOVERNMENT PRINTING OFFICE : 1980 O - 326-621 : QL 2